Joseph P. Vidosic, Ph.D. Mechanical Engineering,
Purdue University, served for many years as Regents'
Professor of Mechanical Engineering at the Georgia
Institute of Technology, and is a Fellow of the
American Society of Mechanical Engineers. He is
currently Dean of Administration at Middle Georgia
College. Dr. Vidosic is a Registered Professional
Engineer in the State of Georgia and also serves as an
industrial consultant in mechanical engineering. He
is author of *Metal Machining and Forming Technology*,
published by The Ronald Press Company.

ELEMENTS OF
DESIGN ENGINEERING

JOSEPH P. VIDOSIC
GEORGIA INSTITUTE OF TECHNOLOGY

THE RONALD PRESS COMPANY · NEW YORK

To Dorothy and Richard

Preface

This book is intended for courses in design engineering in which the interdisciplinary nature of the design function is emphasized. Traditionally such courses are found in departments of mechanical or industrial engineering. The topics covered, however, are not confined to these areas alone; sciences and technologies which may appear to be of little concern to design engineering are involved. The student using this book is assumed to have reached a level of maturity in his engineering education where the broad implications of a given design problem take on increased interest. His curiosity leads him naturally to seek information beyond that contained in the class textbook or even expounded by the instructor. At this stage in his studies the student is knowledgeable about the fundamentals of his own particular engineering discipline and has been exposed to elements of a few other disciplines.

It is extremely difficult for an engineering student to become fully conversant with each of the many disciplines that will affect his work as a practicing engineer; the time available for formal education is much too limited. As a consequence, the truly universal engineer is a rarity. Yet it is important that every engineer (student and practitioner) know at least enough to recognize the diverse areas into which he is led in his search for the solution of a problem. A major objective of this book is to make the student aware of the existence of these areas within the context of practical design situations. By gaining an insight into the interdisciplinary nature of problem solving, the student also acquires a deep appreciation of the cooperation and teamwork so essential to good design engineering.

Sufficient material is contained in this book for the usual one-semester course. It is obvious, however, that each chapter can serve as the basis for expanded studies of its particular topics. The book can thus serve equally well in expanded courses in which specific areas of design engineering are examined in depth. The abundant problem material at the end of each chapter permits variety and flexibility in the choice of topics to be emphasized. For many chapters, design problems are included, in addition to the academic problems, discussion questions, and drill exercises. The primary aim of these open-ended design problems is to give the student practice in applying the design principles discussed in the particular chapter and in using his individual initiative in solving problems for which single unique solutions do not exist. Most of the problems require the student to do research outside of his textbook.

The appendices at the end of this book furnish the student with two forms of practical experience. The first appendix is concerned with the experience of others as presented in case studies of actual design engineering problems. Emphasis is on the highlights of a particular problem which illustrate the process of design, depict the thoughts involved and the creativity exercised, and indicate the evaluation of possible alternatives. The case studies may be considered and analyzed profitably in conjunction with any of the chapters after Chapter 3 or 4.

The design projects in the second appendix provide opportunity for the student to exercise his mind in the solution of realistic engineering situations and to practice creativity, if this can, in fact, be practiced. The problem statements are intentionally brief, so that the student will gain experience in defining what is to be solved and in gathering the data required. Use of a design laboratory to accompany class study is often an effective way to present the design projects.

The author cannot claim to have originated the ideas expounded in this book; many have contributed. He is grateful to all who have extended permission to use their material. Any mistakes contained within the book are nevertheless the responsibility of the author. Several of my colleagues have been most helpful. Among these are Drs. H. L. Johnson, J. H. Murphy, F. R. E. Crossley, E. Harrison, and S. L. Dickerson, who have taught using my notes and then offered many valuable suggestions. Much appreciation is also expressed to Mrs. Lucille F. Whitt, who carefully typed most of the manuscript. Finally, appreciation is expressed to my wife, Martha, whose patience and understanding permitted me to work on the manuscript.

JOSEPH P. VIDOSIC

Atlanta, Georgia

Contents

ELEMENTS OF
DESIGN ENGINEERING

1

Design Engineering

Engineering has dominated and will continue to dominate large and small enterprises that produce the things that make our society what it is. The tremendous productivity that supports our high standard of living is the result of the efficiency and economic utilization of our resources of land, capital, manpower, and brainpower with constant technological improvement.

1-1. ENGINEERING

Mr. Ronald B. Smith, Past President of the American Society of Mechanical Engineers, said [1]:

Engineering is the art of skillful approximation; the practice of gamesmanship in its highest form. In the end it is a method broad enough to tame the unknown, a means of combining disciplined judgment with intuition, courage with responsibility, and scientific competence within the practical aspects of time, of cost, and of talent.

This is the exciting view of modern-day engineering that a vigorous profession can insist be the theme for the education and training of its youth. It is an outlook that generates its strength and its grandeur not in the discovery of facts but in their application; not in receiving, but in giving. It is an outlook that requires the many tools of science and the ability to manipulate them intelligently.

In the end, it is a welding of theory and practice to build an early, strong, and useful result. Except as a valuable discipline of the mind, a formal education in technology is sterile until it is applied.

Another, Mr. Philip Sporn, a renowned engineer and utility executive, has stated [2] that an engineer "must be able to conceive, to design, to synthesize, be able to build and operate systems representing great aggregations of capital and energy and human abilities. He's got to be vastly concerned with efficiency and costs and economics . . . ."

Professionally, engineering has been defined many times and in many ways. A completely acceptable definition has not been agreed upon and probably never will. One recent "official" definition [3] reads as follows:

Engineering is the Profession in which a *knowledge* of the mathematical and natural sciences, gained by *study, experience,* and *practice,* is applied with *judgment* to develop ways to utilize *economically* the materials and forces of nature for the benefit of *mankind.*

The statement defines comprehensively the nature, scope, goal, and responsibility of engineering. Among the key words that bear note are *knowledge, study, experience, practice, judgment, economically* and *mankind.*

If engineering is categorized as to function, the following may be considered: *research, development, design, production, operation, marketing,* and *administration.* The more demanding of these

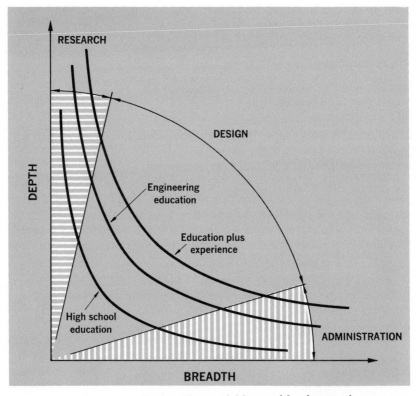

Fig. 1–1.   Engineering activities and background.

activities are research, development, design and administration. The greatest number of practicing engineers probably fall in the *design* category. Engineering activities can thus be well depicted as in Fig. 1–1. The contour lines indicate, qualitatively, the breadth and depth of individuals with differing educational and experience levels [4]. The curves probably run asymptotic to the axes. It is amusing to note that at the limits, the administrator knows "nothing about everything" whereas the researcher eventually knows "everything about nothing."

1–2. DESIGN

Webster defines *design* as a "plan or scheme," or "a preliminary sketch of something to be executed." *Plan* is further defined as a "method of procedure or arrangement," and *scheme* as a "theory of action." Thus design is an idea or plan of something, anything, formulated into a configuration for communication and action. For present purposes, the scope is narrowed down. Four definitions, each encompassing a successively smaller area of activity, are suggested.

1. *Design* is the creation of an end result that satisfies a human need by taking definite action.
2. *Engineering Design* is the process that uses engineering tools—mathematics, graphics, language—and scientific principles to evolve a plan which when fully carried out will satisfy a human need.
3. *Mechanical Engineering Design* is the formulation of plans to satisfy human needs using the disciplines—engineering sciences, techniques, and other mental processes—that are studied by mechanical engineers.
4. *Machine Design* is the formulation of a plan for a mechanism or device capable of transmitting forces and motions, and doing work or accomplishing a specific function that must be done to satisfy a human need as economically as possible.

It should be observed that definite action, a need for the item of design, and economics are contained or implied in these definitions. Thus design is a human, not just an engineering, activity for a purpose, directed toward the goal of satisfying an individual or social need. The designer does not usually produce the final, physical product nor provide the actual service; but rather he creates the model used by the producer or the servitor to provide one or more of *something*. Generally then, a design could be many things—a mosaic for a cathedral floor, a garment for the fashion world, the configurations for a monument, a toy, plans for a shopping center, a power plant, a machine, a missile, or a weapon system. Of course, the last six are more likely to be the "somethings" engineers are concerned with.

1-3. ENGINEERING DESIGN

Design is the primary function, the essential function, of engineering. Engineering design has been defined [5] "as an iterative decision making process for developing engineering systems or devices whereby resources are optimally converted into desired ends." For the General Electric Company, one of the largest users of engineering talent, it has been written [6]:

The principal results of all engineering (and all scientific research, as well) of concern to the Company was stated to be designs of products, of applications of those products, and of ways and means of designing, producing, applying, and servicing these products. In this view, those designs are then the generic end-subjects of engineering in the Company.

Because of the wide variety of products a company of this scope deals with in its many designs, it may be more meaningful to use the *value-added concept,* as indicated in the Fig. 1–2, to depict contributions

VALUE ADDED
(Qualitative)

Stages	Value Added	Marketable
Natural Resource Materials	0	
Extracted Natural Resource Materials	1	Possibly
Refined Natural Resource Materials	2	Possibly
Basic Materials	3	Possibly
Intermediate Materials	4	Possibly
Primary End-Use Materials	5	Possibly
Modified Materials	6	Possibly
Materials of Standard Shapes and Sizes	7	Probably
Composite and Directional Materials	8	Possibly
Pieces	9	Possibly
Parts	10	Possibly
Functional Elements	11	Probably
Functional Assemblies or Systems	12	"Final" Product

Fig. 1–2.   Value-added chart.
After General Electric Co. chart.

at successive levels.   It is assumed it all starts with nature's providing the raw materials.   Since such natural materials are only rarely immediately marketable, something must be done to change them into *products for which there is a market*.   Thus engineering, and in turn processing, confer value at every stage.   The *product* may be sold at the end of any stage, or it may be processed further into a higher stage of value added.   Furthermore, the cost of bringing the raw material to that stage and to the marketplace must be less than the price the market is willing to pay for it; there must result a profit if capital as well as manpower and brainpower are to remain active.

How does the engineer accomplish his designs?   What is the "raw material" available to him?   The raw material can probably be grouped in four categories:

1. NATURAL SCIENCES AND MATHEMATICS
   Chemistry
   Physics
   Life Sciences
   Earth Sciences
   Space Sciences
   Oceanography
   Elementary Mathematics
   Higher Mathematics
   Advanced Mathematics

2. ENGINEERING SCIENCES
   Mechanics of Solids
   Mechanics of Fluids
   Thermodynamics
   Transfer Phenomena
   Materials Science
   Electrical Theory

3. ENGINEERING TECHNOLOGY
   Techniques
   Manipulations
   Empiricism
   Experimentation
   Experience
   Industrial Architecture
   Manufacturing Methods
   Environmentals

4. OTHER RELEVANT KNOWLEDGE
   Communications
   Economics
   Psychology

Social Science
History
Philosophy
Geo-Physics
Information Theory
Political Theory
Literature

As illustrated in the design flow chart, Fig. 1–3, the engineer must govern the flow in appropriate proportions, if he is to end with an optimum, economical design.

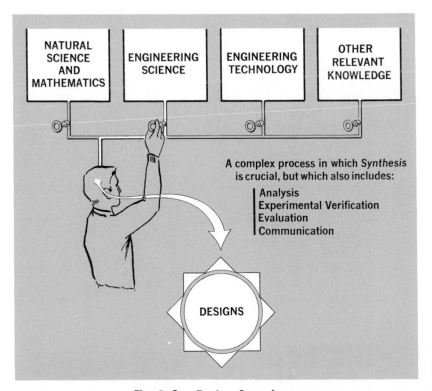

Fig. 1–3.   Design flow chart.

Narrowing the scope to *mechanical engineering design* necessitates no changes in the category listings above. The life, earth, space, and ocean sciences have not to date become common mechanical engineering studies; the others in Category 1 have of course been in the curriculum for some time. All the engineering sciences are also to be found in most mechanical engineering curricula. Some are emphasized more in one curriculum than in another; in mechanical engineering appear more of some but, nevertheless, some of each. The listings in Category 3 are all part of required knowledge. It is only essential that these apply to "the art of the generation, transmission, and utilization of heat and mechanical energy, and the design as well as production of tools and machines and their products." [7]

All *other relevant knowledge* must be used as required as well. If the area of mechanical engineering is "separated" into its two traditional subdivisions, machine and thermal systems design, each draws from the four categories, and they then combine to solve mechanical

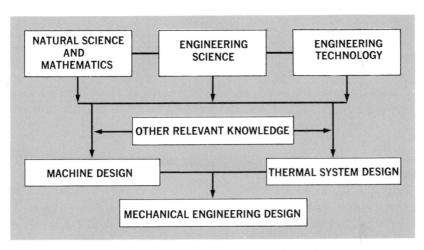

Fig. 1–4. Mechanical engineering flow chart.

engineering design situations, as depicted in the mechanical engineering flow chart, Fig. 1–4.

1-4. PHILOSOPHY OF DESIGN

Education does, or certainly should, aim at engendering independent thinking. In addition, it must of necessity imbue the student with reasonable proficiency in theory and with factual information such as is contained in many of the disciplines named in the preceding section.

To teach and to learn these things with at least some efficiency requires an individual possession of *feeling* and *wisdom*, which can be referred to as a philosophy. In this sense, *philosophy* is a major, rather than the usual, kind of discipline. It is a body of broad principles, and concepts, and general methods that underlie a given branch of learning; it deals with whole classes of problems. It must condition the individual with a consistent and integrated attitude toward life, and reality, and work, and, in this case, design. Since all principles are proven "true" only on the empirical evidence of experience, there cannot be *one* philosophy of engineering design. It is inevitable that it should be flavored by personal experience, and idiosyncrasies, and bias; this is not necessarily bad, nor should the philosophy go unformulated. The foundation, if not the choice and exact formulation of principles, must nonetheless be bound by the laws of logic.

The philosophy must contain a *consistent set of principles* within which contradiction does not exist. It must possess an *operational* aspect, or lead to action, because an exercise without consequences is useless. Since its origin is empirical, it must contain a *feedback mechanism* capable of evaluating the success with which principles are applied to particular situations and of revealing shortcomings. Such a philosophy of design can probably be best propounded diagramatically

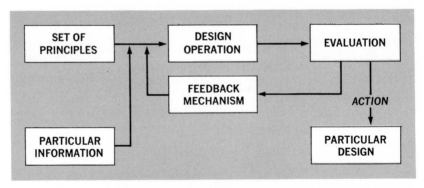

Fig. 1–5. Philosophy of design.

(Fig. 1–5) as Prof. M. Asimow did at the First Conference on Engineering Design Education. (See also Reference [8].)

Some of the general concepts involved are as already indicated:

1. *Need.* Individual or social need must exist for the item.
2. *Action.* The material item must actually be realized.

3. *Economic Utility.* The item must be made available at a marketable price that includes profit as well as cost.
4. *Design Procedure.* Design proceeds iteratively from the abstract concept to the concrete item.
5. *Judicious Compromise.* The basically empirical nature of all engineering dictates a constant need for decision.
6. *Evaluation.* The many designs must be evaluated to establish the best alternative.
7. *Optimality.* The best alternative is optimized with respect to the most significant criterion.
8. *Communication.* To gain existence, the design must be communicated to the producer.

Individual designers should also possess a personal-action philosophy that manifests itself in the following design attitudes:

1. Willingness to proceed in the face of incomplete data and knowledge and even contradictory data.
2. Recognition of necessity to use engineering judgment in arriving at best possible decisions.
3. A questioning attitude, about data, theory, problem, specifications, answers, etc.
4. Recognition of experiment as the ultimate arbiter.
5. Willingness to assume full responsibility for the final design.

1–5. THE SCHEDULING PRINCIPLE

Human nature, being what it is, tends to encourage individuals to put off. There always are other days; eventually one of them becomes the deadline of that dreadful tomorrow on which the finished task is to be reported. Resort is made to the last-minute-rush technique that adds much to the possibility of error-making in decision, in evaluation, and in computation. To prevent this, it may be better to divide the whole task into several appropriate bundles of effort with a sub-deadline for each. Spurts of energy still occur, fatigue sets in, and warm-ups are required; but because of the smaller scope of each sub-task, the energy output will more nearly approach the ideal uniform distribution. The probability of numerous and possibly costly errors will diminish, and the total energy expenditure will likely reduce. This scheme of task division and subdeadlines is illustrated in Fig. 1–6.

The individual contribution principle formulated below has been suggested.

$$\text{Contribution} = (\text{Aptitude} + \text{Knowledge} + \text{Experience})(\text{Efficiency})$$

The efficiency factor might well help to explain why a brilliant individual can be a failure and an average person a success.   Everyone has a chance.

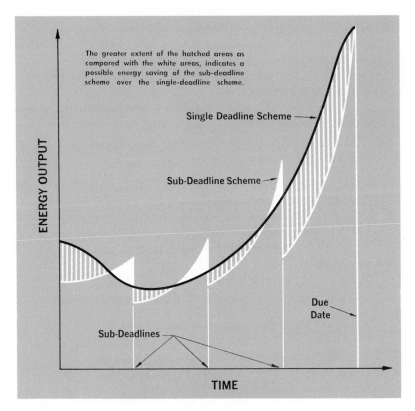

The greater extent of the hatched areas as compared with the white areas, indicates a possible energy saving of the sub-deadline scheme over the single-deadline scheme.

Single Deadline Scheme

Sub-Deadline Scheme

ENERGY OUTPUT

Due Date

Sub-Deadlines

TIME

Fig. 1–6.   Scheduling diagram.

Organization is the one important factor in work efficiency and the resulting productivity.   Self-discipline and self-motivation are valuable and necessary habits the dedicated engineer develops.   Do not procrastinate, nor panic when the workload appears to become overwhelming.   Schedule routine and uncreative jobs for your less productive hours.   Lump similar tasks together, make quick decisions on minor details, be systematic and develop a sense of time and responsibility.   But beware of distractions and of over-concentration, and do not permit the work to become a chore.   Relax fully when not working so that the relaxation becomes a battery-charging period that will provide the energy for the next spurt of real productivity.

REFERENCES

1. R. B. Smith, "Professional Responsibility of Engineering," *Mechanical Engineering*, v. 86, n.1 (Jan. 1964).
2. Philip Sporn, "The Forgotten Engineer," *Intern'l Sc. & Tech.*, Nov. 1963, pp. 57–60.
3. Ralph A. Morgen, Letter of Jan. 2, 1963, written while its author was president of the Engineer's Council for Professional Development.
4. J. Modrey, "On the Incompatibility of Present Graduate Schools and Engineering Education," *Proc. First Conf. on Eng. Des. Educ., 1960*, 38, Case Inst. of Tech.
5. A. B. Rosenstein and J. M. English, "Design as a Basis for a Unified Engineering Curriculum," *Proc. First Conf. on Eng. Des. Educ.*, Case Inst. of Tech., Sept. 8–9, 1960.
6. General Electric Company, *Some Key Terms and What They Mean in Research and Engineering*, ENS-R-111, March, 1963.
7. *Bulletin—General Catalog and Announcements, 1966–67*, Georgia Institute of Technology.
8. Morris Asimow, *Introduction to Design*, Prentice-Hall, Inc., Englewood Cliffs, N.J., 1962.

PROBLEMS

1–1. Prepare a table comparing the per-capita productivity of the United States of America with that of six other nations.

1–2. Analyze the courses you have had in college thus far, deciding how much of each is breadth material and how much is depth, and then compute the percentage of each. Plot the result on an Engineering Activities diagram such as Fig. 1–1, assuming a 5-in. length of each axis represents 100%. Have your expectations been met? Why? Where do you estimate you stood on this diagram at the end of your high school career?

1–3. Classify each of the courses in your curriculum according to the four raw material categories indicated, and compute the percentage distribution among them.

1–4. Classify the courses in your curriculum according to the two traditional sub-divisions of mechanical engineering, and compute the percentage of each. Place the courses that clearly do not belong in either sub-division in a third *other* group. If not an M.E., establish the sub-divisions of your curriculum, and do the same.

1–5. How would you explain the reason(s) for the high productivity of the United States of America?

1-6. Discuss why there may not be a single philosophy of design engineering.

1-7. Discuss the key words in Morgen's definition of engineering given in the text.

1-8. Explain and discuss the engineering functions of research, development, and design.

1-9. Present and discuss your views as to what the philosophy factor *a consistent set of principles* means and implies.

1-10. What habits would you try to develop as a dedicated engineer?

1-11. Discuss efficiency as a factor that will permit you to make a contribution to your chosen profession.

1-12. Show how the key words appearing in the official definition of *engineering* apply to a common device such as a wrist watch, an electric shaver, or a bicycle.

1-13. Define *design engineering* in your own words.

1-14. Distinguish clearly between design engineering and your particular area of design (e.g., mechanical design). Illustrate each by an actual example.

1-15. You have been given the job of designing a speed reducer. It is to transmit 100 hp at 500 rpm of the pinion at a speed ratio of 4:1. You have one week to complete the design. Schedule the work day by day so that the design will be finished in five 8-hr days without a last-minute rush.

1-16. Identify an industry that would be marketing the product at the end of each of the value-added stages shown in Fig. 1-2. For instance, the mining industry represented by the Consolidated Coal Company markets a product categorized by value-added stage 1.

1-17. Which of the four areas does the design of the following items fall in and why? Gear reducer, power plant, monument, nuclear reactor, air-conditioner, and hydroship.

2

The Design Process

It is believed by some that a single, or at least unified, design methodology does not exist. It is therefore claimed that design cannot be taught, because it relates only to each specific engineering system; it can only be learned by experience, is the argument. Those who have been studying the problem seriously, however, have felt strongly that a design process is identifiable, and that it can, therefore, be realistically taught. It is now well established that the general techniques, concepts, and procedures are common to all designers. This specialized, logical reasoning is the engineering method or the design process.

2-1. THE PROCESS

The discipline of design involves knowledge, skill, and attitude. The liberal as well as technical knowledge required is normally studied by way of the many disciplines of a college curriculum. Manipulative and other such skills are also acquired during the college career. Proper design attitudes, including an action philosophy and thoughtful responsibility, are developed as the individual matures mentally, professionally, and socially. Throughout his life, the normal competent engineer continues to gain in each.

The most crucial part of the design process is "creative synthesis." [1] Also included are analysis, experimental verification, evaluation and selection, description, and communication. But the fact that conceptualizing a satisfactory solution to a problem depends critically on synthesis should be well noted.

Edward Hodnett [2] has indicated that the major steps in problem solving are *diagnosis, attack, the scientific method* (probably more applicable to research phases), and *art*. Von Fange [3] has identified the steps, on the other hand, as *define, search, evaluate,* and *select*.

Generally, the design process is the solution of problem situations in which:

1. Pertinent information must be gathered, critically analyzed in terms of the existing problem situation, and organized for solution of the particular situation.
2. Decisions must be made, tested, evaluated, optimized, and communicated.
3. Iteration and feedback must underlie each step so that new discoveries and insights become involved in repetitions of previous manipulations.

More specifically, the solution of design problems may be considered to involve, in the horizontal structure of design, the following eight stages:

a. Recognition
b. Definition
c. Preparation
d. Conceptualization
e. Synthesis
f. Evaluation
g. Optimization
h. Presentation

It should be noted that the stages are not independent. All are interrelated; findings at any stage may affect results of any or all previous stages. Re-consideration, re-decision, re-formulation, re-examination, and re-computation are continuously carried out as needed in the design of most structures, engines, machines, or systems. A complete feedback is an absolute necessity. To strengthen the process description, the stages are depicted graphically in the design process flow chart, Fig. 2–1. The opposing arrowheads on the interconnecting lines are indicative of the interdependence and feedback principles.

An additional explanation of each stage will further clear the nature of the design process.

Recognition. This is the initial encounter with the situation that constitutes or contains the need. It establishes the general problem area and identifies the particular need. It may have all started with an expression of a desire for an item by the consumer, or by a superior, or even by the designer himself. It may be a request for a man–machine system that will perform a new task, or an idea that will utilize a newly discovered principle.

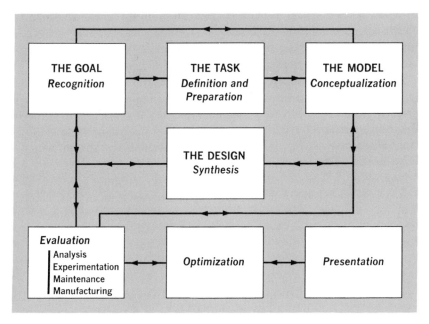

Fig. 2-1.   Design process flow chart.

Definition. The problem must be exactly identified and defined. A clear statement of the particular task must be understandably evolved.

Preparation. All pertinent information must be collected. Data, formal knowledge, and empirical know-how that bear upon the problem must be gathered, reviewed, and organized. Where anything is lacking, as it often is, the gap must be filled in with the proper assumptions, compromises, and sound engineering judgment.

Conceptualization. Configurations of elements, devices, mechanisms, etc., that may in one combination or another perform the desired function and yield possible solutions, must be generated. No alternative arrangement that holds promise of probable success can be omitted. Creativity is of particular importance at this point. All basic scientific principles and laws of nature that may lead to a solution should be carefully investigated as possible starting platforms.

Synthesis. The concepts that appear to contain the desirable solution may be just a "black box" at this stage. They possess no real material substance. Each must, therefore, be sized (capacity) and dimensioned (strength). Details must be conceptualized. Exact mechanisms are synthesized to supply the required motions, dynamic characteristics, and time sequences. Components must be selected, materials decided upon, parts and subassemblies designed, and fabricating processes considered.

Evaluation. The designs, models, or possibly analogs must now be analyzed; critical parameters must be checked to see that all is satisfactory. The real physical system must be analytically or experimentally evaluated. Its fabrication must be finalized. The evaluation may have to be performed on all alternatives not previously eliminated. The "best" design must be selected.

Optimization. Such criteria as reliability, economy, weight and space limitations, and life requirements can be very important factors. Any one, or more, of them may be determining. The design may thus have to be optimized with respect to the particular criterion in question. That is, the best design is explicitly maximized for the significant desirable, or minimized for the significant undesirable, factors.

Presentation. Communication, both verbal and graphic, becomes of prime importance at this stage, because the design has no value until utilized. It must be sold to the builder who will realize it, as well as to the consumer who will put it to use. Communication is actually of importance throughout all stages, especially in systems projects, because management must be kept informed at every step, in order that it can decide upon discontinuation whenever economics may dictate the design unworthy of further expenditure.

2-2. THE PROCESS ILLUSTRATED

A window-and-door line manufacturer contemplates the large number of apartment houses being constructed all around the country in urban developments. Its management decides that a window whose outside glass surface could be easily reached from the inside for cleaning would be a profitable product.

This is no doubt a relatively simple problem for engineers with experience in the window manufacturing industry. To a beginner it could prove an innovation of considerable difficulty. In either case, it well illustrates the stages of the design process.

It can be safely assumed that when the problem first arose, sash windows were common. To wash the outside surface of such a window is not an easy matter, because one has to reach around a long way, or sit precariously on the window ledge to get to the lower- and upper-pane surfaces. To eliminate the difficulty, it is necessary either to develop a device that will somehow spray and remove the cleaning medium while the operator is standing safely on the inside, or to somehow bring the outside surface to the inside so it can be washed as simply as the inside surface. Since the manufacturer does not consider gadget design and marketing to be within his domain, he decides not to pursue this approach, but instead directs his engineers to concentrate on a window so designed that the outside surface can be readily brought within easy reach of the housewife standing on the inside.

As a result of the management's analysis and decision, engineering proceeds with the design as below.

Definition. The problem is already clearly defined. Wanted is a window that can easily be so manipulated that the outside glass surface is readily accessible for cleaning from the inside. The window must also permit, of course, the usual opening and closing for ventilation control.

Preparation. Standard window dimensions, window materials, and their properties (wood, aluminum, steel) are the data needed. Such information is, quite obviously, in the files of this alert window concern. It is quite possible, however, that as specific window concepts are evolved, additional data may be required. Such would be gathered as needed.

(It should be noted that though the eight stages are separated for instruction, several steps could actually be going on simultaneously. A design engineer is continually working back and forth among the stages, feeding knowledge gained in one to improve or complete another.)

Conceptualization. The designer generates one or more possible solutions. In this problem, he must devise some way of making the outside surface of the window easily accessible from inside the room. The first thought could well be to make the window removable so that it could be carried to the sink and washed like most other household items a housewife cleans. A farfetched idea; possibly, but then a lightweight design involving a metal frame that lifts out easily and yet retains features of tightness, easy opening and closing, and good appearance offers a challenging concept. It is decided, however, that although this is a most worthy long-range project, work on which will be continued later, for the present a "simpler" concept must be found.

A more direct possibility is to redesign an ordinary sash window so that it can be rotated about a vertical pivot, as in Fig. 2–2, or about a horizontal axis, as in Fig. 2–3. Either of these, it is realized, would

Fig. 2–2.   Sash window, center vertical pivot.

involve a redesign of the woodwork surrounding sash windows so that guides could be moved out of the way and sash weights disconnected. Engineering decides this might well result in too cumbersome and costly an arrangement and so discards the concept.

A louvered window of suitable depth and swing, providing sufficient hand space, as illustrated in Fig. 2–4, constitutes a highly competitive concept.   In order to reach the entire glass surface easily, the glass panes should not exceed a width of around twelve inches.   Thus an ordinary window may require six to eight such panes.   The idea is quite feasible, but the details of properly sealing several panes to dust, dirt, and noise indicates that a single pane might be preferable. Thus the concept of a casement window of the type in Fig. 2–5, designed to move away sufficiently from the corner as it is rotated open, appears the best alternative.

Synthesis.   Window concepts other than the casement have been eliminated for the various reasons stated.   The casement type must, therefore, be designed in detail as to the frame structure, the supports and pivots, and the mechanism that will rotate it and move it about

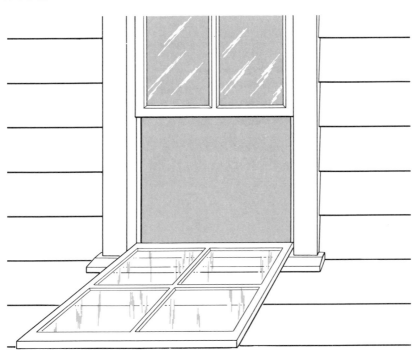

Fig. 2-3.   Sash window, base horizontal pivot.

five inches away from the window frame at one end. It is not the purpose presently to develop the detail design of the window, but only to establish that synthesis of the window and its components is the design stage performed at this point.

Evaluation. Obviously much evaluation has already taken place, prior to and along with the part synthesis of the alternatives.   The one idea accepted and completely synthesized is carefully evaluated at every step to assure a good, workable, safe window.

Optimization. Again, much of this occurred during synthesis. Selection of material to minimize weight represents optimization. Another criterion was handled in the design of dependable mechanism, economy was carefully considered in the selection of standard sections for the frame and of fabrication processes.

Presentation. As in other phases, a good deal of this has already been accomplished. Management was sold on the need for such a window originally. As design proceeded, management had to be and was kept informed and agreed to the type of window, the material

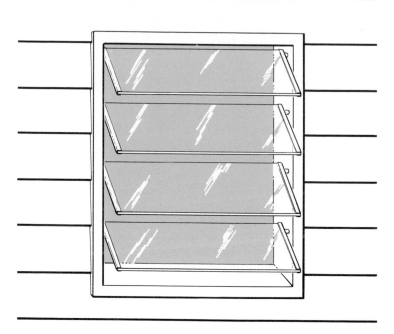

Fig. 2–4.　Louvered window.

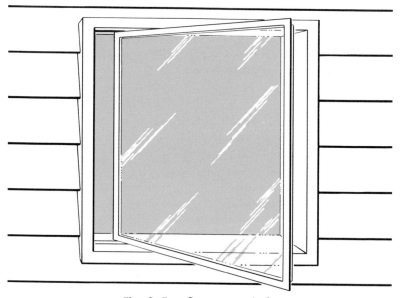

Fig. 2–5.　Casement window.

it is to be made of, and the details of its fabrication. Nevertheless, another very important bit of communicating remains to be done. Builders and contractors must be convinced of its utility, and ethical advertising must obtain its acceptance by housekeepers.

The above is not a very glamorous or extensive project, but to a concern making and selling the product it is an exciting problem.

2–3. CHRONOLOGICAL OR VERTICAL STRUCTURE OF DESIGN

A project must often be carried through a series of design phases as well as the stages that transform the abstract idea into a physical object or, more likely, system. It must also be taken through a series of planning phases to make it commercially available. In general, the design phases, at least, are separately performed; that is, the next phase is not begun until the previous is finished. The planning or production–consumption phases are more closely interdependent with each other. The phases are:

a. Feasibility Study
b. Preliminary Design
c. Detail Design
d. Production Planning
e. Market Planning
f. Obsolescence Planning

Although not all of these phases are within the scope of the present study, each is briefly explained.

2–4. DESIGN PHASES

Feasibility Study. A need that starts a design project may be real, but it can also be hypothetical. In any case, its identification at this point is likely very nebulous; its reality is likely based on observations that may lack much proof. The need may have found seed in someone's mind as a result of a scientific, technical, or economic advancement. The need may be only latent; the probable consumer must still be made aware of it and of his need for it. A technical success can easily go bankrupt when a financially sound need is not realized. Many stage plays, for instance, ended their existence in bankruptcy after the first night's performance. And, several automotive companies have tried and failed over the years because the need for their particular model of car could not be generated.

The existence of a real need is established only when the consumer, the general public or some portion of it, some industry, or a government agency is willing to pay the marketplace price. Evidently, the need is difficult to determine, particularly since the product is not even designed. But a careful analysis of the potential market, a diligent study of social trends and individual tastes, and considerations of national aspirations does assist in establishing the reality of a need. Of course, sound engineering judgment, common sense, and cautious predicting must be practiced.

It should be noted that the above discussion implies that the product must exist at least on paper if its need and feasibility are to be established. The feasibility study does therefore also involve generation and evaluation of design concepts that may possibly satisfy the need at hand.

Preliminary Design. Solutions that may have been suggested during the feasibility phase, as well as other possibilities, are considered, and the better alternatives established. Surviving alternatives are conceptualized and synthesized sufficiently to reveal over-all features, function characteristics, special-component or material requirements, weight and space needs, fabrication tolerances, life expectancies, and costs. Thus specific design concepts are thoroughly evaluated.

Detail Design. With the concept generally developed and accepted, and the components or subsystems tentatively defined, the design can now be fulfilled. Capacities are exactly sized, dimensions calculated, wear accounted for, parts detailed, tolerances established, and treatments determined. Thus all components are synthesized, tested, and modified as required, and the machine or system laid out. The design becomes fully developed, completely detailed, and clearly described. It is now a producible design.

2–5. PLANNING PHASES

Production Planning. Although this, as well as the two succeeding phases, is not usually the work of the design engineer who worked on the previous design phases, many of the requirements have been anticipated by him, and he is therefore involved. It is very likely, however, that the chief engineer or even the project group should share responsibility with those doing the planning. Certainly the engineers most acquainted with the product, machine, or system are in good position to provide reliable leadership.

The major task involves planning for manufacturing the product. Processes, tools, fixtures, production control, inventory control, and quality control must each be economically planned and effectively carried through to the completion of the product or system. Sometimes it may even involve specifying new production equipment or laying out new plant facilities.

Market Planning. Again, the designer as such is involved only indirectly. Nevertheless, marketing requirements could well have influenced his design, and he should be concerned. Packaging, warehousing, and advertising the product are the important tasks of marketing planners; some real engineering problems may well be present: for instance, suspension arrangements to prevent shock damage in transport, or coatings to prevent corrosion of surfaces in storage, or color and shape to permit attractive display. Furthermore, safety measures, reliable and economic operation, convenience and aesthetic features, and maintenance feasibility are of great concern here and must be understood and properly designed into the product.

Obsolescence Planning. Some products are simply designed for a predetermined life. Others, like the automobile, are subject to deliberate fashion changes. And still others, like spacecraft, really become technically obsolescent. To the design engineer the question whether to design for ordinary wear and physical deterioration or for technical obsolescence can be quite troublesome. Thus he may attempt designing product life to match required service life, or reduce possible obsolescence by anticipating future technical advances. He may even design a downward service escalation into the product so that it can be utilized at different levels—a new model each year does not completely nullify the value of the older car.

The problem of retiring a production machine or a public utility system, for instance, poses a deep and difficult decision requirement. The economics dealing with the replacement candidate or "defender" versus the new asset or "challenger" must be given careful consideration [4, 5]. The mere act of substitution may raise serious questions, such as how do you replace a machine without stopping needed production, or how do you replace a fossil-fuel power plant with a nuclear one without disrupting service? It should thus be obvious that although not solely engineering problems, obsolescence, replacement, and equipment retirement must be taken into some account during the design phases.

2–6. RESEARCH, DEVELOPMENT, DESIGN

Normally the activities connoted in the three terms are not too distinct, one from the other. They may be distinguished, but the activities are so intermingled in today's science and technology that this is often difficult. The first two categories are defined by the National Science Foundation as follows:

Research. Basic and applied investigation to advance scientific knowledge in the Physical Sciences, Life Sciences, and Engineering.

Basic Research, also termed fundamental or pure research, is concerned primarily with developing new or fuller scientific knowledge rather than applications thereof.

Applied Research is concerned with discovering new scientific knowledge primarily for its immediate or specific applications.

Development. Technical activity on non-routine problems encountered in translating research findings or other scientific knowledge into products or processes.

The term *engineering* is not defined by NSF. It places it, however, in parallel with the natural sciences when it indicates that research advances engineering along with the sciences. Applied research is sometimes referred to as *industrial research,* a phrase that is quite meaningful.

Applied or industrial research, development, and design are each concerned with problem-solving. Each plays its part in, and each is best carried out by following, the stages described as the design process. The details of procedure and the tools are different, but the objective in each case is to reach a goal originally set. In a real sense, development forms a bridge between applied research and design. All three may or may not have the same goal; all three may be leading to fulfillment of the same need.

On the other hand, research may be general, development can be of a device that only promises possible future use, while design is directed at a specific answer, a piece or system of hardware. In design, a solution must be found; research can be discontinued if the effort appears fruitless.

2–7. DESIGN AND DRAFTING

Design is often associated, unfavorably, with drafting. Neither is the other, although each depends on the other. The design engineer need not be well skilled at drafting, but he must be able to communicate his ideas and designs graphically, even if only to the draftsman for final presentation. Furthermore graphics, generally considered, is not only a communicating language but a symbolic one as well; it can be used to solve problems. Note, for instance, graphic statics; graphical quadrature; the geometric solution of point, line and plane situations; velocity and acceleration analysis; psychometric charts; and the schematic diagram of a vapor-heat engine system.

Though drafting is largely a recording process, drawing can be and is used as a pictorial extension of the mind. In the early phases of design, layout can be very useful in helping to determine compatibility, misfit, or disproportion among interacting members, parts, and components, and can even provide a means for estimating cost or deciding

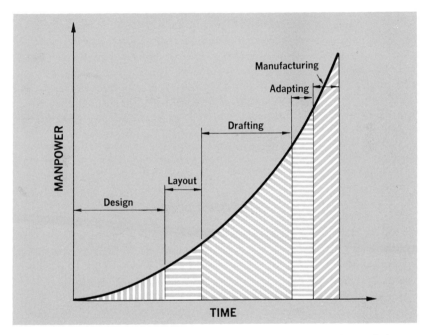

Fig. 2–6.   Manpower requirements diagram (qualitative only).

the economic suitability of continuing a design. A sketch may suggest the best way of proceeding with the synthesis or analysis, and a schematic diagram can reveal the omission of a piece of equipment needed to complete the system cycle.

An approximate indication of how much and what kind of manpower is used in the evolution of a design project is depicted in the manpower requirements diagram [6], Fig. 2–6. It is interesting to note the relatively large amount of energy expended by draftsmen in the preparation of such as working drawings, manufacturing specifications, and parts lists. The adaptation time represents the man-hours used to transform manufacturing information into the form understood by computers and numerically controlled tools where such manufacture is warranted. It is also interesting to note the relatively smaller effort expended in finally manufacturing the physical item itself when the design is complete and realizable.

REFERENCES

1. General Electric Company, *Some Key Terms and What They Mean in Research and Engineering*, ENS-R-111, March 1963.
2. E. Hodnett, *The Art of Problem Solving*, Harper & Row, 1955.
3. E. Von Fange, *Professional Creativity*, Prentice-Hall, Inc., Englewood Cliffs, N.J., 1959.
4. E. L. Grant and W. G. Ireson, *Principles of Engineering Economy*, The Ronald Press Co., 4th ed., 1960, Rev. Ptg., 1964, Ch. 17.
5. J. P. Vidosic, *Metal Machining and Forming Technology*, The Ronald Press Co., 1964, Ch. 16.
6. R. W. Mann, "Engineering Design, Professional Practice and Educational Implications," *Engineering Design and Graphics Education Conference*, Massachusetts Institute of Technology, August 13–24, 1962.

PROBLEMS

2–1. Identify the most crucial part of the design process.

2–2. Distinguish as clearly as possible, and illustrate the difference between, the Recognition and Definition stages.

2–3. Distinguish clearly between research, development, and design.

2–4. Define drafting and contrast it with design.

2–5. It has been indicated that the stage structure of the design process is a horizontal structure, whereas the chronological phase sequence is vertical. Explain what is meant by this.

2–6. Discuss how the designer is involved in the production planning phase.

2–7. Explain and discuss the sentence concerning design and drafting that states "Neither is the other, although each depends on the other."

2–8. Discuss the feedback-iterative nature of the design process.

2–9. Discuss how the design process may have been applied in connection with the original T-rail by Robert Livingstone Stevens, circa 1830.

2–10. Recognize and discuss honestly and intelligently three different problem areas in your engineering curriculum.

2–11. Millions of words have been written and spoken about the merit and demerit of more science and less professional courses in the engineering curriculum. Enumerate three merits and three demerits in this trend, and evaluate them as you see them.

2-12. It has been established that astronauts must land on the moon in the early 1970's if the United States is to retain leadership in space. Discuss the decision from the feasibility point of view.

2-13. How may obsolescence considerations be designed into modern expressway systems in large urban areas?

DESIGN PROBLEMS

2-D1. Imagine yourself chief of works for the Egyptian king Cheops, who had the Great Pyramid of Gizeh built circa 2700 BC. Prepare a proposal for the construction of this large pyramid, using the tools and slave labor available at the time.

2-D2. Write a specification (definition) for an automatic registration-time-card dispenser or a desk with a book holder and page turner.

2-D3. Write a specification (definition) for a refrigerator butter conditioner, to keep butter at its best spreading temperature, or for rough-terrain landing gear.

2-D4. Cheop's Great Pyramid of Gizeh was a monument and burial tomb for the king. Propose another type of monument and tomb that would have served as well and could have been built with the tools and labor of the time.

2-D5. A one-way system of streets is proposed for the downtown section of a large city. Outline the study that should be undertaken to investigate the feasibility of the proposal.

2-D6. Provide a preliminary design of a simple unit for demonstrating the first law of thermodynamics.

2-D7. Identify several principles that may be used to base the design of a pleasure-boat speedometer upon.

3

Analysis and Synthesis

Engineering is an exciting business, especially for those who engage in creative design. Truthfully, design has been said to be the "mainstream of the engineering profession." As a process, design resembles problem-solving. It handles, however, somewhat more; design deals with an engineering situation rather than just a problem, and hence requires not only analysis but also synthesis, composition as well as dissection, imagination as well as reason.

3–1. HORIZONTAL STRUCTURE OF DESIGN

As described in detail in a previous chapter, the process of engineering design or, simply, complete problem-solving, consists of several stages: broadly conceived, *understanding*, *solving*, and *evaluating*. Within these are two basic activities, analysis and synthesis. These are, in a real sense, counter-actions, because the one untangles while the other unites. Analysis is probably used more during the understanding and evaluating stages, whereas synthesis may be used more during the solving stage.

Both *analysis* and *synthesis* have many shades of meaning, even with regard to their significance in design. For instance, a designer is analyzing when computing the stress in a beam, but synthesizing when using a pre-established design stress to determine what its sectional dimensions should be. On the other end of the spectrum, a traffic engineer is analyzing when trying to uncover the reasons for rush-hour congestion, whereas the nuclear engineer is synthesizing when deciding how to shield a reactor pile against gamma radiation.

Considered from the point of view of design, the terms *analysis* and *synthesis* can be said to have each a kind of dual meaning, depending upon the particular, immediate occasion:

Synthesis—mind is the creation, the conceptualization, in the mind of a combination of elements forming the whole. The elements may be mental images of specific components; or facts; or such relationships as material properties; or the first law of thermodynamics; or Newton's laws of motion; or more likely some combination of these.

Synthesis—paper is a case of combining elements into a new form, here implying creation on paper for eventual production of a configuration of components possessing capacity for sufficient performance. It can include computing how large the cylinder must be to contain a given weight of gas at a specified pressure; or how thick the wall must be for the cylinder not to burst under the existing pressure.

Analysis—mind is performed when, on the other hand, the mind isolates the already synthesized idea into its components to evaluate the elements for conditions or limitations that make it valid, consistent, exact, economical, for the purpose at hand.

Analysis—paper is the resolution into parts or elements to determine whether it possesses the capacity to perform as intended. To illustrate with the previous example, the strength of the cylinder wall is calculated to see if the established safe stress is exceeded.

3–2. PICTORIAL ASSISTANCE

Graphical representations sketched by the engineer as he proceeds through the "mind" stages of synthesis and analysis constitute an essential solution tool. It is generally not too difficult to get a beginner to use this tool. The matter of somehow picturing an idea on paper seems to be an almost natural thing. Constructing a free-body useful during the "paper" stage is, on the other hand, another matter. Yet, a correct free-body diagram accounts for a good portion of the solution. A complete free-body signifies knowledge and understanding of the problem because it contains what is known as well as what is unknown and yet to be found.

A free-body diagram shows all the forces and entities acting or effective upon the body. All influences of other bodies on the isolated body under consideration are indicated. Everything that exerts a force or causes an effect is removed from contact and replaced by expressions of the reactions or effects each causes upon the free or isolated body. The concept may best be depicted by means of an example.

Example 3–1. The action of the road upon a stationary automobile may be shown in free-body style (Fig. 3–1):

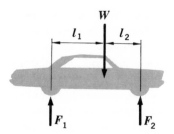

Fig. 3–1. Free-body diagram for stationary automobile.

W = weight of automobile shown at center of gravity of car
l_1 and l_2 = distances from center of gravity to center of tire contact with road
F_1 and F_2 = reactions or forces exerted upon tires by the road (force acts on two wheels at each end)

When the engine is turned on, the many internal actions and reactions cancel each other, but a torque results upon the driving wheels. With the brakes off, the wheels rotate and with the help of friction between tire and road the car is accelerated; see Fig. 3–2, in which the additional symbols represent:

F_{r1} = friction force generated at driving wheels
F_{r2} = friction force generated at front wheels
F_d = drag force (small at usual speeds)
a = acceleration produced by unbalanced force ($F_{r1} - F_{r2}$)
v = velocity of automobile

If the acceleration is replaced by the reverse effective force (D'Alembert's principle), the body is placed in equilibrium.

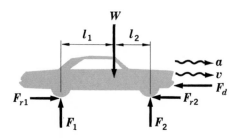

Fig. 3–2. Free-body diagram for moving automobile.

3–3. CHECKING SOLUTIONS

Professional competence as well as pride prevail upon the engineer to produce correct results. Although engineers often work in teams, each must assume responsibility for his part of the job. There are no answer books, or filed solutions, or classmates to compare answers with, or teachers with whom to ascertain the solution. Thorough and constant checks for correctness of one's solution are an absolute necessity. Self-confidence is developed and correct results produced when one can assure oneself that one's work is performed correctly. Carefully checking every step is proper procedure whether analyzing or synthesizing, whether evaluating or conceptualizing.

Checking can take different forms. Theory must be critically reviewed to ascertain its appropriateness to the problem, and equations should be dimensionally checked to see that all terms result in the same unit or units. Arithmetical, algebraic and other mathematical manipulations should be checked as solution proceeds. Results can be checked by extending and extrapolating to some known limiting case or boundary condition. Sometimes it is possible to check over-all results by considering whether the solution is reasonable in the light of experience. Finally, the most conclusive assurance of correctness might be found in a properly planned and conducted experiment. Experimentation thus becomes an important engineering tool, though it can be expensive; experimentation and instrumentation are, however, extensive subjects falling outside the scope of this book.

An equation is said to be homogeneous when all terms have the same unit. This homogeneity constitutes a base for an often effective checking method; it will detect misplacement or omission of terms at every step in the derivation and manipulation of algebraic equations in finite or infinitesimal form.

In making a dimensional check, one investigates to insure that all terms of the equation have the same unit quality. For instance, the equation

$$8 \text{ pencils} - 5 \text{ pencils} = 3 \text{ pencils}$$

is homogeneous and so dimensionally correct, whereas

$$8 \text{ pencils} + 5 \text{ erasers} = 13 \text{ (what?)}$$

is not. The second equation is obviously meaningless. Representative of a more typical equation is the homogeneous

$$12 \text{ pencils per box} \times 3 \text{ boxes} + 12 \text{ boxes per case} \times$$
$$5 \text{ cases} \times 12 \text{ pencils per box} = 756 \text{ pencils}$$

A working equation will depict the method even better. The deflection y of a beam fixed at both ends and supporting a uniformly distributed load w lb/in., starting a units from one end is expressed by

$$y = -\frac{1}{6EI}\left(R_l x^3 - 3 M_l x^2 - \frac{w(x-a)^4}{4}\right)$$

The homogeneity check can be made by substituting dimensions for each symbol. Thus

$$\text{in.} = -\frac{1}{\text{lb/in.}^2 \times \text{in.}^4}[(\text{lb} \times \text{in.}^3) - (\text{lb-in.})\,\text{in.}^2 - \text{lb/in.}(\text{in.} - \text{in.})^4]$$

$$= -\frac{1}{\text{lb-in.}^2}[(\text{lb-in.}^3) - (\text{lb-in.}^3) - (\text{lb-in.}^3)] = \frac{\text{lb-in.}^3}{\text{lb-in.}^2} = \text{in.}$$

Note that the process checks the dimensions only. The meaning of each term in the equation must be implicitly understood and the constants checked otherwise. For instance

$$s = \frac{Mc}{I} + \frac{Tc}{J} = \frac{6Fl}{bh^2} + \frac{3T}{bh^2} = \frac{\text{lb-in.}}{\text{in.} \times \text{in.}^2} + \frac{\text{in.-lb}}{\text{in.} \times \text{in.}^2} = \text{lb/in.}^2 = \text{psi}$$

is homogeneous, but wrong because non-parallel vector quantities cannot be added algebraically.

The deflection equation above can also be used to demonstrate the check where a derived equation is taken to a known limit. The maximum deflection of a fixed beam uniformly loaded occurs at the center:

$$y_M = \frac{wl^4}{384EI}$$

when the load w exists all the way across the beam. The original equation should, therefore, reduce to the above maximum deflection, if correct, when $a = 0$ and $x = l/2$. It can easily be found first that $R_l = wl/2$ and $M_l = wl^2/12$. Thus

$$y = -\frac{1}{6EI}\left[\frac{wlx^3}{2} - \frac{3wl^2x^2}{12} - \frac{w(x-0)^4}{4}\right]$$

$$= \frac{1}{6EI}\left(-\frac{wlx^3}{2} + \frac{wl^2x^2}{4} + \frac{wx^4}{4}\right)$$

$$= \frac{wx^2}{24EI}(l^2 - 2lx + x^2) = \frac{wx^2}{24EI}(l - x)^2$$

and

$$y_M = \frac{w(l/2)^2}{24EI}[l - l/2]^2$$

$$= \frac{wl^2}{96EI}\left(\frac{l}{2}\right)^2 = \frac{wl^4}{384EI}$$

which checks.

Sometimes the check can be an easy inspection matter, as in checking the following grinding chip length equation. It can easily be seen that the unit is the square root of in.^{2} or in.

$$l = \sqrt{\frac{Dd}{1 + D/D_w}} \left(\frac{1 + v}{V}\right)$$

3–4. ANALYSIS

The process of analysis can best be explained in illustrating the method by means of examples. The problems used are simple, selected so as not to obscure what is being explained, that is, analyzing an engineering situation to see whether capacity is satisfied, specifications are met, or limitations are exceeded.

Example 3–2A. The calorific value of a fuel is being determined by burning a small amount of the fuel, 0.002 lb, in a closed container immersed in 15 lb of water in a well-insulated tank. What is the calorific value of the fuel, if the water temperature rises 2° F?

Solution: The Joule equivalent not only provides the quantitative relationship between two units of energy, the Btu and the foot-pound, but also yields the amount of internal energy absorbed by one pound of water while its temperature rises 1° F.

Thus, if the fuel sample raises the temperature of 15 lb of water by 2° F, the total energy given off by the fuel is

$$1 \times 15 \times 2 = 30 \text{ Btu}$$

But the fuel sample weighs only 0.002 lb. Therefore, the energy that would be given off by 1 lb of fuel, or in other words its calorific value, is

$$\frac{30}{0.002} = 15,000 \text{ Btu/lb}$$

A dimensional check of the two equations yields

$$\text{Btu/lb-°F} \times \text{lb} \times \text{°F} = \text{Btu}$$

and

$$\text{Btu/lb} = \text{Btu per lb}$$

The equations are homogenous and, therefore, dimensionally correct.

Example 3–3A. A simple pendulum swinging through an angle of 160° is 3 ft long. Find the period of oscillation.

Solution: The first relation likely to come to mind is one learned in elementary mechanics:

$$T = 2\pi \sqrt{\frac{L}{g}}$$

Further consideration, however, recalls that the equation is based on the assumption that the angle of swing is small enough to permit replacement of sin θ by θ, making the period independent of the swing angle. It is soon realized that the error that would occur in this case, where the swing is large, would make the computation far from correct. The exact solution, therefore, which does not involve the above assumption, must be resorted to. In this derivation, [1] solution of the non-linear differential equation plus the application of appropriate boundary conditions results in

$$T = 4 \sqrt{\frac{L}{g}} K(k)$$

where $K(k)$, the complete elliptic interval of the first kind, is

$$\int_0^{\pi/2} \frac{d\theta}{\sqrt{1 - k^2 \sin^2 \theta}} \quad (0 < k < 1)$$

The value of the integral may be obtained from tables of integrals, such as those of Dwight or Peirce. In this case $k = \sin (80/2)$ or $\sin (40°)$ and the complete integral is 1.787.

Thus

$$T = 4 \sqrt{\frac{3}{32.17}} \times 1.787 = 2.183 \text{ sec}$$

A dimensional check, recognizing 4 and k dimensionless, reveals

$$T = \sqrt{\text{ft/ft per sec}^2} = \text{sec}$$

Example 3–4A. A steel lever is oscillated by the action of a high-speed cam. It deflects slightly but sufficiently, as a result of its inertial forces, to cause some misalignment difficulties. It is suggested that the substitution of a lighter material, such as aluminum or magnesium, be made.

Analysis: The inertial force is, of course,

$$F_I = \frac{Wa}{g}$$

where W is the weight of the lever in pounds, a is the tangential acceleration of the center of gravity of the lever, and g is the acceleration of gravity, 32.17 ft/sec^2 for the purpose at hand.

Since the lever is pivoted at one point (Fig. 3–3), and the inertia force is applied at the center of gravity, the deflection is defined by that of a cantilever beam.

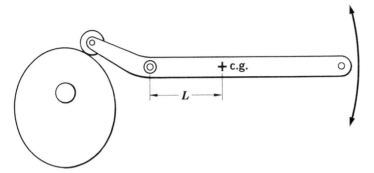

Fig. 3–3.   Steel lever of Example 3–4A.

Thus

$$y = \frac{FL^3}{3EI} = \frac{Wa}{g}\left(\frac{L^3}{3EI}\right) = \frac{V\rho a L^3}{3gEI}$$

The volume of lever V, acceleration a, length from pivot to center of gravity L, acceleration of gravity g, and second moment of area I are the same regardless of material.   Therefore

$$\frac{y_{\text{non-ferrous}}}{y_{\text{ferrous}}} = \frac{\rho_{nf}E_f}{\rho_f E_{nf}}$$

The pertinent material data are as follows.

	Steel	Aluminum	Magnesium
Density, ρ in lb/in.^{3}	0.283	0.100	0.066
Modulus E, psi	30×10^6	10.5×10^6	6.5×10^6

Thus

$$\frac{y_{\text{Al}}}{y_{\text{Fe}}} = \frac{0.100 \times 30 \times 10^6}{0.283 \times 10.5 \times 10^6} = 1.009$$

and

$$\frac{y_{\text{Mg}}}{y_{\text{Fe}}} = \frac{0.066 \times 30 \times 10^6}{0.283 \times 6.5 \times 10^6} = 1.076$$

The analysis shows, therefore, that if made of aluminum, the lever would deflect 0.9% more than the steel lever and, if of magnesium, 7.6% more.   The solution is thus not to be found in material substitution, and so the suggestion is not valid.

Example 3–5A.   Figure 3–4 shows a component part of an instrument. Each beam is $2c$ units deep by c units wide and L units long; the spring constant is k.   Derive the simplified expression for the maximum flexure stress in the lower beam.

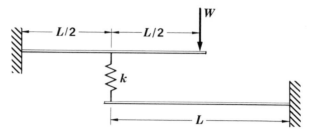

Fig. 3-4.   Component part of an instrument shown schematically.

Solution: The free-bodies of the elements of the system are shown in Fig. 3–5. The free-bodies reveal three unknown forces on the top beam, which also supports the only known force W.   The case is thus statically indeterminate and so deformation relations must be involved.   If the deflection down at the mid-point of the top beam is denoted by y_1 and the deflection up due to spring force P at this same point is identified as y_2, and it is recognized that the end of the spring moves down y_2 or P/k as well, then the deflection of the end of the lower beam is

$$|y_3| = |y_1| - |y_2| - \left|\frac{P}{k}\right|$$

The deflection y_1 is

$$y_1 = \frac{Fx^2}{6EI}(3a - x) = \frac{WL^2}{24EI}\left(3L - \frac{L}{2}\right) = \frac{5WL^3}{48EI}$$

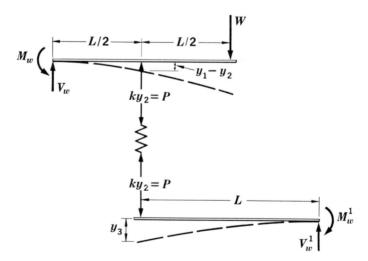

Fig. 3-5.   Free-body diagram of component-part system.

while

$$y_2 = \frac{PL^3}{24EI}$$

and

$$y_3 = \frac{PL^3}{3EI}$$

Therefore

$$\frac{PL^3}{3EI} = \frac{5WL^3}{48EI} - \frac{PL^3}{24EI} - \frac{P}{k}$$

or, solving for P,

$$P = \frac{5L^3Wk}{6(3L^3k + 8EI)}$$

But $I = 8c^4/12$; thus

$$P = \frac{5WkL^3}{(18L^3k + 32Ec^4)}$$

It may be wise to check the above equation dimensionally before proceeding:

lb × lb/in. × in.³/(lb/in. × in.³ + lb/in.² × in.⁴) = lb²-in.²/lb-in.² = lb

The stress can now be found using the flexure theory:

$$s = \frac{Mc}{I} = \frac{PLc}{I} = \frac{15WkL^4}{(36kL^3c^3 + 64Ec^7)}$$

The dimensional check below proves the last equation is homogenous.

lb × lb/in. × in.⁴/(lb/in. × in.³ × in.³ + lb/in.² × in.⁷)
= lb²-in.³/lb-in.⁵ = lb/in.²

The four examples worked above illustrate analysis as used in problem-solving, each example representing a different degree of difficulty and complexity. Example 3–2A is, of course, quite simple. But it does require some recognition and analysis of the situation, followed by a very simple manipulation of values. Example 3–3A required a slightly deeper analysis that, in turn, revealed the inadequacy of a possibly common assumption in the application in question.

Example 3–4A is illustrative of mind analysis where an alternative solution is analyzed to check its suitability. In this, an apparently logical solution is proved wrong. Illustrated in the last example, 3–5A, is the need for some deep thinking. Recognition and reasoning as well as knowledge of certain theories are applied to execute the analysis. All examples are quite simple but worthy of much student attention.

3–5. SYNTHESIS

Just as for analysis, the process of synthesis can be best explained by illustrating with examples. The four analysis situations of the previous section will be converted into synthesis problems. In this way the difference between the two processes should become quite clear.

Example 3–2S. The calorific value of a fuel is to be checked every few thousand cubic feet of production. It seems desirable to keep the test sample rather small, say around 0.002 lb. The calorific value is to be determined measuring the temperature rise of the medium in which the burning fuel is to be immersed, enclosed in a container of course. A temperature-rise range of 2° to 5° F is believed suitable. The calorific value of the fuel is estimated to be somewhere between 14,000 and 17,000 Btu/lb. What size container is needed, if the energy-absorbing medium is to be water.

Note: Some synthesis as well as analysis has already been performed, or the problem statement could not have been made. The method of testing has been decided in someone's mind—a case of synthesis. Decision of sample size is also a matter of synthesis. Furthermore, estimation of the approximate calorific value range has been arrived at by analyzing the chemistry of the fuel.)

Solution: The fuel sample will yield on burning between $14,000 \times 0.002$ and $17,000 \times 0.002$, or 28–34 Btu, of energy. Since water requires 1 Btu/lb for each degree Fahrenheit rise in temperature, the largest amount of water required is

$$\frac{34}{1 \times 2} \quad \text{or 17 lb}$$

and the smallest (only of academic interest) is

$$\frac{28}{1 \times 5} \quad \text{or 5.60 lb}$$

Water weighs approximately 62.4 lb/ft³. Therefore, the volume of water required is

$$\frac{17}{62.4} = 0.272 \text{ ft}^3 = 470 \text{ in.}^3$$

The shape and actual dimensions of the container are matters of choice or possibly space consideration, not a part of immediate concern.

Note that a dimensional check, though not shown, was applied.

Example 3–3S. A switch must be turned on and off every $1\frac{1}{8}$ sec. Of the several devices that may be used to actuate the switch, it is decided to try a simple pendulum.

Note that much synthesis as well as analysis may have already taken place in supposing, evaluating, and eliminating other possible timing devices.

Solution: Review of space availability and convenience of attachment reveals the pendulum pivot can be located about 1 ft above the plane on which the switch is to be mounted. The length of the pendulum (*L*) can therefore be taken as one ft. It is thus necessary to determine only how far from the vertical line through the pivot the switch should be located. Furthermore, since a reasonably precise answer is most desirable, the exact pendulum theory will be used regardless of the swing angle (Fig. 3–6).

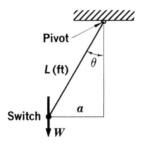

Fig. 3–6. Diagram of pendulum actuator.

The period of a mathematical pendulum is defined by the relationship

$$T = 4 \sqrt{\frac{L}{g}} K(k)$$

from which the complete elliptic integral can be determined:

$$K(k) = \frac{T}{4} \sqrt{\frac{g}{L}}$$

In this case

$$K(k) = \frac{1.125}{4} \sqrt{\frac{32.17}{1.0}} = 1.125 \times \frac{5.67}{4} = 1.595$$

This value of the elliptic integral occurs at 14°. Thus

$$a = L \sin \theta$$
$$= 1 \times \sin (2 \times 14)°$$
$$= 1 \times 0.4695 = 0.4695 \text{ ft}$$
$$= 5.63 \text{ in.}$$

Note that had the pendulum length been unknown as well, possibly a more realistic situation, the solution would have been much more complex, because of the transcendental equation that would then exist.

Example 3–4S. What can be done to eliminate the difficulty in the cam–lever device of Example 3–4A?

Solution: The cam surface could conceivably be changed to reduce lever accelerations during the cycle; a reduction in the angular speed of the cam would also reduce the disturbance. These would, however, modify the functional characteristics, which is probably not permitted. The only possibility appears to be to increase the stiffness of the lever by increasing the depth of cross section. Observe that, in the deflection equation

$$y = \frac{V\rho a L^3}{3gEI}$$

ρ, a, L, g and E are fixed. Therefore

$$y \propto \frac{V}{I} \propto \frac{A}{Ar_g^2} \propto \frac{1}{r_g^2}$$

So, use a section deep enough to make the radius of gyration, r_g, large enough to keep the deflection below the critical value which causes excess bending.

Example 3–5S. The steel beam–spring system shown schematically in Example 3–5A is to support a load W of 100 lb. The length L is to be 30 in. and the spring rate k is 50 lb/in. So design the system that the deflection of the lower beam does not exceed 0.05 in. while the maximum stress in the beams is close to 15,000 lb/in.^{2}.

Solution: The formulation derived in Example 3–5A is used as required. Free-bodies are also as shown there.

$$y_3 = \frac{PL^3}{3EI} = \frac{PL^3}{2Ec^4}$$

or

$$P = \frac{2Ey_3c^4}{L^3} = 2 \times 30 \times 10^6 \times \frac{0.05c^4}{30^3} = 111.1c^4$$

But

$$P = \frac{5WkL^3}{18kL^3 + 32Ec^4}$$

or

$$111.1c^4 = \frac{5 \times 100 \times 50 \times 30^3}{18 \times 50 \times 30^3 + 32 \times 30 \times 10^6 c^4}$$

Thus

$$106,660c^8 + 2,699c^4 - 675 = 0$$

and

$$c = 0.510 \text{ in.} \quad \text{(found by iteration)}$$

The maximum stress in lower beam is

$$s = \frac{15WkL^4}{36kL^3c^3 + 64Ec^7}$$

$$= \frac{15 \times 100 \times 50 \times 30^4}{36 \times 50 \times 30^3 \times 0.510^3 + 64 \times 30 \times 10^6 \times 0.510^7}$$

$$= \frac{60{,}780 \times 10^6}{6.45 \times 10^6 + 17.24 \times 10^6}$$

$$s = 2{,}566 \text{ psi}$$

To find the maximum stress in upper beam, spring load P is found first.

$$P = \frac{5WkL^3}{18kL^3 + 32Ec^4}$$

$$= \frac{5 \times 100 \times 50 \times 30^3}{18 \times 50 \times 30^3 + 32 \times 30 \times 10^6 \times 0.510^4}$$

$$= \frac{675 \times 10^6}{2.43 \times 10^6 + 64.9 \times 10^6} = 10.03 \text{ lb}$$

Then

$$s = \frac{Mc}{I} = \frac{(WL - PL)c/2}{8c^4/12} = \frac{3L(W - P)}{4c^3}$$

$$= \frac{3 \times 30(100 - 10.0)}{4 \times 0.510^3} = 15{,}260 \text{ psi}$$

Stress and deflection requirements insofar as the beams are concerned are, therefore, satisfactory.

The spring is designed next. A spring index, C, of 10 seems reasonable since the spring rate indicates a soft spring. A No. 11 music wire having a diameter of 0.1205 in. and minimum tensile strength of around 260,000 psi is selected. The coil diameter is

$$D = Cd = 10 \times 0.1205 = 1.205 \text{ in.}$$

Based on the distortion–energy theory and a factor of safety of 4 (there are several uncertainties present), the strength of the spring is

$$s_{sd} = \frac{s_{sy}}{f_s}$$

$$= \frac{0.577s_y}{f_s}$$

$$= \frac{0.577(0.75s_u)}{f_s} = \frac{0.577 \times 0.75 \times 260{,}000}{4}$$

$$= 28{,}100 \text{ psi}$$

Wahl's correction factor, K, for index 10 is 1.14.   The maximum stress in the wire is, in turn,

$$s_s = \frac{8FCK}{\pi d^2} = \frac{8 \times 10 \times 10 \times 1.14}{3.14 \times 0.1205^2}$$
$$= 24,100 \text{ psi}$$

which appears satisfactory.   The number of active coils needed may be obtained from the spring rate relation, or

$$n_a = \frac{Gd}{8C^3k} = \frac{11.5 \times 10^6 \times 0.1205}{8 \times 10^3 \times 50} = 3.45 \text{ coils}$$

In order to assure good seating against the beams, the spring should, preferably, be squared and ground.   The total number of coils is, therefore,

$$n = n_a + 2 = 3.45 + 2 = 5.45 \text{ coils}$$

The uncompressed spring will be

$$n_a d + \frac{P}{K} = 3.45 \times 0.1205 + \frac{10.0}{50} = 0.616 \text{ in. long}$$

The center distance between beams is

$$0.616 + 2 \times 0.510 = 1.64 \text{ in.}$$

The results thus are: the beam cross sections are 1.02 in. deep by 0.510 in. wide; the spring is wound of No. 11 music wire to a coil diameter of 1.205 in. and 5.45 coils with both ends squared and ground.

It must be indicated that several alternate spring designs are possible.   It must also be noted that the exact spring attachment details as well as those for the beams are yet to be designed.   Some additional information is needed before this can be properly done, so it is omitted here.   Additional, very informative, examples that actually illustrate both analysis and synthesis as defined in this text, are contained in the first two chapters of a most significant text by Ver Planck and Teare [2].

3–6. IN REVIEW

Professional confidence in problem solving can be acquired only by practice and with the insight gained through experience in working many problems.   Both analysis and synthesis involve anticipation before, as well as perception after, the event.   One must perform in the light of what one anticipates may bring success in a later step.   And simultaneously one must be prepared to go back to an earlier step to correct, or modify, or improve.

A distinction can be made between this, the professional engineering method, and the scientific approach. Generalizations of scientific principles are used to analyze and synthesize the truth of a particular concrete situation. In this sense, the professional method is deductive. In the scientific method, cases are studied sufficiently to produce a hypothesis. The hypothesis is then carefully and thoroughly checked, experimentally, to definitely ascertain its validity and establish a principle.

A critical review of the articles in this chapter will reveal no basic difference in approach between analysis and synthesis. It is primarily a matter of what falls in the unknown area. The professional approach in either case is little, if any, more than the application of common sense. Of course, if this application is to yield satisfaction, it must be backed by a store of knowledge of the laws of nature, of the properties and behavior of materials, of the manipulative techniques of mathematics and communication, and of the art of engineering that has solved problems of the past. The one very important difference between analysis and synthesis, as here depicted, is the extent of creativity required in synthesis. In analysis, since it deals with already created objects, creativity assumes a secondary role. In synthesis, however, the object, or some portion of it, is yet to be designed; creative skills are therefore called upon. As a result, several alternate solutions are possible, and added analytical common sense must be applied to select the best of the alternates.

The professional method for dealing with real engineering problems, whether analyzing or synthesizing, consists of five phases that are not necessarily performed independently of each other. Rather, these are usually so intertwined that the engineer must check and recheck, modify, correct, and improve as the experience that is gained suggests; feedback is a part of the solution. The five phases of the professional method are as follows.

1. *Definition.* The exact problem must be clearly established. Information concerning the problem must be gathered and facts obtained. The ultimate indication of the proper definition is the correct and complete free-body.

2. *Plan of attack.* Having identified the problem and drawn the free-bodies, it becomes possible to recognize the course the solution must take. Theories, principles, formulation and factual information needed can be formalized. The plan of solution approach is established.

3. *Execution.* The plan is carried through to completion of solution.

4. *Checking.* Formulation, manipulation and results are checked at every step.

5. *Feedback and generalization.* The experience gained as one proceeds is used to reevaluate what has already been done and to reconsider what is yet to follow. Knowledge gained is also realistically generalized and added to one's store of professional experience and self-confidence.

REFERENCES

1. H. W. Reddick and F. H. Miller, *Advanced Mathematics for Engineers*, 3rd Ed., John Wiley & Sons, Inc., New York, 1955.
2. D. W. Ver Planck, and B. R. Teare, Jr., *Engineering Analysis*, John Wiley & Sons, Inc., New York, 1954.

PROBLEMS

3–1. A book rests on a desk; construct the free-body of both the book and the desk.

3–2. Draw the free-body of a jet aircraft in flight at constant velocity.

3–3. A vibrating mass is held suspended by a spring and a viscous damper; construct the free-body of the mass.

3–4. Draw the free-body of a particle of fluid flowing through a tube.

3–5. Isolate and draw the free-body of the rotor of an electric motor.

3–6. Draw the free-body of a satellite in orbit.

3–7. Construct the free-body of the movable iron core of a solenoid.

3–8. The equation relating the variables of a magnet-type relay follows; k is a spring constant, and the other symbols are in customary units;

$$v^2(M_1 + M_2) = y[k_1(2x_1 - y) + k_2(2x_2 - y) - 2g(M_1 + M_2)]$$

check the equation dimensionally.

3–9. Derive the relation that expresses the amplitude of vibration of the mass of Problem 3, and check it dimensionally.

3–10. Check the equation of the state of the perfect gas dimensionally.

3–11. The over-all coefficient of heat transfer by convection and conduction through a wall from fluid to fluid is expressed by,

$$U = - \frac{1}{1/h_{c1} + \Delta x/k + 1/h_{c2}}$$

the symbols being in customary units. Check the equation dimensionally.

3–12. The electrical conductance of a combination of series-connected conductors is described by an equation analogous to that of Problem 3–11:

$$C = \frac{1}{(L/\sigma A)_1 + (L/\sigma A)_2 + (L/\sigma A)_3}$$

show the equation is dimensionally homogenous.

3–13. A classroom with a 10-ft ceiling measures 40 ft by 15 ft. Compute the mass of air contained in the room at standard atmospheric conditions.

3–14. Determine the specific volume and density of steam at 100 psi and 800° F.

3–15. Is a round steel rod 30 in. long and 1 in. in diam. likely to bend excessively when driven at right angles into rock by a laborer swinging a 10-lb sledge hammer squarely against its top?

3–16. An aluminum bushing $\frac{1}{8}$ in. thick and 1 in. OD is fitted in a steel cylinder 3 in. OD. Maximum stresses are not to exceed 1,000 psi in the aluminum bushing nor 6,000 psi in the steel cylinder. Determine the maximum diametral interference between bushing and cylinder.

3–17. An AISI-C1045 steel pipe, drawn 800° F, 5 in. OD, and 3 in. ID, is used in drilling oil wells. Drilling through the particular strata in question is expected to require a torque of 180,000 in.-lb, plus an additional friction torque of 25 in.-lb/ft drilled. What is the maximum depth that can be drilled with this pipe?

3–18. Superheated steam flows at an entrance pressure of 100 psi, temperature of 800° F, and zero velocity, through a nozzle. Calculate its velocity at the instant or point where the pressure becomes 60 psi.

3–19. A single cylinder, 4-cycle gasoline engine is needed to deliver 100 bhp at 600 rpm. Determine the cylinder size required.

3–20. A knuckle pin is made of AISI-1050 steel. The joint carries the 1,500-lb load while oscillating a small amount. Calculate the size pin needed to safely support the load.

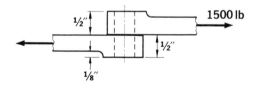

Problem 3–20.

DESIGN PROBLEMS

3–D1. A plate supported on knife edges 3 ft apart is to be used to weigh people in an electric strain-gage demonstration. Design the plate suitable for the set up.

3–D2. Astronauts will eventually have to perform many tasks in space while outside capsules and astroports. They are likely to be beset by many problems unless space-walk control becomes as natural as on earth. Some of the methods proposed are: pack rockets; leg, foot, head or torso motor control; photocell watching the position of the eyeballs; the astronaut's breath; and the astronaut's humming of different notes. Evaluate these suggestions. Can you suggest a better or, at least, another method.

3–D3.* An irreversible drive is needed to power the output shaft in either direction but automatically lock it to prevent rotation in the opposite direction at any given time. The action must be possible in either the clockwise

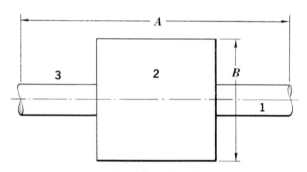

Problem 3–D3.

or counterclockwise direction. Specifically the shaft must satisfy the following requirements; the numbers and letters referring to those in the figure above.

    a. Unit 2 will automatically couple input shaft 1 to output shaft 3, when 1 is turned in either direction.

    b. Unit 2 will automatically lock output shaft 3 in whatever phase it happens to be when rotation of input shaft 1 is stopped, regardless of the direction of rotation.

    c. Unit 2 is to be a mechanical device as simple, foolproof, and economical in manufacture as possible.

    d. Unit 2 must make it possible to provide very small increments of movement, at least 0.2°.

    e. The backlash in either direction must not exceed $\frac{1}{10}$ the increment of movement.

    f. The complete unit must not exceed the over-all dimensions of $A = 5$ in. and $B = 3$ inches square.

    g. Shaft 1 must be capable of transmitting to shaft 3, through unit 2, a torque of 1,000 in.-lb.

    h. Shafts 1 and 3 must be in line.

Prepare the preliminary design of the unit.

    * From Joseph P. Vidosic, *Machine Design Projects*. Copyright © 1957. The Ronald Press Co., New York.

4

Decision in Design

It should be clear that design, whether of a simple machine element or a complex engineering system, requires much deliberation and subjective compromise. Formal knowledge is still so far from complete that unique solutions to engineering situations are not yet possible. Since human tastes are always involved, uniqueness is never likely to be fully realized. Instead, design will continue to involve series of decisions, each of which is hopefully based on accumulated experience, the wisdom of centuries, and good old common sense. At best, however, decisions retain some uncertainty, because decision-making is very complex. The process is subject to human whims and error. It is not fully developed and far from exact, depending as it does upon probability and statistical reasoning. Nevertheless, a rational approach, where it can be applied, is wise and more objective. Decision theory and decision-making are only touched upon in what follows—but it is a start.

4-1. NATURE OF DESIGN

Design depends upon science, technical knowledge, and several intangibles, such as talent, aptitude, physical insight, and judgment. All scientific principles are established via experiment; they are therefore basically empirical in nature. Theory is thus idealized; actual problems, on the other hand, are far from ideal. Before a problem can be solved or an item designed, idealized theory must be shifted closer to the reality of the actual situation while the problem itself is brought nearer to theory by somewhat idealizing it. What is implied is that a successful design depends upon an appropriate balance between the use of fundamental knowledge and the exercise of engineering judgment.

Design centers around the shaping of a new product or modification of an existing one. And the need for balance is noticeably affected by whether the design is of one kind or the other, that is, whether it is by:

1. *Evolution*—new design evolving out of older similar types or class of equipment; past experience is often plentiful and very helpful.
2. *Innovation*—relatively or completely new equipment; little or no past experience available; fundamentals and decision process most helpful.

It must be remembered, however, that at best engineering design is:

Compromise, not uniqueness
Useful, not colorful
Best, not absolute
Marketable, not grandiose.

4-2. DECISIONS

A design decision is usually, as already stated, a very complex task. Discrimination between a "good" and a "bad" decision is not an easy matter [1]. There are many factors that affect decisions; there always have been. But, advancing technology makes most design decisions more sensitive to these same factors, particularly as the design approaches innovation. Therefore, objectivity is as necessary in decision-making as the usual experience-backed intuitive subjective procedure. True, the competent designer carefully considers all evidence that bears on each direction a decision may take the design, and hopefully emerges with the one that promises the best result. He must do this for many factors, each of which affects the design in some way. He must, furthermore, synthesize as many alternate designs as the situation permits and then select the best.

It is the decision (eventually the one that determines the best design alternative) involving the major factors that is better made objectively. Making a decision objectively is to use a rational and formal approach rather than only intuition or even an educated guess or good judgment. The need for better decisions has always existed, but the modern economic situation in industry places a heavier burden upon the process. Some of the reasons for the heavier burden are:

1. Technological knowledge is growing exponentially, exposing more and more theory and principles that must be utilized to stay in business.

2. The number of alternate solutions is increasing, due to greater knowledge.
3. Improved data-processing methods provide more information for synthesizing.
4. Greater competition is such that the potential market becomes more sensitive to small design changes.
5. Equipment and system-performance demands are increasing.
6. Less adjusting time becomes available as expected service life decreases.
7. Large expenditure and hazards to life demand higher reliability in advanced engineering systems.
8. As less design "debugging" time becomes available, the need for speedier decision-making increases.
9. The increasing pressure for automation in industry allows less error in designs.
10. Governmental taxing policy and increased labor costs also leave less margin for error.

4-3. DECISION INDISPENSABILITY

The general reasons why objective decision-making is increasingly necessary in many design situations have been expressed above. To indicate more specifically some classes of questions that arise, as well as some possible alternative answers, groups of decision doubles are enumerated below. In addition to such questions, there arises, particularly in the larger systems, the need to select effectively among alternative designs. Designers must make decisions, among others, as to:

1. *Energy Sources*　　Mechanical or Electrical
　　　　　　　　　　　Chemical or Thermal
　　　　　　　　　　　Rocket or Jet Engine
　　　　　　　　　　　Spring or Battery
　　　　　　　　　　　Hydraulic or Pneumatic
　　　　　　　　　　　Instantaneous or Gradual
　　　　　　　　　　　Just Sufficient or Overload

2. *Component Elements*　Reactor or Boiler
　　　　　　　　　　　Heat Exchanger or Cooling Tower
　　　　　　　　　　　Gears or Pulleys
　　　　　　　　　　　Pipe or Channel
　　　　　　　　　　　Riveted or Welded
　　　　　　　　　　　Plain or Rolling Bearings
　　　　　　　　　　　Transistor or Vacuum Tube

3. *Market*	Custom or Mass Life or Mission Appeal or Engineering Function or Economics
4. *Design*	Exact or Economical Reliable or Passable Life Hazard or Property Damage Modified or New Primary or Secondary Part
5. *Controls*	Automatic or Manual Feedback or Cascade Parameter or Impulse–Response Optimization
6. *Material*	Brittle or Ductile Ferrous or Non-ferrous Special or Commercial Stronger or Smaller Better or Cheaper
7. *Loads*	Static or Dynamic Uniform or Irregular Constant or Spontaneous Measured or Calculated Frequent or Occasional
8. *Design Stress*	Elastic or Fracture Safer or Cheaper Lighter or Stronger Code or Individual
9. *Fabrication*	Machined or Forged Casting or Weldment Turn or Grind Close or Loose Tolerance Custom or Mass Production
10. *Maintenance*	Frequent or Rare Light or Extensive Expert or Average Thorough or Economical

4–4. ESCALATION

The number of required decisions multiplies rapidly as the number of factors increases. As D. L. Marples has indicated [2] the tree can grow to large size. Assume that three solutions exist to a primary problem. Should two sub-problems arise in the case of each solution, six choices are generated. If all six result in two new possible paths each, the number of decisions rises to twelve, and so it can continue. Suppose, for instance, there are m possibilities at the first stage and $(m \pm i)$ at each other stage, then the total number of required decisions becomes

$$1 \times m_1(m \pm i)_2(m \pm i)_3 \cdots (m \pm i)_n$$

Therefore, as already stated, the tree under discussion has

$$1 \times 3(3 - 1)(3 - 1) = 1 \times 3 \times 2 \times 2 = 12 \text{ decision paths}$$

The tree is shown in Fig. 4-1.

Now suppose the factor situation were such that the decision paths could flow from each first stage point to each second stage point, as

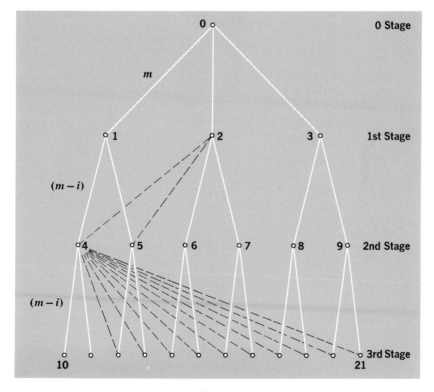

Fig. 4-1. The decision tree.

shown by broken lines generating from point 2, the number of possible alternatives becomes

$$1 \times 3(3 + 3)(3 - 1) = 36$$

Suppose, in addition, each second stage point, like 4, could connect to each third stage point, as shown, again by broken lines, the number of alternative paths now becomes

$$1 \times 3(3 + 3)(3 + 9) = 216$$

It is easy to expect the situation to get quite impossible. It is, therefore, also easy to see why rationalization and objectivity may be necessary. First of all, every possibility of intuitively eliminating as many decision paths as possible should be investigated. Some paths may be relatively unimportant, others meaningless, and still others even undesirable. Thus fewer decisions are left; of these some may be more critical or significant than the rest. The less critical can prob-

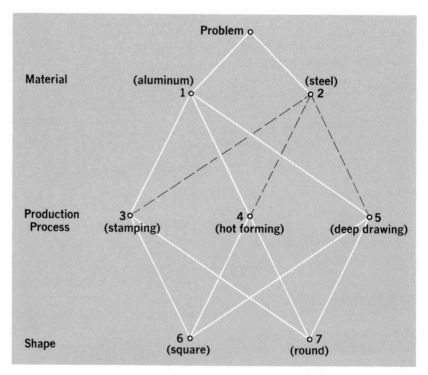

Fig. 4–2.   Decision tree for ice-tray production.

ably be settled via experience-backed engineering judgment.   Decision theory need only be applied to the more critical questions.

For instance, suppose, in a simple but possible case, there are two apparently suitable materials, three possible production processes, and two acceptable shapes for an ice tray.   The materials are aluminum and plain carbon steel; the processes are stamping, deep-drawing, and hot-forming; and the shapes are square and rectangular.   The tree looks as in Fig. 4–2.

Notice that one material offers six possibilities, and both create twelve possible paths.   Further consideration, however, makes it reasonable to eliminate steel, because of aluminum's preferred corrosion-resistance properties.   Furthermore, hot-forming is decided unsatisfactory, because of the better surface finish and dimensional control of cold-working processes.   Thus only paths 1–3–6, 1–3–7, 1–5–6, and 1–5–7 are left.   Objective decisions based on cost of tray material for equal ice volumes and on process characteristics will hopefully determine the best path.

4–5. DECISION-MAKING

Decision-making is concerned in general with the selection of an action that appears to promise the most desirable return; profit, yes, but it could also include such features as utility, safety, or ease of maintenance, for instance.   Thus in making a decision a choice must be made from among several possible acts by considering the consequences that may result as each act is applied to the problem at hand. Decisions are made under:

1. *Certainty*, where the action is known to lead to specific consequences.
2. *Risk*, when the action leads to specific outcomes that occur with only known probability.
3. *Uncertainty*, where the action results in consequences that have unknown probabilities.

Unfortunately most design decisions are likely to fall in the uncertainty classification, which accounts for the great difficulty and complexity in design decision-making.

The benefit to be derived from the appropriate decision may be a matter of economics, social effects, financial feasibility, political consequence, or physical realizability.   Though any one of the measures may be important in a particular case, the designer's direct concern is primarily that of physical realization.   It is, however, clear that budgetary as well as time considerations are likely to be involved. A design manufactured for profit in a competitive market must be developed at cost of time and money, which are not independent of available funds and proper market timing.

Since uncertainty is involved in making decisions, judgment—honest and prejudiced—probability, statistical averages, logic, and of course the human function are bound to be involved. The conservatives are concerned with just avoiding failure rather than being heroic. They will likely try to get the most out of the worst possible situation, such as using lowest daily output as a basis for annual rate. Others, optimistic at heart, will arrive at decisions hoping that the most favorable situation will be effective. Finally, and probably the most scientific, still others will base decisions on the law of averages and formal probability, which will tend to maximize the more stable, long-range outputs.

Such is the process of decision-making. It is formalized and systematized, and yet it is probable and statistical. It is objective and mathematical, and yet it depends upon imperfect human reasoning and attitudes. It tries to be explicit, and yet total facts are not all known. It still leaves much to be desired, but it is the only approach that proves better, because it tends to minimize subjectivity.

4–6. STATISTICS

The statistical evaluation of available data does lead to more intelligent decisions, at least within the framework of specified objectives. And probability principles assist with the predictions that are always involved in decision-making. It is thus proper to briefly review these.

Statistics may be defined as the scientific collection and systematic evaluation of a sufficient amount of proper data. Probability theory permits, on the other hand, the use of these data so one can act with a higher degree of confidence.

It is too costly and physically too difficult to collect all the relevant information in a given situation. A sample of the total (the universe) must therefore be used. The population or universe may be fifty gears that arrive on order, or the 100-gross screw order. Or it could be an almost infinite population, such as may be involved in establishing the exact quality of the water supply in city X. The need for an appropriate sample is made evident by the water example, if not by the others.

Obviously the sample, whatever its size, should be representative of the entire population. Such, of course, is seldom the case except by sheer coincidence. The proper size of a random sample can fortunately be reasonably estimated statistically. For instance, if a study is made of a sample increasing in size, it is found that one of its properties, the standard error, varies exponentially with sample size, as shown qualitatively in Fig. 4-3. Thus in effect the size of a random sample

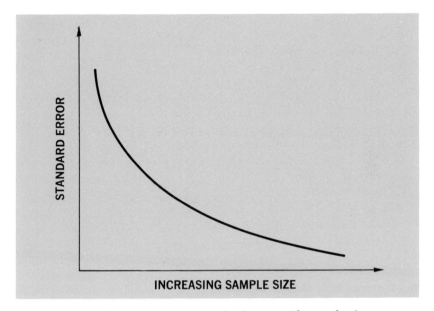

Fig. 4-3. Decrease of standard error with sample size.

reaches a magnitude beyond which the difference between its properties and those of the total population becomes negligible, or at least as small as acceptable.

A plot of the frequency with which a particular value of the variable occurs, called a frequency distribution histogram, can be used to determine sample size via another property (to be defined) identified as the standard deviation. Such a diagram, simplified, is Fig. 4-4. Several types of such frequency distributions are possible—for example, normal or Gaussian, Poisson, binomial, flattened. Probably the most common is the "normal" bell-shaped distribution defined mathematically by

$$y = \frac{h}{\sqrt{\pi}} e^{-h^2 x^2}$$

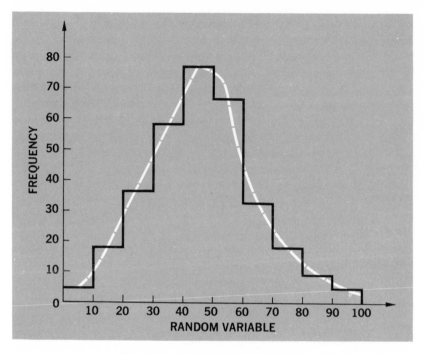

Fig. 4–4.   Frequency histogram.

where x represents the individual values of N readings, e is the base of natural logarithms, and h, the modulus of precision, is

$$h = \sqrt{\frac{(N-1)}{2 \Sigma x^2}}$$

There are three averages obtainable from such a series of data.   The most common is the arithmetic mean, defined as

$$M_A = \frac{\Sigma x}{N}$$

The second representative value is the median or simply the middle value of the array organized by order of magnitude.   It is often more closely representative, because it minimizes the influence of extreme values.   Finally, there is the mode, which is the value occurring most frequently.

The dispersion occurring in a set of values is most effectively described by the *standard deviation*.   This variance measure expresses the magnitude of the difference between the arithmetic average and the individual values in units of the variable. Symbolically it is expressed

$$D = \sqrt{\frac{\Sigma (X - M_A)^2}{N}}$$

It can be shown that for the symmetrical bell-shaped curve [3], 68.26% of the total area under the curve exists within one standard deviation to each side of the mean, 95.6% within $2D$, and 99.72% within $3D$.

The *standard error* of the random sample mean can be computed from

$$S_e = \frac{D}{\sqrt{N}}$$

Thus the standard deviation of the random sample can be computed and then the standard error found. This can be used to judge the appropriateness of the sample data. An example is worked to illustrate the estimation.

Example 4–1. One hundred pieces of $\frac{1}{4}$-in. rod are cut to a length of 67.5 in. A check of 20 rods selected at random is made. Compute the standard error. The measured length of each of the 20 sample rods is presented in Table 4–1.

Solution: The arithmetic average and standard deviation are determined, using the values in Table 4–1.

$$M_A = \frac{\Sigma X}{N} = \frac{1349.62}{20} = 67.48 \text{ in.}$$

$$D = \sqrt{\frac{\Sigma (X - M_A)^2}{N}} = \sqrt{\frac{1.2730}{20}} = 0.2523 \text{ in.}$$

and

$$S_e = \frac{D}{\sqrt{N}} = \frac{0.2523}{\sqrt{20}} = 0.05638 \text{ in.}$$

The value of the arithmetic average is, therefore,

$$M_A = 67.48 \text{ in.} \pm 0.056$$

meaning that the rods vary in length between 67.43 in. and 67.54 in. Whether the variation is excessive depends upon the accuracy of length required (not given in the problem). Whether the sample size is sufficient could be established by making a, say, thirty- or forty-sample run and noting how much the standard deviation and error change. If no change occurs in the second significant figure, the twenty-size sample would be sufficient as a running check.

Table 4–1
Rod Lengths

Reading	M_A	$(X - M_A)$	$(X - M_A)^2$
67.05	67.48	−0.43	0.1849
67.06		−0.42	0.1764
67.13		−0.35	0.1225
67.16		−0.32	0.1024
67.27		−0.21	0.0441
67.35		−0.13	0.0169
67.37		−0.11	0.0121
67.44		−0.04	0.0016
67.49		0.01	0.0001
67.50		0.02	0.0004
67.50		0.02	0.0004
67.51		0.03	0.0009
67.54		0.06	0.0036
67.60		0.12	0.0144
67.62		0.14	0.0196
67.69		0.21	0.0441
67.73		0.25	0.0625
67.80		0.32	0.1024
67.87		0.39	0.1521
67.94		0.46	0.2116
1349.62			1.2730

4–7. PROBABILITY

Probability involves chance, the chance that a particular consequence will occur under a particular set of conditions. It studies random phenomena occurring in an aggregate of a large number of equal-state items. Probability is often a matter of purely inductive reasoning, where personal judgments predominate. "You will probably be a successful engineer" is a subjective judgment. Probability can deal, however, in its more rigorous approach, with outcomes that are more certain, or at least more concrete, because they are statistically supported. Feller [4] calls this, quite appropriately, *physical probability*. Gnedenko [5] refers to it as *real occurrence*. The numerical determinations so made require sophisticated statistical methods, themselves based on refined probability theory.

Three types of events may be defined. A *certain event* is one that occurs inevitably whenever a set of conditions is imposed. For instance, the first law of thermodynamics is such a case, because the energy always remains constant (the event) in an isolated system, no matter what the conversion process, since energy can be neither created nor destroyed.

An *impossible event* is, on the other hand, one that cannot occur when the set of conditions is realized. That the velocity of a missile orbiting a planet is constant is an impossibility, because the missile is changing direction as it speeds along.

An event that may or may not occur when the set of conditions is applied is a *random event*. An example of such an event is the claim that you will make 92 on the next test; it is quite possible to earn this grade, but so are many other scores possible. A random event is thus neither inevitable nor impossible.

The probability that a random event will occur whenever the set of conditions is realized is said to equal P. Probabilistic theory holds that the probability P implies that between an event and the set of conditions there exists a relation that is independent of the observer. Finding the nature of this relation can, however, be quite a task. It is a statistical matter expressing the relative frequency of occurrence in a large number of trials. Since the required data are not always available nor possibly even feasibly obtainable, probability estimates are sometimes more subjective than desirable. For instance, it has been pointed out that there are 10^{30} possible card distributions in bridge, each distribution usually assumed equally possible. This cannot be feasibly proven, because it would require billions of years to conduct the experiments with every living person playing some 80,000 games each day. Sensible judgments are therefore necessary; they do help to systematize the determination and so are most useful.

References [4] and [5] are suggested to those wishing to study probability beyond the brief review given here.

The probability that a reading will fall within a given range of the variable, say $\pm x$, is mathematically expressed for the common, normal distribution by

$$P_{(X)} = \frac{h}{\sqrt{\pi}} \int_{-x}^{x} e^{-h^2 x^2}\, dx$$

which is, of course, the area under the normal distribution curve between the given limits. The above requires prior knowledge of the distribution. Since this is often not known, a more empirical probability definition is more useful. Thus the probability that event A will occur in N outcomes is expressed as

$$P(A) = \frac{\text{Number of ways in } N \text{ possibilities that produce } A}{\text{Number of possibilities } N}$$

Analysis of the above formulation indicates that the probability scale runs from *zero*, when event A cannot occur, to *one*, when event A can happen N ways, that is the event must happen.

Some additional rules can be very helpful in arriving at probability estimates. The principles can best be expressed symbolically, but to do this a symbolism must be decided upon. The probability that event A will happen if conditions X occur may be represented symbolically as: $P(A/X)$, or $P(A)$ for short. Also if B is a second independent event, then AB means "both A and B," and $A + B$ means "either A or B or both." Furthermore, the complementary or denial of event A is expressed as $\bar{A}$ and vice versa.

$P(A) + P(\bar{A}) = 1$ (Complementary Law)

$P(AB) = P(A) \times P(B)$ (Multiplication Law)

$P(A + B) = P(A) + P(B) - P(AB)$ (Addition Law)

$P(A + B) = P(A) + P(B)$ if A and B are mutually exclusive, which makes $P(AB) = 0$

$P(A) + P(B) + \cdots = 1$ if the events are mutually exclusive and collectively exhaustive (all possible events included)

Example 4–2. The weather bureau predicts that the probability of rain Sunday is 60%, of snow, 70%, and of both rain and snow, 20%. The WGIT announcer wants to spice his report with additional predictions, so he asks you to compute three additional probabilities.

1. That it will rain Sunday but not snow.
2. That it will rain and/or snow Sunday.
3. That it will either rain or snow, but not both, on Sunday.

Solution: The solution can be made using the rules stated above. Rain is identified as event A, and snow as event B.

1. The denial of B is

$$P(\bar{B}) = 1 - P(B) = 1.0 - 0.7 = 0.3$$

Therefore rain but no snow has a probability of

$$P(A\bar{B}) = P(A) \times P(\bar{B}) = 0.6 \times 0.3 = 0.18$$

2. The probability that it may rain or snow or both Sunday is found thus.

$$P(AB) = P(A) \times P(B) = 0.6 \times 0.7 = 0.42$$

and

$$P(A + B) = P(A) + P(B) - P(AB)$$
$$= 0.6 + 0.7 - 0.42 = 0.88$$

3. To find the probability of either rain or snow, but not both,

$$P(\bar{A}) = 1 - P(A) = 1 - 0.6 = 0.4$$
$$P(B\bar{A}) = P(B) \times P(\bar{A}) = 0.7 \times 0.4 = 0.28$$

Therefore, since $A\bar{B}$ and $B\bar{A}$ are mutually exclusive,

$$P(A\bar{B} + B\bar{A}) = P(A\bar{B}) + P(B\bar{A})$$
$$0.18 + 0.28 = 0.46$$

4-8. DECISION PROCESS

Arriving at a conclusion as to which alternative solution, answer, decision, or design is best in a particular situation is a weighty and not absolutely defined matter. As already indicated, it can be subjective, because personal desirabilities and probability estimates, often unsupported by conclusive data, are involved. A systematic approach is, nevertheless, much more likely to lead to a more appropriate decision than is mere guessing or even contemplating.

One of the more satisfactory methods of decision-making is based on the Bayesian model [6]. The model consists of a matrix in which an expected consequence results when a condition is applied to each possible act. Two additional matrices, formed by assigning numerical values to the desirability and probability of the occurrence of each consequence, are also involved.

The first of these matrices expresses the relative desirability of the particular consequence. The desirability can be negative, since it is more or less relative. Thus the desirability scale can be anything whatsoever, just so the algebraically larger number is assigned to the more desirable consequence. It might, however, be simplest to use the scale 0-to-1 where 0 identifies the least desirable or least liked consequence and 1 the most desirable or best liked. For the decision to be as impartial as possible, desirability figures must, of course, be established as objectively as possible, free of all personal bias but incorporating all the experience and knowledge that can be summoned. Partiality must be kept at the very minimum in the probability matrix as well.

The second of the additional matrices is the one expressing the probability that a consequence will occur when the condition is applied to the act. Probability theory should be applied whenever the situation permits. If conditions are so set up that all consequences of any one act are mutually exclusive, each row of the probability array must add to one unit when normalized. The essential convention is, however, only that all entries in each row of the probability matrix add to the same positive sum.   Thus, the simplest conclusion is to always normalize each row of figures to say, the base 1.   The sum will, therefore, always have to be 1—an easy check.

The expected desirability of each act, establishing the preference order of the acts, is computed by algebraically summing the products of corresponding entries in the two matrices.

The process is probably best explained by means of an example or two.   The first deals with an important general question, whereas the second is a matter of design.

Example 4–3.   The history of boilers and power plants is based on the combustion of fossil fuels.   The nuclear reactor now appears to hold promise for the larger power plants of the future.   Local as well as general factors affect its choice.   What are the advantages, disadvantages, cost and the overall choice?

The more significant factors concerning conventional and nuclear power plants enumerate as follows:

1. For large plants the initial *cost* of nuclear power plants is only about 10–25% higher; the cost of fuel, and its transportation, storage, and feed to furnace, is much less.   Over the life of the plant it is therefore estimated that the cost of power to the consumer will not be much, if any, more than for the conventional plant.

2. About 4 electron-volts of energy are released when a molecule of carbon combines with oxygen as compared to about 200×10^6 ev when uranium-235 captures a neutron.   The tremendously larger energy release affects the *size* and design of the combustion device.   Thus the nuclear reactor is much smaller than the conventional boiler furnace for the same thermal output.

3. A reactor is much more self-sufficient, because the reactor *fuel* core contains a two- to three-year's supply.   However, the fuel is expensive, and in case of a malfunction delays due to radioactivity can prevail.

4. Boilers require a continuous removal of combustion *waste* products while nuclear waste generally is not removed until the fuel is replaced.   Radioactivity, however, adds to the problem of even the less frequent removal.

5. No visible flame is present in the reactor.   Thus the operator must work *blind*, depending entirely on the readings of instruments.

6. *Shielding* against radioactivity and containment in case of malfunction are major problems in reactor design and operation.

7. The public consideration of a power plant as a *nuisance* can have an effect upon the selection of an otherwise suitable plant location.   The extra potential hazard of a nuclear plant engenders an even stronger aversion.

8. Design and construction of the nuclear plant are more demanding, because of the essential greater structural *reliability*.

9. The greater seriousness of a breakdown requires more and better trained operational and preventive maintenance *manpower*.

Solution: The acts to be investigated are *nuclear* or *conventional*. Based on arguments recorded above, conditions are *cost, size, fuel, blind, shielding, nuisance, reliability,* and *manpower*. The consequent, desirability and probability matrices follow.

	Cost	Size Advantage	Fuel Advantage	Waste Disposal	Blind Operation	Shielding	Nuisance	Structural Reliability Required	Manpower Skill Required
Nuclear	Higher	Exists	Some	Simple	Yes	Req'd	Greater	Greater	Higher
Conventional	Lower	Absent	Absent	Cont.	No	Unnec.	Lesser	Lesser	Lower

The desirability matrix is established by assigning values relatively expressing the estimated desirability of each consequence. These relative values are impersonally established, judging as objectively as possible how desirable each condition seems to be when applied to each act.

	Cost	Size	Fuel	Waste	Blind	Shielding	Nuisance	Reliability	Manpower
Nuclear	0	1	0.6	0.9	0.6	0	0.5	0.8	0.5
Conventional	1	0	0.2	0.7	0.9	1	0.7	1	0.9

The probability matrix establishes the probability of the stated consequence occurring when the condition is applied to the act. It, of course, extends in the range 0 to 1; that is, the chance a consequence will obtain is 0%, 100%, or something in between. Judgments should be most impersonal based on knowledge and understanding. Where facts and figures are available, statistical techniques should be used to determine probabilities. In general, probabilities are established by deciding how likely it is that a consequence will occur. For instance, considering the cost column, one asks "How likely is it that the construction cost of a nuclear plant will be higher than that of a conventional?" Based on present trends, chances are 100% that it will. Thus the 1. Similarly the probability that the cost of the conventional fossil-fuel plant will be lower is 100%.

	Cost	Size	Fuel	Waste	Blind	Shielding	Nuisance	Reliability	Manpower
Nuclear	1	1	0.8	0.7	1	1	0.6	1	0.9
Conventional	1	1	0.9	1	0.8	1	0.8	1	0.8

The probability matrix is next normalized to cause both rows to add to the same amount; thus, for the first value,

$$\frac{1}{1 + 1 + .8 + .7 + 1 + 1 + .6 + 1 + .9} = \frac{1}{8} = 0.125$$

	Cost	Size	Fuel	Waste	Blind	Shielding	Nuisance	Reliability	Manpower
Nuclear	0.125	0.125	0.100	0.088	0.125	0.125	0.075	0.125	0.112
Conventional	0.120	0.120	0.108	0.120	0.096	0.120	0.096	0.120	0.096

The expected desirability of each act, is computed by multiplying corresponding entries in the two matrices (desirability and normalized probability) and summing the products. Thus,

Nuclear: $0 \times 0.125 + 1 \times 0.125 + 0.6 \times 0.100 + 0.9 \times 0.088$
$+ 0.6 \times 0.125 + 0 \times 0.125 + 0.5 \times 0.075$
$+ 0.8 \times 0.125 + 0.5 \times 0.112 = 0.533$

Conventional: $1 \times 0.120 + 0 \times 0.120 + 0.2 \times 0.108 + 0.7 \times 0.120$
$+ 0.9 \times 0.096 + 1 \times 0.120 + 0.7 \times 0.096$
$+ 1 \times 0.120 + 0.9 \times 0.096 = 0.705$

This analysis, therefore, favors the conventional power plant. If the base is set at 1.00 for the less desirable, the conventional becomes

$$1 + (0.705 - 0.533) = 1.17$$

and the increasing order of preference is

Nuclear: 1.00
Conventional: 1.17

The decision should be the conventional fossil-fuel power plant. It is probably the American pioneering spirit, which fosters the desire to innovate and progress, that has led the power industry to decide to make half of its new plants nuclear.

Example 4–4. A large counterweight is to be made. Two questions needing decision confront the design engineer. Should the counterweight be cast or forged, and should it be made square or round in cross section?

Solution: The consequence matrix is established as shown below. These consequences are obviously based on a knowledge of the processes of casting and forging involved as well as considerations of the relative strengths of different sections.

	Square	Round
Cast	Cheapest	Cheaper
Forged	Faster	Stronger

The desirabilities appear to be as shown in the following matrix. A desirability range other than 0–1 is used to illustrate its validity.

	Square	Round
Cast	2.0	1.0
Forged	0.5	1.5

The probabilities are judged in normalized form, because of the simplicity of only two columns in this case.

	Square	Round
Cast	0.4	0.6
Forged	0.5	0.5

Thus the expected desirabilities are

Cast: $2 \times .4 + 1 \times .6 = 1.4$
Forged: $.5 \times .5 + 1.5 \times .5 = 1.0$

The better choice then seems to be to cast the counterweight. And since there appears a fair chance that the square section will prove cheaper, it is decided upon.

4–9. EVALUATION PROCESS

Another approach to decision-making is particularly suitable where the apparently best solution is to be selected out of a group of alter-

TABLE 4–2

Evaluation Table

Common Characteristic	Weighting Factor	System A Pitot Tube		System B Nozzle		System C Orifice		System D Lift		System E Propulsion	
		Capability	Value	Capability	Value	Capability	Value	Capability	Value	Capability	Value
Range	8	10	80	8	64	8	64	10	80	10	80
Low Speed Sensitivity	10	3	30	2	20	2	20	8	80	8	80
Mounting Ease	9	7	63	7	63	7	63	9	81	9	81
Cost	7	10	70	10	70	10	70	9	63	9	63
Bulkiness	8	9	72	8	64	7	56	7	56	6	48
Ruggedness	4	8	32	9	36	9	36	10	40	10	40
Reliability	6	6	36	6	36	6	36	7	42	7	42
Durability	8	5	40	6	48	6	48	9	72	9	72
Totals			423		401		393		514		506

nates. For instance, the selection of the most suitable path of those left on a decision tree could well be made, provided proper value measures are set up. The method is more subjective and not as sound mathematically as the previous but, nevertheless, it is rational and systematic.

Appropriate characteristics common to the solutions being considered are established. These are specified requirements dealing with such as function, cost, wear, and aesthetics. The capability of each system with regard to each characteristic is established on a numerical-value scale. The relative importance of each characteristic can also be expressed as a numerical weighting factor. The sum of the products of system capability by weighting factor is used as the final selection measure. The process can best be explained with an illustrative case.

Example 4-5. The speed of motor boats must be controlled in order to assure greater safety and, sometimes, less disturbance to shore property. Speeds down to below 5 knots must be measurable. A manufacturer of marine accessories decides to enter the business by marketing a suitable speedometer. His preliminary designs are based each on a different basic principle of flow measurement. The manufacturer must evaluate these possible solutions and decide upon the best approach.

Solution: The eight characteristics enumerated in Table 4-2 are considered important, with the second and third being the most critical. Weighting-factor and system-capability scales of 1 to 10 are used. The weighting factors are a matter of subjective evaluation based upon the designer's careful consideration of his understanding of each characteristic.

From a glance at the totals in Table 4-2, System D appears best.

REFERENCES

1. M. K. Starr, *Product Design and Decision Theory*, Prentice-Hall, Inc., Englewood Cliffs, N.J., 1963.

2. D. L. Marples, *The Decisions of Engineering Design*, The Institute of Designers, London, July 1960.

3. A. M. Mood, and F. A. Graybill, *Introduction to the Theory of Statistics*, 2nd Ed., McGraw-Hill Book Co., Inc., New York, 1963.

4. W. Feller, *An Introduction to Probability Theory and Its Applications*, Vol. I, 2nd Ed., John Wiley & Sons, Inc., New York, 1957, p. 4.

5. B. V. Gnedenko, *The Theory of Probability*, Chelsea Publ. Co., New York, 1962, p. 17.

6. R. C. Jeffrey, *The Logic of Decision*, McGraw-Hill Book Co., Inc., New York, 1965.

PROBLEMS

4–1. Explain the difference between an objective and a subjective decision.

4–2. Which five reasons for the currently heavier burden upon the decision process do you consider more important and why?

4–3. Define a random event. What other kinds of probability events are there?

4–4. Add one more alternate pair to any three groups of decision questions of Article 4–3.

4–5. There are two alternate designs, each of which can be made of any one of three materials, and each material can be obtained either in the hot-rolled or cold-drawn condition. Draw a decision tree indicating all possible paths. Select the path you believe best. Why?

4–6. Compute the maximum number of paths in the case where the 0-stage contains one point, and the 1st-stage has two, each of which goes to four possibilities in the 2nd-stage.

4–7. One hundred readings of the thickness of a metal strip are as given below. Compute the standard error.

Thickness (in.)	Frequency	Thickness (in.)	Frequency
0.0408	2	0.0415	14
0.0409	2	0.0416	18
0.0410	3	0.0417	17
0.0411	5	0.0418	13
0.0412	3	0.0419	5
0.0413	7	0.0420	1
0.0414	10		100

4–8. Identify a personal judgment statement that you often make representing pure inductive reasoning on your part.

4–9. Prove conclusively that the order of preference would not have changed had the desirability interval in Example 4–3 been increased by a positive factor m.

4–10. Two-hundred wrist watch shafts of the same diameter and length are contained in a box. One-fourth of these are, however, of a tolerance closer than the rest. If ten rods are randomly picked out of the box at once, what is the probability of half of them being the closer tolerance shafts?

4–11. Considering such factors as loss of full earning years, availability of fellowships, later earning power, professional contribution capacity, prestige and personal satisfaction, determine the expected desirabilities for earning the B.S., M.S., and Ph.D. degrees.

4–12. Determine the order of preference for earning the B.S., M.S., and Ph.D. degrees using the evaluation-table method. Base it on the factors given in Problem 4–11.

4–13. Are unique solutions to real engineering problems probable? Discuss.

4–14. Define and discuss design by evolution and by innovation.

4–15. Discuss your understanding of what is meant by "best not absolute" and "marketable not grandiose."

4–16. Discuss three benefits that may be derived from appropriate decision-making.

4–17. Explain and discuss why objective decision-making is better than subjective.

4–18. Discuss the matter of a proper statistical sample.

4–19. Discuss the effect of the size of a random sample upon its properties as compared to those of the total population.

DESIGN PROBLEMS

4–D1. The Mark Machinery Company is designing a new series of axial compressors. Sizes are to vary from 100,000 to 1,000,000 cfm at speeds of around 12,000 rpm. Using the Bayesian approach, decide whether plain (hydrodynamic) or rolling bearings should be selected for the series. Such factors as capacity, speed, overload, space, weight, lubrication, starting and running friction, and maintenance should be taken into account.

4–D2. Develop the evaluation table needed to determine the relative values of the Gathering methods shown along the vertical axis in Fig. 5–2. Utilizing the evaluation-process approach, select the gathering method that appears to possess preference for the design of the yard raking machine.

4–D3. A high-speed, long-life, 1 hp electric motor is to be mass produced. The decision as to whether to use standard or precision ball bearings must be made. Initial cost of the standard bearing is $3, whereas that of the precision is $5: Cost of installation of the precision bearing is estimated 25% higher than that of the standard bearing. The standard bearing must, however, be lubricated three times as often. Which of the two bearings does the Bayesian technique favor?

4–D4. Determine the preference of bearing for the axial compressor of Problem 4–D1 using the evaluation-table process. Base the selection on the factors given in the problem using a weighting-factor scale of 1 to 10.

4–D5. Using the evaluation-process approach, establish the order of preference for the nuclear and conventional power plants of Example 4–3. Use the nine factors given in the example.

4–D6. Re-evaluate Example 4–3, adding the pioneering spirit of American industry as a tenth factor.

5

Creativity

Alfred N. Goldsmith's definition of creativity reads: "Creativity is the production and disclosure of a new fact, law, relationship, device or product, process, or system based generally on available knowledge but not following directly, easily, simply, or even by usual logical processes from the guiding information at hand." And Calvin W. Taylor wrote that "Creativity at its highest level has probably been as important as any human quality in changing history and in reshaping the world."

Creativity does not, however, imply that the total idea is necessarily formulated at once. The process instead consists usually of some anticipation of the whole idea, which is gradually elaborated one detail upon another until a clear structure is formed. The process is not necessarily spontaneous; it can be a slow development of an intuitive feeling as to what belongs and what does not.

Evidence seems to point strongly to the probability that creativity can be developed. It is, therefore, essential that a study of it be made; and what follows deals with creativity, the process, and the ways of developing one's potential in this connection.

5–1. COMPREHENSIVE DESIGNER

The late John E. Arnold, who conducted extensive investigations in the area and was one of its early expounders, held that all people have potential for creative activity. He also wrote that a comprehensive designer possesses the following attributes [1].

1. He is motivated by very broad concepts of human activity, thought, and behavior.
2. He has a complete understanding for and knowledge of the organisms for which he is designing, and the total environment in which the product will be conceived and used.

3. He is articulate in all types and levels of communication.

4. He is able to balance his ability to analyze, synthesize, and evaluate.

5. He possesses a mastery of the creative process.

It is quite obvious that the above defines a real and complete designer. It is also suspected that such individuals are as rare as geniuses. Arnold, however, believed that the lower "rank" of "creative engineer" can be attained by many, because the creative process is a disciplinary matter that can be studied and developed. On the other hand, J. A. Anderson of the AC Spark Plug Division of General Motors reported [2] that psychologists disagree on the possibility of training people to be more creative. Some claim, instead, that one is either born creative or not. However, when AC conducted an investigation of its engineers, it found otherwise. The creative ability improved by forty-one per cent, as measured by aptitude tests, among their engineers as a result of training in creativity. Another authority, Dr. Anne Roe of Harvard put it this way [3]: "I think that the creative approach to life is built into the human species—as part of normal functioning—and that our problem is to let it go rather than get it started." And Calvin W. Taylor wrote in his enlightening book *Creativity* [4]: "Because creative acts affect enormously not only scientific progress, but society in general, those nations who learn best how to identify, develop, and encourage the creative potential in their people may find themselves in very advantageous positions." Luis DeFlorez put it another way [5]: "The ingenious man, the ingenious organization and the ingenious nation—other things being equal—have the best prospect for survival and success in the world today."

Creation is an infinite, continuous process. It keeps growing faster and faster, because there are more things on which to build. Each new creation presents applications in many directions and each application raises new questions and new demands. Close to three million patents have been granted in the United States since the head of the Patent Office predicted in 1833 that "Everything seems to have been done. I just don't see how anything else can be invented, because the U. S. Patent Office is running over with inventions." And, of course, patents do not include all ideas that leave an impact upon humanity.

5–2. SOME CONCEPTS OF CREATIVITY

All problems that confront the engineer, or any human being for that matter, are in their solution either *analytical* or *creative*. When a problem has a single right answer it is analytical in nature; problems in mathematics and the sciences are ordinarily of this kind. Those having a multiplicity of acceptable solutions, like most real engineering problems, are creative. This is not, however, to imply that a multi-solutional problem is necessarily always solved creatively. It is possible to arrive at a solution by routine methods and possibly even by chance. Nevertheless, it has been shown that such solutions by non-creative engineers are usually more costly in time and sometimes not quite as good. Furthermore, the nation cannot afford, in this fast modern age, many such inefficient and wasteful approaches which depend on sheer quantity of men and facilities.

Creativity, like ability to teach and even learning capacity, is difficult to measure. One can not tell by examining the end product whether its design involved creativity. And, furthermore, one can not look at the situation that is to be solved and decide that it can be solved only by creative means.

Creativity must not be confused with productivity. The former is a high level of mental activity, quality conceptualism; the latter implies quantity instead of quality.

It is claimed that in order for something to be creative, it must be useful and of benefit to mankind. But being creative does not necessarily add value. In fact, achievements of no value can be useless, harmful, immoral, and even criminal. What is significant, however, from the engineering design point of view, is that the most brilliant idea remains useless, and therefore not a creation, until it is developed, communicated, and made ready for use by others. Creativity occurs in many professions, but in engineering it is most important. Engineers are the creators who take the discoveries of science and the results of research and transform them into design creations of real benefit to mankind (unfortunately, the benefits to one group of people are sometimes harmful to other groups). The entire scientist–engineer–technician–management team must be creative, each in his area of effort, for greatest over-all benefit.

Scientists create new knowledge and new understanding of nature and thus open new fields of activity.

Engineers create by taking the findings of research and transforming them into new designs that benefit mankind.

Technicians create by improving the techniques and methods used to carry designs to detail conclusion.

Manufacturers create by transforming raw materials into economical products.

Salesmen create the desire for useful products.

Management creates the operating business firm.

Von Fange summarizes [6] creativity this way. "The opportunity for creative accomplishment exists in every vocational pursuit. The rate of improvement depends not on the contributions of a few, but on the sum of the changes conceived by the many. To clarify what professional creativity is, we should consider one aspect at a time. Confusion about creative work exists due to pride of one's own profession, ambiguous considerations of usefulness and timeliness, and the shades of meaning given words. A creation is simply an association new to us. It can be undirected, directed for good, or misdirected, depending on our purpose and the motives of those who use it. The worth of creative work depends greatly on the worth of the objective chosen for effort."

5-3. THE CREATIVE PERSONALITY

What constitutes the creative personality is an interesting question. As already mentioned, the claim has been made that all are born with the potential. The essentials are present initially, but effort must be exercised to develop them. Heredity seems to provide the "equipment," but a specific person must get to understand it, to improve it, to maintain it, and to apply it in the environment of his own being and his own society. He must learn how to interact effectively with people and climate. He must develop interests, and motivation, and values.

Creativity can be either fostered or inhibited by one's vision, attitude, and mental health. Good mental health permits an individual to function more naturally, more freely, because he is not overly concerned as to what others think about him or, more specifically, about his thoughts and ideas. His attitude becomes more independent and yet not objectionable nor intolerant of the opinions of others. The real creator's vision is bold but clear, knowledgeable but adaptable, curious but sensible, conventional but skeptical, egocentric but open to new experience. He is willing to work hard and yet is dissatisfied with merely routine work. He has to be precise, critical, honest, and adventuresome. Above all he must develop confidence in himself and a deep internal desire to create and to contribute.

A patent examiner conducted an analysis in an attempt to uncover the mental processes of inventors. Among the results reported [7] are the motives given by inventors for working on their creations. In the order of frequency with which the motives were given by the inventors, they are: the love of inventing, the desire to improve, financial gain, necessity or need, desire to achieve, part of the job, prestige, altruistic reasons, and just plain laziness. The love of inventing, the desire to improve, and the desire to achieve account for fifty-three per cent of the motivation.

5–4. CREATIVE PROCESS

The creative process is the mental activity by which man uses knowledge, experience, and available information to arrive at a rational and good solution. It requires fluent and flexible thinking. It is both challenging and rewarding. Except for the good fortune of an occasional chance inspiration, the better solutions are created deliberately and consistently only by the full force of all mental powers.

Thinking, mental powers, what are these? Webster's dictionary defines the verb *to think*: "to exercise the faculties of judgment, conception, or inference." The significant words in the definition need to be defined for a stronger appreciation of the meaning:

> *Judgment:* "The operation of the mind, involving comparison and discrimination, by which knowledge of values and relations is mentally formulated."
>
> *Inference:* "The deriving as a consequence, conclusion, or probability; the necessary consequence of a chain of reasoning."
>
> *Conception:* "The power . . . to form . . . ideas. . . ."

Thus the three mental powers involved in thinking constitute a process in which ideas are formed and discriminated, and their consequences reasoned. The power of conception permits the synthesis of alternative ideas. Judgment and inference, on the other hand, are powers that assign values, compare, and conclude. Thinking, then, which very nearly everyone can do at least to some degree and certainly anyone who has reached the state of being able to understandably read this, is the activity that must be used to create designs, alternative designs. It is this ability that must be developed to the utmost. Thomas Alva Edison, a man with a most imaginative and creative mind, once said [8]:

> The man who doesn't make up his mind to cultivate the habit of thinking misses the greatest pleasure in life. He not only misses the greatest pleasure, but he cannot make the most of himself. All progress, all success, springs from thinking.

Could there be a greater plea, by a greater engineering creator?

Formal knowledge and technology can be learned; experience is slowly gained. Thinking must be practiced until it becomes a habit. Creative ability and creative designs are then possible.

The divergent production of ideas, concepts, and designs, that is, the production of several possible solutions, is one important creative ability; it is the procedure followed by many.   Others do better by using the convergent approach, by narrowing the possibilities down and concentrating on a single solution.   Furthermore, there appears to exist little correlation between measures of creativity and those of intelligence or scholastic aptitude. [9]   When emphasis is placed on quantity of creation rather than quality some correlation begins to appear.

Everyone who is willing can thus become creative to greater or lesser extent.   There are, however, certain barriers that can be eliminated, remedies gained, and problem-solving techniques mastered to help the development of stronger creative ability.

5–5. BARRIERS TO CREATIVITY

It is explained by students of creativity that the process of creativity is stifled, and therefore greater creative productivity denied most individuals, because of custom and traditional reactions that bind people to the near and even distant past [3, 6].   Background, habit, environment, unwritten law, all form the personal blocks that the designer must recognize and dispel if he is to become highly creative.   To break through these barriers is not an easy matter, but it must be tried. Some of the more common barriers are said to be:

Habit transfer	Distrust of intuition
Functional fixedness	Overdependence on others
Practical mindedness	Stagnation
Overspecialization	Overmotivation
Incorrect problem statement	Fear of criticism

This is quite a collection and there are, no doubt, more.   It may be well to consider each separately.

Habit Transfer.   Habits can be good or bad, they can prevent as well as accelerate thinking.   Without some habit, man would be a beginner at everything; with too much habit, the engineer may attempt to solve problems with old approaches which could have been quite successful in earlier situations but may not necessarily be best in the current one.   To maintain a proper balance, habits must be appraised, so they can be used when beneficial and discarded when something else proves better.   Habits can make life simpler by eliminating the sometimes frustrating necessity to think and study, but they can also cause a man, an industry, a nation to stand still and therefore, in effect, to recede.

Functional Fixedness. Psychologists claim that humans may acquire or inherit a trait that tends to blind them to other possible uses for a product once he has ascribed a particular function to it. John E. Arnold said: "Familiarity with certain objects or concepts is frequently apt to establish a functional fixedness in our minds, and we are unable to see this object as part of a number of relationships. We see a pencil as only a writing instrument. We never see it as a tool for propping open a window, or as fuel for a fire, or as a means of defending ourselves in an attack. A pencil is a pencil. It is not a combination of graphite, wood, brass and rubber, each of which has multiple properties and multiple uses."

Practical Mindedness. Almost everyone wants to get down to "facts" as soon as a problem is posed, usually before the problem is even understood. Roaming imaginatively around the problem as long as new thoughts concerning it arise can be fruitful. William J. J. Gordon of the Invention Research Group said: "It is dangerous to particularize a problem too soon, because this kind of early definition may mean that the broad scope inherent in the situation will never be liberated. Premature particularization is very often a symptom of an individual's concern with being impractical."

Overspecialization. The specialized engineer tends to reach conclusions so rapidly, based on his one field of specialization, that he disregards the contribution other basic findings can make to his problem. He therefore falsely excludes certain solutions as unworkable without even trying them. William O. Felsman suggested that: "An approach which is often very valuable in designing a system is to deliberately design it in a fashion which one knows will not work and then attempt to prove it won't work. It is often a great surprise to the designer to find that, upon strong analysis, he cannot prove that this system does not work. . . . At this point, he has achieved a different viewpoint toward one system, and he may proceed to show just what there is about their particular configuration which might work. In so doing, he gains facts of a different nature from those which he already knows."

Incorrect Problem Statement. The real theme of a problem should be stated clearly and precisely, but it must not be so stated that it tends to indicate one solution and exclude all others. As Arnold pointed out, in calling for the design of a bread-toaster one should say "a device for dehydrating and browning the surface of bread" rather than just "a device that uses radiant electrical heat" for the purpose. Many principles of dehydration and browning may then be thought of, instead of only the one.

Distrust of Intuition. Intuitive hunches, particularly those stemming from experience, cannot be ignored. Furthermore, there are times when not all parameters can be measured exactly, and so the engineer must resort to intuition. This should not be done when decisions can be established from fact, but when it offers the only possibility it must be performed with confidence.

Overdependence on Others. One can become overimpressed with the knowledge and judgment of others and fail to exercise one's own creativity. This dulling of one's ability, and cultivation of complete dependence upon others, has a lowering effect upon one's professional potential. Professor Ross L. Mooney described the failure this way. The typical engineer "wants to be stimulated by others and he expects response from others. . . . He is challenged, not to be an independently creative man in his production, but a dependently adaptive man, using his energy to adjust to groups and keep in line with the multiple group-belongings necessary for the support of his being."

Stagnation. The tendency to become so self-satisfied and content that ideas cease to flow and routine action sets in, resting oneself in the status quo, is easy to succumb to, because less effort, particularly of the mind, is required. An incessant, dogged effort can also still the mind, whereas prudent relaxation often stimulates the mind and provides incubation time during which a brilliant idea may emerge spontaneously.

Overmotivation. Although intense motivation must exist if one is to be creative, it is possible to overdo it. One can try being a perfectionist, setting goals too difficult to reach, and actually accomplish little, if anything. Overmotivation can blunt one's vision, narrow one's field of observation, and so reduce his real effectiveness in problem-solving.

Fear of Criticism. Anxiety in apprehension of disapproval and possible criticism, plus the fear of disappointment, often prevents one from proposing one's inner ideas which, because out of the ordinary, could prove brilliantly different. Unfortunately, the more original and unique an idea is, the more vulnerable it is to criticism, no matter how valuable it may eventually prove to be. Thus fear stifles thinking and creative productivity. Dr. Richard W. Wallen of the Personnel Research and Development Corporation spoke this way: "Anxiety about social disapproval not only prevents people from making suggestions; it can even prevent them from thinking of new suggestions. It actually seems to interfere with free-ranging, flexible thinking. The anxious person is so concerned about his relationships with other people that he cannot give full energy to the problem."

The above then are the counter-forces that must be neutralized if creative productivity is to reach a maximum. Their negative nature dictates that the designer do all within his power to optimize his thinking by minimizing these tendencies within him. He can do this, of course, only by conscientiously striving to practice the positive at every occasion. He must realize that the barriers do exist, that he is a creature of habit, that he is vain, that he is subject to mistaken notions. For once he realizes this, he will seek ways of overcoming them. He will tend to use the natural creative ability he possesses, no matter how small, to imagine the means by which he can minimize the barriers and

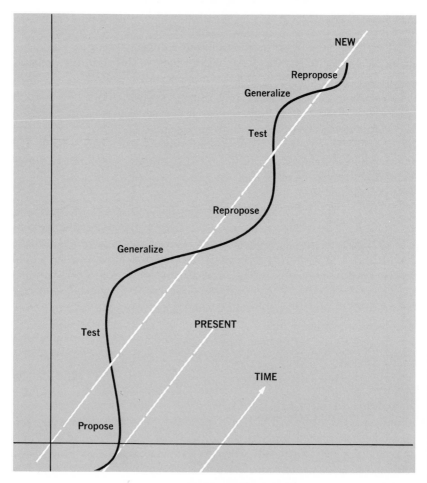

Fig. 5–1. Understanding spirals.

make himself gradually more and more creative. Once this becomes commonplace, ideas will no longer be "good" or "bad," "white" or "black," but instead each idea will naturally provide a stepping stone to a better and higher idea. Conformist attitudes and habit reflexes will no longer hinder thinking and misdirect conceptual powers down a marked, narrow path. It is the spirals to better understanding (see Fig. 5–1) suggested by Von Fange [6] that must become more gracious, that must permit better speeds, that must diminish in number in reaching the new level. Each spiral represents a trial in an iteration that will hopefully take the designer to a better solution or design. Each time an improvement is proposed and tested, knowledge is gained that adds to the general understanding of the problem and in turn brings one closer to the desired or expected result. The more imaginative the designer, the more significant will be his proposed refinement and the fewer attempts (or spirals) he will need in his approach to the better "new" state.

5–6. CREATIVE TECHNIQUES

The human mind responds quicker to emotion than to reason, it conforms with much less effort than it leads, it finds it simpler to remain dull than to become imaginative, and of course, it prefers to stagnate rather than to think. It is therefore productive to stimulate the mind to a maximum of creativity by keeping it as free of barriers and inflexibilities as possible. High intelligence is not a prerequisite to creativity, but independent thought is. Thus anything that gives a fresh, a new, point of view becomes a gimmick that may stimulate creative activity; it assumes the role of a creative technique.

Many such techniques, some of which are to be described below, have been proposed and found helpful. Some are subjective and suited to one temperament and not to another. If a technique does not revitalize your mind to new activity, to a fresher point of view, after a sincere try, discard it, for it is not likely to result in noticeable productivity. Try another, it may prove quite a creative stimulus.

5–7. ASSOCIATION

Probably the most common way of explaining a new and unfamiliar object is to compare it (and probably even contrast it) with another similar and familiar item. Conceptual powers are greatly stimulated by such association. For example, by meditating upon the flight of birds, man has developed aircraft that today surpass in performance the fondest "hopes" of the mighty hawk. How association can play a large part even in the creative mind of probably the greatest analytical genius the world has ever known can be found enumerated several times in O'Neill's biography of Nikola Tesla [10]; for example:

In the tremendous burst of revelation which he received in the park at Budapest as he gazed into the flaming orb of the setting sun, there had flashed into his mind, as we have seen, not only the marvelous invention of the rotary magnetic field and the many uses of multiple alternating currents, but also the grand generalization that everything in Nature operated on the principle of vibrations that corresponded to alternating currents. The host of inventions and discoveries which he made in all succeeding years had their roots too, in that sublime experience.

Each engineer is likely to have stored in his memory-complex many bits of knowledge and experience of things seen and things done. Although fading memory shrouds these events, a small stimulus may bring them forth in vividness again. And the vividness of recall may in turn lead a solution to the particular problem being considered.

Nature can be a great teacher as well as a great source of ideas. There are few, if any, performance devices that do not have their counterpart in nature. Many have been developed by directly imitating nature's way of performing a similar function. As a matter of fact, the new science of *bionics* is used by engineers in applying knowledge about living systems to problem situations. Examples of this are the knee and the toggle mechanism, animal color adaptation to environment and camouflaging, rattlesnakes and infrared homing devices, bat navigation and sonar. Here is what Michael Pupin wrote in his Pulitzer Prize winning autobiography [11] about one of his many experiences in this connection:

. . . a young Italian student by the name of Marconi, while experimenting with Hertzian waves, had demonstrated that a Hertzian oscillator will send out electrical waves which will penetrate much longer distances when one of its sides is connected to earth. "Of course it will," said I, "the grounded oscillator takes the earth into close partnership." When as a herdsman's assistant on the pasturelands of my native Idvor I stuck my knife into the ground and struck its wooden handle, I knew perfectly well that the ground was a part of the vibrating system, and that the sound-producing stroke was taken up by the ground much better than when I struck the knife-handle without sticking the knife into the ground. But I also knew that unless the boy who was listening pressed his ear against the ground he would not hear very much. It was, therefore, quite obvious to me that the best detector for a Hertzian oscillator which is grounded must be another Hertzian oscillator which is also connected to the ground. Grounding of the sending and receiving Hertzian oscillator was in fact the fundamental claim of the Marconi invention.

5-8. EXPLAINING THE DIFFICULTY

One explains the problem, the difficulty, to a good listener and then carefully attends the listener's reactions and statement; he may not come up with a direct solution, but what he says could well stimulate the poser of the problem with a good idea. The technique seems to be especially useful when the problem is explained to someone who has little background in the area. The extra effort made to communicate the unknown to him may stimulate ideas in the mind of the expounder, and one of these may turn out to be just the right one.

5-9. FUNCTION MATRIX

Another method that can be worked quite effectively on an individual basis, like playing solitaire, is the matrix method proposed by Arnold [12]. The designer (or for that matter a group) determines, from the specification covering the device, two or three, or more, of the major functions that it must perform. The engineer next considers each function separately and establishes different ways for each function to be carried out. He then sets up a matrix, making each major function an axis and each way in which the function can be performed a coordinate. In the matrix array he will find a possible design-concept solution in each box. He can, furthermore, obtain additional subideas by repeating the process for each box.

An example will serve to illustrate the method. A yard-raking machine that will gather, pulverize, and dispose of leaves and pine needles is to be designed. The major functions obviously are: gathering, pulverization, and disposal. The next question is, in how many ways can the material be gathered, pulverized, and disposed of. Possible methods are shown in the major-function matrix, Fig. 5-2. Notice that forty-eight possible solutions are indicated. One now reviews or analyzes each solution concept for possible additional considerations. Some boxes may not be worth additional thought and are discarded at this point. For instance, it may be wisely decided that to attempt to burn the vegetation inside the machine and then discard the ashes could well prove too much of a hazard, especially if a gasoline engine is to be used as the power source. By removing the burning coordinate, one can eliminate twelve boxes. Additional boxes may be dropped from consideration for other reasons. Or one might simply select two or three that seem to hold the greatest promise.

These special boxes can probably be expanded by considering, as already stated, different ways of carrying out each particular function.

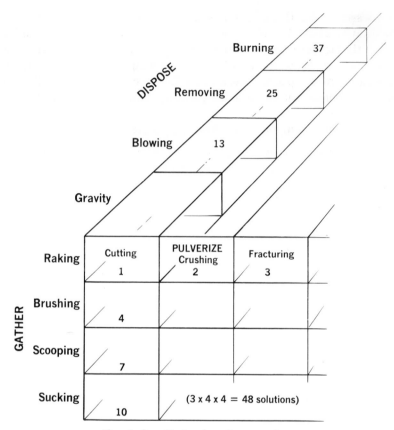

Fig. 5–2.   Major-function matrix.

As an illustration, the origin or first box may be handled as shown in the function-box matrix, Fig. 5–3.   The single-solution concept multiplies into an array of eighteen ideas.   These are analyzed, evaluated, and either retained or discarded.   The process is continued until the best configurations are found and adapted for final design.

5–10. BRAINSTORMING

A popular creative technique is that of the brainstorming session, first introduced by Alex Osborn in 1939 [13].   It can be used either individually or by groups, and when sessions are properly conducted, good ideas can flow quickly from the minds of the participants.   The atmosphere must be fully relaxed, the session must take on the air of a bull session.   Anything goes, and no remarks or criticism of any kind are allowed about the ideas being put forth.   All ideas are recorded. When the last idea has been freely made, the participants begin to go down the list, exploring each and overlooking the non-relevant, discussing the more appropriate, and finally selecting the best.   The session atmosphere can be quite invigorating, and the resulting ideas are often ingenious.

The brainstorming session follows this pattern:

1. The problem is clearly posed, with only one focal point voiced.
2. Ideas are not criticized even if obviously non-relevant to the problem at hand, or even if obviously just fillers.   Instead, everyone reaches for as many ideas as possible.   Competition is certain to set in, if freedom of thought prevails.
3. Following the statement of the last idea, the group proceeds to analyze, criticize, eliminate, and discuss until only ideas worthy of further consideration are left.

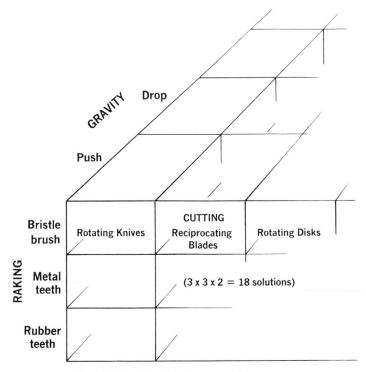

Fig. 5–3.   Function-box matrix.

The session must be serious and the attitude sincere, if it is to be productive. It can degenerate into the customary jury deliberation on the one hand, or become fully nonsensical on the other. The leader should keep in mind its proper path, and no one should throttle the flow of ideas. At a General Electric brainstorming session, 150 ideas on new ways of crossing a stream were proposed in 30 minutes at a demonstration for a group of Army engineers.

5-11. SEEKING NEW POINTS OF VIEW

A quite natural and more personal approach to the stimulation of ideas is to seek a new point of view when the old fails to bring results. Inventive ability is not a common trait; it does not seem to correlate with a person's IQ. The inventor must, however, possess the knowledge, the art, and the experience upon which the solution depends. The more perceptive people see, hear, and remember more and may therefore be better able to view a problem from more angles.

To be more creative, to find new ideas, one must look at the problem from many viewpoints. One can dream, in a sense, about the problem and its possible solutions, play make-believe, and wish for the ideal solution. Venturing into *fantasy* can stimulate ideas, one of which may well be just the right one [4]. Taylor points out that children often attack problems through fantasy and eventually arrive thereby at a resolution of what may be troubling them. The point here is that fantasy can be a method of idea- or concept-generation.

Another way of availing oneself of a new viewpoint is by *inversion*. The engineer considers the problem from some opposite point of view. For example, suppose the design of a diving vehicle that must descend safely to great depths is sought. Designers are likely to approach the problem with considerations involving a propulsion system for descending to the sea floor. It could well be that consideration of vehicle ascent from the bottom up may produce a better alternative method of propulsion and design.

Empathy, too, the ascription of emotional feelings, can prove a fruitful method of creative attack. It is a matter of personal attachment to the problem. One imagines himself to be the problem; he then tends to acquire a closer feeling for the problem, which can provide a new outlook and in turn a preferable concept and solution.

Fantasy, inversion, and empathy, like association and incubation, are not creative devices that can be turned on to unquestionably yield ideas and solutions every time. They are not systematic procedures that can be formulated in terms of rules and steps. Instead, they are thinking processes that may assist and inspire the mind to something it would not otherwise conceive. One begins to imagine and consider the impossible as well as the possible, the obscure as well as the obvious, the fantastic as well as the real. Results are rare, but when they come they are startling and rewarding.

Engine-knock caused Charles F. Kettering much trouble while he was perfecting battery ignition and electric lighting for the new horseless carriage. It caused him particular difficulty when he had to resort to kerosene for fuel. He speculated that the trouble had something to do with vaporization. He recalled that the wild trailing arbutus with the red-backed leaves bloomed early in the spring, even in the snow. Possibly the red had something to do with it? Did it make the plant absorb more heat? If kerosene were dyed red it might absorb more heat, too, and vaporize easier. There was some iodine around; it ought to dye kerosene red, so it was tried. Knock was not completely eliminated, but this speculation eventually led to tetraethyl lead and anti-knock gasolines.

Michael Faraday tried for a long time to obtain electricity out of magnetism. When electricity was sent through a coiled wire, magnetism developed in an iron core within the coils, so why didn't current flow in a wire coiled around a lodestone? Where did the magnetism go, anyway, when the current is shut off? Did flow have something to do with it? Magnetism at rest did not generate electricity, but magnetism in motion might. So the lodestone was moved within the coil, and electricity was generated. The important phenomenon of electromagnetic induction became part of our knowledge, along with a generator.

Edison dreamed about a machine that would do for the eye what the phonograph does for the ear. So he devised the first moving-picture camera, the kinetograph. Then he speculated what the result would be if these were somehow combined, and the combination led to talking pictures.

The need for accurate current measurement became a serious problem when the first power station was opened in 1882. The principle of electroplating was applied, a known amount of metal was transferred from the anode to the cathode by each ampere of current. Imagine the cumbersome task of collecting plates at each premise, taking these back to a central location for weighing, and then returning each to its proper cell. Just keeping track of each plate, its weight before and after, and its proper location was a difficult, clumsy, uneconomical chore. Mistakes were made. Elihu Thompson, the beloved teacher, scientist, and engineer, considered the method totally unsatisfactory. An electric motor converts electricity into shaft energy; why not let this energy to measure itself? A tiny electric motor connected into the customer's circuit, using an almost negligible amount of power, with its shaft operating a train of gear-dials, would register cumulatively the total energy going through the circuit. Its design presented many problems but the kilowatt-hour meter still measures the electricity used in household, plant, and office, whatever the need.

Although the above methods may develop the creative capacity, per se, of a young mind so that it will continue to be creative, this is not necessarily the purpose. The methods are intended to help average engineers with the solution of the design situations they must solve. Any of the techniques may assist with the generation of solution ideas. As stated the methods are subjective, and if one technique fails to arouse a new point of view, to provide new ideas, discard it and try another.

Like the comprehensive designer, a creative person possesses an attitude involving an open mind, constructive discontent, positive outlook, course of conviction, and self-confidence. And, these attitudes can be developed to a satisfying extent by the man who willingly tries.

REFERENCES

1. John E. Arnold, *The Creative Engineer*, ASME Paper No. 55-A-163, Nov. 1955.
2. J. A. Anderson, *Evaluation, Distribution and Training of Creative Men*, ASME Paper No. 55-A-211, Nov. 1955.
3. E. Raudsepp, "Removing Barriers to Creativity," *Mach. Des.*, May 24, 1962, pp. 138–43.
4. C. W. Taylor, *Creativity—Progress and Potential*, McGraw-Hill Book Co., Inc., New York, 1964.
5. Luis DeFlorez, "Ingenuity: A Quality of Victory," *The Technology Review*, Massachusetts Institute of Technology, June 1962, p. 35.
6. E. K. Von Fange, *Professional Creativity*, Prentice-Hall, Inc., Englewood Cliffs, N.J., 1959.
7. J. Rossman, *Psychology of the Inventor: A Study of the Patentee*, Inventors Publishing, New York, 1931.
8. D. D. Runes, *The Diary and Sundry Observations of Thomas Alva Edison*, Philosophical Library, Inc., New York, 1948.
9. H. L. Hargreaves, "The Faculty of Imagination," *Brit. J. Psychol.*, 1927.
10. John J. O'Neill, *Prodigal Genius—The Life of Nikola Tesla*, Ives Washburn, Inc., New York, 1944.
11. Michael Pupin, *From Immigrant to Inventor*, Charles Scribner's Sons, New York, 1923.

12. John E. Arnold, "Useful Creative Techniques," *Creative Eng'g Seminar*, Stanford U., 1959.
13. Alex F. Osborn, *Applied Imagination*, Charles Scribner's Sons, 1953.

PROBLEMS

5–1. Why is it extremely important that creativity be encouraged and all possible be done to develop it to a maximum throughout the population?

5–2. Distinguish between creativity and productivity.

5–3. Define *thinking* as clearly and precisely as you possibly can.

5–4. Explain the difference between the divergent and convergent production of ideas.

5–5. Describe what you think life will be like thirty years from now and list six new items, devices, or what have you, that engineers will have to bring to realism by then to make that life possible.

5–6. Thinking is mentally directed creativeness. Estimate the percentage of your average day you spend in thinking. Make your estimate realistic and substantiate it.

5–7. What creative technique do you habitually employ? Illustrate.

5–8. Select three devices that have their functional counterpart in nature. Clearly describe the similarity.

5–9. Discuss whether an idea ahead of its time benefits anyone.

5–10. Was Leonardo da Vinci creative or merely ingenious when he sketched a flying machine and other devices? Discuss.

5–11. Should the restriction of usefulness be imposed upon the definition of creativity? Discuss.

5–12. Is a computing machine that can yield new combinations very rapidly creative, productive, neither, or both? Discuss.

5–13. Discuss K. G. Johnson's statement "Education is man's going forward from cocksure ignorance to thoughtful uncertainty."

5–14. The test is the common method used to provide the teacher with facts and figures that help him establish grades. Suggest and discuss other realistic ways of arriving at course grades.

5–15. Can you uphold the idea that the day of the individual inventor is past? Discuss and illustrate your claim.

DESIGN PROBLEMS

5–D1. A special bathroom lock must be created. Normally the lock must work as it commonly does, but it must be child-proof; that is, if a child locks itself in, the lock must be capable of being opened from the outside with possibly a little more than the usual effort. Start with a stapler. List at least six of the stapler's characteristics and then show how three of these may be applied to the problem at hand, the doorlock.

5–D2. A brake for small pleasure craft must be designed. Consider a parachute. List at least five of its characteristics and then explain exactly how two of these could be applied to the design of the boat brake.

5–D3. An automatic floor washer that will scrub, rinse, and dry the floor is to be designed. Draw a function matrix and expand the most promising box.

5–D4. A device that will automatically assemble ten sheets of $8\frac{1}{2}$-in. $\times$ 11 in. notes is needed. It will fasten them in such a way that they can be paged through and stack them in groups of twenty. Draw the major function matrix, and expand the most promising box.

5–D5. Conduct a systematic study of a home heating and cooling system. Construct a matrix using heat sources as one axis and distribution methods as the other. Select the most promising boxes, and explain why.

5–D6. Conduct a brainstorming session on the problem of developing a universal landing gear that will work acceptably on land, water, and snow.

5–D7. Conduct a brainstorming session on the problem of developing a device for an automobile that will continuously indicate the instantaneous gasoline consumption rate in miles per gallon.

5–D8. Obtain the following items: 10 paper clips, 6 rubber bands, 4 thumbtacks, 4 pencils, 2 safety pins, 2 pieces of poster paper, 1 piece of aluminum foil, 1 razor blade, 1 large envelope, and a length of cord. None of these items can be cut to produce more of the item; they can be distorted as needed. In no more than four hours, use all of these items to build a working model of some useful device.

5–D9. Obtain a small, common household mouse trap. Convert it into some other device in no more than 3 hr. You may use, if you wish, up to 3 paper clips and 3 pencils in addition to the mouse-trap components.

5–D10. List at least ten properties a common red brick possesses. How many alternate uses can you suggest for the brick that would utilize one or more of the characteristics enumerated.

5–D11. Name ten alternate uses for the common wire coat hanger.

5–D12. You have available a pile of bricks, a few pieces of board, some wire coat hangers, a length of rope, and three pieces of pipe. Sketch clearly three different play things that could be fabricated out of these items for your children. All five types of items must be in each of the three play things. The only tools available are a hammer, pair of pliers, wood saw, and a hand drill with wood and metal bits.

5–D13. Air pollution is a major problem in our large cities. It is well established that automobiles are one of the major contributors to this pollution. Your employer, a large automobile manufacturer, has decided that legal restrictions on pollutants emitted by automobiles would be undesirable. Management therefore decides to spend some money to investigate the problem. You are assigned the task of considering the problem and suggesting approaches to the development of a pollution-free automobile at only a small price increase.

5–D14. Cooking fuel is very scarce in such arid areas as the Middle East. A small, portable solar cooker of low cost ($5.00) would be of great benefit to the village peasants and bedouins. Suggest a possible design for such a solar cooker.

5–D15. Much energy leaves the ordinary home through the chimney during the winter months. Sketch your concept of a device that could be safely placed over the chimney to use some of the escaping energy. The device is to be an appropriate depiction of the spirit of Christmas.

5–D16. You are to design a small power package for a research rocket. Identify ten physical laws or principles that may be used in solving the problem. Show how and why.

5–D17. A recent report claims that a large percentage of the wheat, bean, and potato crop of a certain country has been chewed up by a large, growing horde of aggressive mice. The unusual propagation of the mice is blamed on the virtual extermination of snakes, martens, and foxes native to the country. This resulted because of the need to cultivate more of its forested land as a result of its population explosion. One of the federal agencies is requested to help solve the problem. As a reliable member of the American engineering profession, propose a sensible, realistic solution to this food- and, probably, disease-problem.

6

Aspects of System Engineering

Generally speaking, and as defined by Webster, a system is "an aggregation or assemblage of objects united by some form of regular interaction or interdependence." It may be defined more specifically for engineering purposes as a combination of elements and components —mechanical, electrical, thermal, hydraulic, pneumatic, etc.—synthesized into a complex for performing a function and satisfying a need. System engineering is a broad, comprehensive approach to the physical realization of equipment. The equipment can be a single unit designed to perform a required function or a series of units combined to provide possibly a broader but still unified output. A bicycle provides transportation, but so does a truck. A single truck is a transportation vehicle, and a number of trucks under single management can be a freight delivery system.

The broad vision, the whole approach, has been the way to thought for many people through the centuries, but it has not been systematically applied in equipment design until rather recently. The conceptualizing, and capacity-size synthesizing, of a scheme of elements may be called *system design;* whereas the whole of what must be done to bring it to reality—planning, design, construction, and initial operation—may be referred to as *system engineering.*

6–1. SYSTEMS

As stated above, a system is a combination of elements designed and constructed for performing a function and satisfying a need in a terrestrial, marine, atmospheric, submarine, industrial, or space environment. A machine or a complex of machines, a structure or a combination of structures, an energy plant, an aircraft, an underwater vehicle, a missile, a highway complex, a weapon, an automobile, all are systems.

Neither size nor complexity necessarily determines whether the design is of a system or just an item. Instead, the word *system* is often used where interdisciplinary knowledge is needed to solve the problem. In this sense the design of a machine tool involving the mechanics of solids in the strength of its members, fluid flow in its bearings, metallurgy in the selection of its materials, electricity in its power supply, and friction heat in its function is as much system design as is the design of a large missile or of an interstate highway complex. Yet, when no particularly great amount of planning and design effort is required, the project is not normally considered one of system engineering. When it is, however, all of what was studied as design process, decision theory, and creativity holds true for system design and system engineering. All of what follows here is presented as well, because it is part of system design.

Primarily then large-scale works are normally considered systems. These are the ones that contain a large number of parts and components; several inputs are required and many unified functions are performed, and quite noticeable is the high cost. Therefore, decisions must be thoughtfully made, all variables accounted for, and precise evaluations conducted. Many such systems exist. The railway network is one such large system; a missile is another example, and so is an expressway system; the air-defense complex of the nation is another. Air traffic with its requirements for planes, airports, communication equipment and control apparatus is another large system, and so are shipping networks, a submarine, and a power plant. It becomes obvious that sociology, biology, politics, and even philosophy form important considerations in many of these systems. Engineers, however, are concerned primarily with the equipment and the man-machine relations, although the rest cannot be neglected because all affect the final outcome.

Such systems are really not as new as might be supposed. The first intercontinental rail track was completed in 1869 to furnish about 30,000 miles of road, which by the 1950s had grown to around 222,000 miles. The first transatlantic cable was laid in 1886. Hunt of Bell Labs enumerates the size of the 1953 telephone system [1], when there were 50 million telephones (up to 71 million by 1960), 150 million miles of wire, and 200 million relays in operation. In 1953 alone, over 6 billion telephone calls were placed over the system. Such performance does not just happen. Rather, it is planned, designed, operated, controlled, and maintained. This is system engineering at its best, even though it may not have been called that twenty years ago. For instance, to transmit the number of calls made in 1953, over one and a half million operators would have been needed had the telephone engineers not foreseen the future as early as 1910 and made plans to develop individual dial phones.

6-2. LARGE-SCALE SYSTEMS

Systems such as those under consideration have been spoken of as large-scale. The adjective contributes little in identifying what a large-scale system really is. Furthermore, complexity is of necessity involved. For instance, designing a multistory building having a total of 200,000 square feet of floor space at 20,000 square feet per floor presents many more problems than would arise if the entire 200,000 square feet were to be a single ground floor. A helpful set of criteria may exist in the following series of characteristics that appear to be fairly common to large-scale systems:

1. *Knowledge Requirement.* The science, technology, art, information, and techniques that must be used to realize the system are many and interdisciplinary.
2. *Component Numerosity.* A great many parts or components, as well as a large number of different types of parts, are contained in the system.
3. *Integrity.* All parts contribute to the function of the system; that is, all parts play some part in converting a given set of inputs into a desired set of outputs.
4. *Complexity.* There are many effective variables in both inputs and outputs.
5. *Feedback.* Feedback loops exist at every stage and phase. New discoveries, improved interpretations, and more facts present themselves at each step; these must be fed back at many places to change decisions, modify calculations, and renew conclusions.
6. *Economics.* The cost of carrying the system through to completion and realization is very costly. The fiscal requirements are demanding and the expenses are many and high.

It should be evident that system engineering deals with extensive projects requiring not only many engineers, but mathematicians, physicists, economists and market specialists, and social, biological, medical and even political scientists. Much time and money are likely to be needed to carry out a single phase or stage of the work. The length of time between initial recognition of the possible need and completion of system is said to be from 2 to 15 years [2]. The period can actually be so long that business, taste, political or financial changes or reversals may cause its termination before the system can be completed. It is, furthermore, apparent that any single engineer is not likely to be involved in all of system engineering. He is probably more likely to be involved in the design of the various equipment needed to physically realize the functioning system.

As a matter of fact, system engineering could be classified as consisting of *equipment design* and *fiscal analysis*. The output of those contributing to the fiscal effort is primarily reporting, while the output of the first effort, though communication is definitely involved, is the hardware itself. It is this latter task—preliminary and detail design—that the competent design engineer is primarily concerned with. Schematically, the above may possibly be depicted as in the system engineering organization chart Fig. 6–1. All of what has been studied,

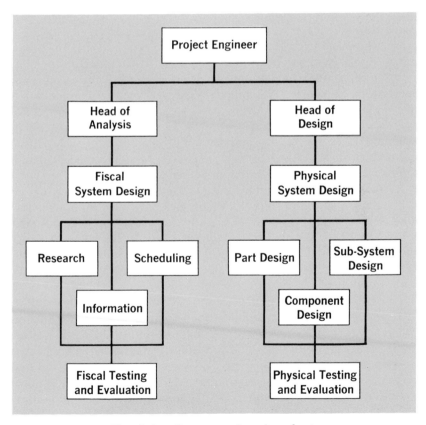

Fig. 6–1.   System engineering chart.

as well as all that is yet to be considered, is involved in system design. Synthesis and analysis are the basic processes that are applied. Much of the same is also involved in fiscal analysis. Sound planning, thorough scheduling, and complete control are essential if a large-scale project is to be accomplished within reasonable time and cost brackets.

6–3. FISCAL DESIGN

Planning, scheduling, and control must have been applied in some way even by the Pharaoh Cheops in pyramid-building days. Although ten thousand or more slaves were made available, fiscal analysis was at least threateningly applied to assure the pyramid would be finished with existing resources before Cheops' death.

Many years later a more scientific method was developed by H. L. Gantt [3]. His load and progress charts, both bar and curve, have long been useful. As systems became larger and more complex, the Gantt procedures proved too difficult to apply effectively. The engineering time factor was missing, and details lacking, so that the progress of a job could not be properly followed. Critical activities that actually determine cost and time-to-finish cannot be singled out and analyzed on bar charts. To complete an extensive project at minimum cost, or time, or both, the critical activity must be considered. This can be accomplished only if scheduling is optimized and maximum attention given the critical activity. The shotgun approach of the bar method does not provide the possibility, because sufficient detail is lacking; much effort is wasted on non-critical activities.

In the nineteen fifties engineers at Du Pont de Nemours, Remington Rand, the U. S. Navy, and other agencies developed more effective methods for fiscal control of new plant construction and weapons systems. Probably the two most favored methods are CPM, Critical Path Method, and PERT, Program Evaluation and Review Technique. These procedures permit easier comprehensive planning, optimum scheduling, and positive control.

The two methods were developed almost simultaneously. CPM evolved within the construction industry, where previous experience permitted better prediction of time and cost figures. PERT, on the other hand, developed along a probabilistic basis, in research and development projects where no previous experience existed. CPM has therefore enjoyed greater industrial acceptance. More recently, however, dollar considerations have been added into the PERT procedure [4] making it more like CPM. Other modifications of it, and of CPM as well, have been made and used by various concerns to best meet their particular needs. Basically, the procedures are as follows.

6–4. CRITICAL PATH METHOD

A system or a machine is designed to convert a required input into a desired output by means of the flow function provided by the equipment itself.   Basically, CPM consists of three corresponding phases, that is, planning, scheduling, and control.

The first step, planning, is the detailed analysis of the entire project undertaken to determine all the various items that make up the job. This is accomplished most usually by a graphical technique called the arrow or logic diagram, illustrated in Fig. 6–2.

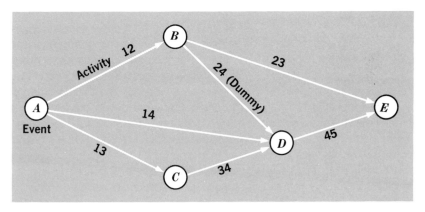

Fig. 6–2.   Arrow diagram.

Each node (circle) represents a point in time, called an event, when some particular item is finished.   For instance, in the fabrication of the automobile, node A may represent the very start of fabrication, and B the completion of say the body, C of the chasis, D of the engine, and E of the assembled vehicle.   The solid lines represent, on the other hand, the activities (operations) that must be performed to build the body, the engine, etc.   Thus activity *12* includes all work done to build the body, *14* to build the engine, etc.   The lines are not scaled vectors; they are only symbolic representations of time/cost estimates.   A dummy activity is one requiring neither time nor cost; it is used only to keep the sequence correct.

It must be appreciated that the illustration is much abbreviated and simplified.   It would actually be much larger and much more complex, because many activities are involved in the fabrication of any one of the subassemblies mentioned.   Arrow diagrams can easily contain hundreds of events and activities, and become rather extensive even for simple systems.

To complete the planning phase, time and cost estimates are assigned to each activity. These can be assigned on many bases, but the more common probably are [5]:

1. *Normal time/cost estimate*—The time needed to complete the item at minimum cost.
2. *Crash time/cost estimate*—The minimum time needed to complete item at increased cost.

A third basis that may be more suitable in some industrial situations is added:

3. *Market time/cost estimate*—The time needed to complete item at some marketable cost.

The *critical path* is the chain of activities through the arrow-diagram network with longest time period between start and completion of project. These become the activities that must be carefully controlled in order that the project be completed as planned. Any delays in an activity contained in this path must be immediately checked and corrected. Remaining activities may "float" by an amount of time that can be determined by subtracting the time of an activity from the time available for the job based on the critical path requirement. Suppose that activity *13* took 5 days; *34*, 3 days; and *14*, 6 days; then the critical path from event *A* to event *D* would be via activities *13–34* or 8 days. Activity *14* would thus have a float or slack of 8 − 6 or 2 days.

The over-all success of CPM depends primarily upon the planning phase. If performed properly, scheduling and control follow easily.

Example 6–1. A project has been broken down so that its arrow diagram is as given in Fig. 6–3. (The analysis that resulted in the diagram is not; it would have to be carefully performed by people thoroughly familiar with all details.) Time and cost estimates per activity are given in Table 6–1, established on both the normal and crash bases. Fiscally analyze the situation.

Solution: The normal critical path duration is by *12–23–36;* that is, 5 + 3 + 6 = 14 days at a total cost of $1,190.

The crash critical path duration is also by *12–23–36;* that is, 3 + 2 + 5 = 10 days at a total cost of $1,960.

To determine the optimum schedule, linearity is assumed between time and cost, and the cost rate calculated for each activity.

$$\text{Cost rate} = \frac{\text{Crash cost} - \text{Normal cost}}{\text{Normal time} - \text{Crash time}} \text{ Dollars per day}$$

Cost rates are computed and entered in the last column of the table.

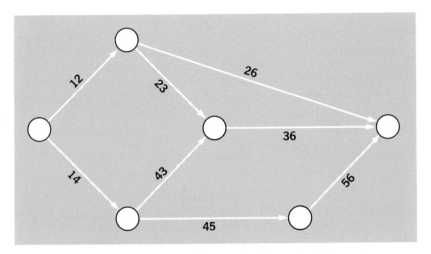

Fig. 6–3.   Arrow diagram for Example 6–1.

TABLE 6–1

Cost Table for Example 6–1

	Normal		Crash		
Activity	Days	Cost	Days	Cost	Cost Rate
12	5	$200	3	$350	$75
14	4	100	2	180	40
23	3	110	2	150	40
43	3	80	1	150	35
26	8	300	7	450	150
36	6	210	5	250	40
45	6	160	5	205	45
56	2	30	2	30	—
		$1,190		$1,765	

To shorten time-to-completion, activities *12*, *23* and/or *36* should be expedited first.   Thus

14 days: normal duration at $1,190

13 days: gain 1 day in activity *23* at $40 with cost increase to $1,230

12 days: gain 1 day in *36* at $40, plus a must day in *26* at $150, increasing cost to $1,420

11 days: gain 1 day in *12* at $75, but also 1 day in *14* at $40 and 1 day in *43* at $35, increasing the cost to $1,570

10 days: gain 1 day in *12* at $75 plus 1 day in *45* at $45, to increase cost to $1,690.

Note that the crash cost does not have to be considered, because the gain of 1 day in *43* as well as 1 of the 2-day gain in *14* are not needed.

The direct costs computed above as well as indirect overhead costs—provided by accounting—are tabulated below and added for total cost.

Days	14	13	12	11	10
Dir. Cost	$1,190	1,230	1,420	1,570	1,690
Ind. Cost	$ 950	850	770	720	690
Total Cost	$2,140	2,080	2,190	2,290	2,380

If the costs listed above are plotted as in Fig. 6–4, the optimum schedule can be read at the minimum point on the Total Cost curve as $13\frac{1}{4}$ days at $2,080.

In projects involving hundreds of activities, the scheduling computations explained are carried out on a computer. The information developed in the planning phase is fed to the programmed computer where all mathematical manipulations are performed. Not only will the computer select the optimum

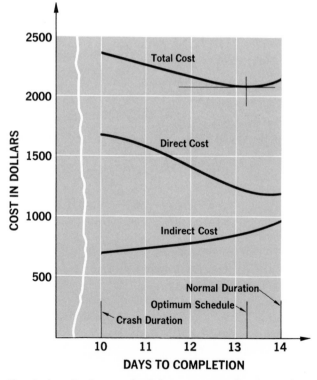

Fig. 6–4. Optimum schedule cost curves for Example 6–1.

schedule, but it can be instructed to yield such additional information as:

1. The status of each activity, whether critical or not
2. The cost of each activity
3. The time required by each activity
4. The scheduled start and finish of each activity, and
5. The float of activities containing same

A flow diagram of a computer-oriented CPM is illustrated in Fig. 6–5.

6–5. PERT/COST METHOD

PERT is based on and uses the same arrow network that underlies the CPM technique. Each arrow-line represents an activity that leads to an event. The activity represents an expenditure of such resources as time, labor, and materials. The event is a definable point in time that signifies the start or termination of an activity and does not require the expenditure of resources. (An excellent presentation of arrow diagram construction is found in Albert Battersby's book [6].)

The major difference between CPM and PERT lies in how the activity time is estimated. In CPM the most likely, or normal, or modal time m is used. In PERT, activity time is a weighted mean t of three time estimates: the optimistic time o, the pessimistic time p, and the most likely time m. Based on the Beta Distribution, the time estimates are as indicated in Fig. 6–6. The statistical nature of these fiscal controls is quite obvious. The optimistic time is an estimate of the minimum time an activity may take if everything goes fully right as the work proceeds. The pessimistic time is, on the other hand, the maximum time the activity would take should bad luck be a constant companion. The most likely or normal time is what occurs most often. The time relation is

$$t = \frac{o + 4m + p}{6}$$

and its standard deviation becomes

$$\sigma = \frac{p - o}{6}$$

As in CPM the path requiring the longest time (sum of the t's) is critical. Every other path has some slack time.

Up to this point, PERT/COST and PERT are the same. In PERT/COST, cost estimates are now introduced. The cost of each activity, based on expenditures for manpower and other resources required to

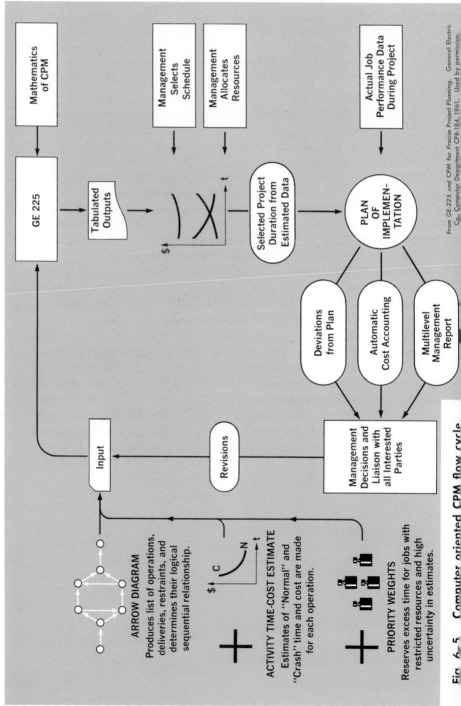

Fig. 6-5. Computer-oriented CPM flow cycle.

From GE-225 and CPM for Precise Project Planning. General Electric Co., Computer Department CPB-184, 1961. Used by permission.

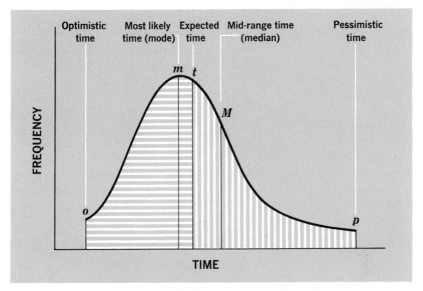

Fig. 6–6. PERT and CPM time estimates, beta distributions.

perform the work on schedule, is derived. Those in control are thus enabled to keep in constant touch with fiscal progress. Management can balance manpower utilization to assure the project is completed on time, at the lowest possible cost.

PERT/COST collates detail time estimates and job-cost data into an information tool and summarizes these into various output reports useful at all levels. Explicit relationships must of necessity be established, however, between the time network and the job-cost structure. This is possible only when complete accounting systems are in effect. Profitable time-cost trade-offs (adding to or subtracting from one at the expense of, or in favor of, the other) become possible as ultimate objectives. The relative progress of a project with respect to total cost is best evaluated as follows [7].

$$V = \frac{A}{R} C$$

where V = value of work performed to date
A = actual cost to date
R = latest revised estimate of total cost of an activity
C = contracted planned total cost of the activity
The A/R ratio is the percentage of the total estimated (not contracted)

dollars spent to perform the work. When this percentage is applied to the contracted planned cost, a reference value is determined that indicates what should have been spent for the work completed to date. PERT/COST is not applicable to all forms of industrial production. It is not suitable, for instance, in manufacturing where the majority of tasks are repeated as in the fabrication of multiple replicas of the same piece of hardware. Where hundreds of non-repetitive interdependent tasks are to be accomplished, as in building construction, new plant or product development, and research, the technique is most beneficial. The over-all duration of the project must, furthermore, be sufficiently long to permit feedback to affect the program.

It should be realized that all critical path methods are primarily management tools used in controlling large projects. Each method has its own possibilities. Each method is being extended, modified, and improved in the attempt to simplify the technique and make it more widely useful.

6-6. SPECIAL FACTORS AND TOOLS

The effective pursuit of system engineering requires, in addition to equipment and fiscal design, knowledge of probability theory, statistical techniques, human factors, block and mathematical models, transfer functions, information theory, and computers. Each of these is a subject in itself. This exposition is not intended to deal extensively with these topics, but rather to point out the need for such knowledge. Although time cannot be taken here to go deeply into any of them, the models, as design implements, are described in the following, and several of the other topics will be covered lightly in other sections.

It was the practice in the past to build to some desirable scale physical models, often called mock-ups, for performance checks and necessary correction prior to final design and production. The cost of this became very high as systems grew in size and complexity. Furthermore, how does one build a suitable physical model of a city's traffic system and habits, or for that matter of a scaled and operating space vehicle. The mathematical model is much less costly and affords much more accurate predictions. Its highly theoretical nature constitutes a disadvantage, but for complex machines and systems it is the only answer, and it enables one to study one component of the system at a time.

The mathematical model is a description of the components of a system and all interrelations by mathematical equations. The performance of each component is represented by the transfer function, which is the ratio of output to input for each component and eventually for the entire system. Probably the most critical skill is the ability to write algebraic and differential equations that fully and correctly represent the physical system. Of course, these relations must eventually be solved; it is here where deep knowledge of mathematical processes and computers become necessary. When solutions are possible in closed form, output can be obtained explicitly in terms of input; when not, the effects of sets of variables or parameters can be investigated via computers, both analog and digital, whereupon numerical procedures and iteration become rather important. It is possible, and customary, to ascertain the transfer function of individual components by test; that is, the transfer calculation is compared with the actual component performance. If the agreement is not adequate, the function is revised until the prediction becomes true, or at least as true as practically required. After all transfer functions are corrected the circuitry of the system, as depicted by the model and as expressed by the proper interrelation of individual functions, is used to determine the output or performance of the system.

To illustrate construction of a mathematical model, the simple case of a single degree of freedom, damped vibrating mass is used. The conventional system schematic and the free-body diagram, Fig. 6–7, are drawn first to depict the situation.

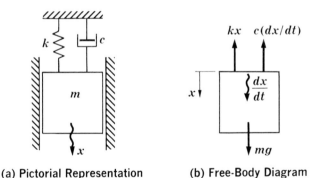

(a) Pictorial Representation   (b) Free-Body Diagram

Fig. 6–7. Damped vibrating mass system.

A better short-hand portrayal of the system for present purposes is the block diagram, Fig. 6–8, showing the instantaneous disturbance and the decaying amplitude x.

Newton's second law of motion, $F = ma$, permits determination of the system's interaction between output and input. Any vibration

Fig. 6–8.   Block diagram of system.

text, such as [8], contains the derivation and solution, which is

$$x = e^{-(c/m)t}\left(x_0 \cos \sqrt{\frac{k}{m}}\, t + \frac{\dot{x}_0 + (c/m)x_0}{\sqrt{k/m}} \sin \sqrt{\frac{k}{m}}\, t\right)$$

Thus the mathematical model becomes as shown in Fig. 6-9.

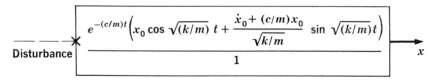

Fig. 6–9.   Mathematical model of damped vibrating mass.

Another mathematical model, illustrating the use of the model where a closed solution is difficult or not possible, is the one used in an investigation of a shock absorber designed to reduce jerk by means of an inertial valve within it [9]. The shock absorber contains a valve the opening of which depends upon the acceleration of a part of its mass, the damping coefficient decreasing when the acceleration of the unsprung mass increases. In an ordinary shock absorber, the force needed to move the piston is primarily a function of its velocity.

A schematic of the automobile system where the shock absorbers are to be used is shown in Fig. 6–10. Actually, an automobile has seven degrees of freedom of motion; that is, the vertical motion of each of the four wheels, the pitch and the roll of the body, and the vertical motion of the center of gravity; and one could even go further by including the elasticity of the frame and the motion of seated passengers. Thus taken, however, the model becomes too complex and unworkable, and it was therefore decided that a simple two-degree of freedom model was appropriate and sufficient for the study of the inertial shock absorber.

The diagram actually represents one-fourth of the car, that is, the masses associated with one wheel and one shock absorber. The irregularities of the road surface cause a displacement z which constitutes the input to the system. K_t is the equivalent tire spring constant, m_2

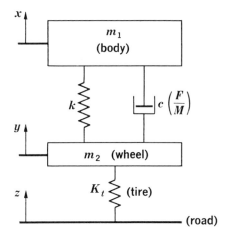

Fig. 6–10.   Schematic of automobile system.

the mass of the wheel and its support, y the motion of the wheel, k the constant of the springs between the body and wheel structure, c the shock absorber damping coefficient (where F is the force transmitted by the absorber and M is the mass of the inertially controlled valve within the absorber), m_1 the mass of the chassis and body, and x the body displacement. Figure 6–11 represents the system mathematically. The road irregularity z is the input to the system and x is the output. What happens between the input to the tire and the output of the automobile are shown in the figure.

The mathematical model contains blocks depicting not only body, wheel, tire and shock absorber, but some of the mathematical manipulations that must be performed to complete the solution. Derivations are too lengthy, though based primarily on Newton's laws of motion, and not exactly necessary for the purpose of this presentation. A brief explanation, however, of the model should reveal its significance.

Input z effects, of course, mass m_1 as well as m_2. It is thus directed to both body and wheel boxes. Within each box is the transfer function (output/input) x/z and y/z. In order to determine the shock absorber velocity, $(dy/dt) - (dx/dt)$, both x and y are taken through differential operators s. The shock absorber action depends on the initial spring force, f_i, on the acceleration, d^2y/dt^2, as well as the velocity, V, of the shock absorber mass M. All three of these combine to govern the inertia valve opening and so must be manipulated and directed along with velocity V to the shock absorber, which in turn provides force F to both the body and wheel masses.

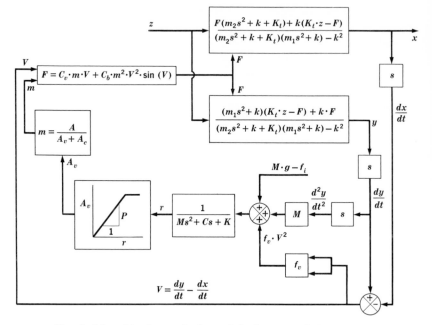

Fig. 6–11.   Mathematical model of automobile system.

6-7. SYSTEM EVALUATION

It has certainly become evident that system engineering considers the entire physical complex implementing the over-all operational process as an integrated whole rather than just an assembly of parts. It establishes objectives, allocates resources and organizes information so that the problem is understood sufficiently to assure achievement of established goals as closely and effectively as humanly possible. It bridges the rocky walls between what is needed and what is technically feasible and economically practical.

The evaluation of such systems is obviously not a straightforward task. The criteria for measuring and ascertaining such technological, financial and functional properties must be carefully selected. A criterion might be cost, performance, strength, capacity, efficiency, noise level, aesthetics, reliability, or some other aspect of effectiveness, or there might be many of these in combination. Proposed solutions, solutions under test, and completed solutions must each be effectively evaluated by means of properly established criteria. As an illustration of a wrong measure, a World War II incident is often related [10].

Merchant ships traveling in convoys were provided with antiaircraft power to ward off planes. After a time, an evaluation of the plan revealed that only a very few planes had been shot down. It was almost decided to remove the guns before it was realized that "how well the ships survived" was the real measure of effectiveness rather than the number of planes downed. An investigation of this point revealed that apparently only 10 per cent instead of around 25 per cent of the ships were being sunk. The armed ships may not have been in position to shoot down many planes, but by keeping the planes at a greater distance they caused the bombing attacks to be much less accurate and therefore less damaging.

In closing, the student must realize that this coverage is meager to say the least. Some major concepts have been introduced just sufficiently to whet the curiosity. Authoritative material, such as referenced, should be studied and consulted if system engineering is to be practiced with any success.

REFERENCES

1. M. M. Hunt, "Bell Labs' 230 Long-Range Planners," *Fortune*, May 1954, p. 120.
2. H. H. Goode, and R. E. Machol, *System Engineering*, McGraw-Hill Book Co., New York, 1957.
3. W. Clark, *The Gantt Chart*, The Ronald Press Co., New York, 1922.
4. Department of Defense and NASA Guide, *PERT/COST System Design*, Office of the Secretary of Defense, June 1962.
5. General Electric Company, Computer Department Bulletin CPB-185, Phoenix, Arizona, May 1962.
6. A. Battersby, *Network Analysis for Planning and Scheduling*, St. Martin's Press, Inc., New York, 1964.
7. D. M. Stires and R. P. Wenig, *Concepts–Principles Applications, PERT/COST*, Industrial Education Institute, Boston, Mass., 1964.
8. S. Timoshenko, *Vibration Problems in Engineering*, D. Van Nostrand Co., Inc., Princeton, N. J., 1937.
9. F. H. Speckhart, "The Design of a Shock Absorber to Improve Ride Comfort by Reducing Jerk," unpublished Ph.D. thesis, Ga. Inst. of Tech., 1966, 108 pp.
10. W. E. Wilson, *Concepts of Engineering System Design*, McGraw-Hill Book Co., Inc., New York, 1965.

PROBLEMS

6–1. Define *engineering system*, and illustrate by indicating major characteristics.

6-2. Distinguish between system design and system engineering.

6-3. Explain the meaning of each box in the system engineering chart.

6-4. Name an early method used for fiscal control of projects.

6-5. What do CPM and PERT do?

6-6. Define a dummy activity.

6-7. How does one ascertain the correctness of the transfer function for a complex system that is too extensive to be simulated as a whole?

6-8. If the critical path activities *12* and *23* require 5 + 3 or 8 hr, how much float or slack does activity *13* have if its duration is 4 hr?

6-9. What is a transfer function? Illustrate by writing a simple one based on some simple situation.

6-10. Which criterion is likely most important in the evaluation of each of the following systems: a boiler, a space capsule, a lawn mower, an air conditioner, and an automobile? Why?

6-11. Discuss thoroughly the difference and similarity between CPM and PERT.

6-12. Describe and discuss the use of mock-ups, block diagrams, and mathematical models.

6-13. Draw an arrow diagram for a project consisting of four events and five activities.

DESIGN PROBLEMS

6-D1. Analysis of a project results in the time/cost estimates given in the table below. Draw an arrow diagram for it and show the critical path thereon.

	Normal		Crash	
Activities	Days	Dollars	Days	Dollars
12	3	60	2	110
13	6	140	4	260
14	2	30	1	55
23	5	90	3	180
43	2	90	2	90
25	7	115	5	175
35	4	100	2	240

6-D2. Assume the indirect cost at $900 for the normal critical path duration of Problem 6-D1. Also assume that the indirect cost drops 10% the first day, then by 9%, 8%, etc. as the number-to-completion days are reduced down to crash time/cost. Determine the optimum schedule.

6–D3. Same as required for Problem 6–D1 but for figures listed in cost table below.

Activities	Normal		Crash	
	Days	Dollars	Days	Dollars
12	3	100	2	140
13	5	240	3	300
14	2	60	2	60
15	1	90	1	90
16	6	300	4	360
23	7	380	4	480
36	3	80	2	100
45	2	50	2	50
56	3	160	2	200

6–D4. Starting with an indirect cost of $1,200 and reducing it by 10, 9, 8, etc. per cent as in Problem 6–D2, determine the optimum schedule for the time/cost data of Problem 6–D3.

6–D5. Explain how any of the block diagrams of Problems 6–D1 to 6–D4 may be changed into mathematical diagrams.

6–D6. Construct a simple mathematical model of an automobile, accounting only for friction on tires, drag resistance, and the result when these differ in magnitude.

6–D7. Construct the block diagram for a simple boiler.

6–D8. Construct a block diagram for a gear speed-reducer.

6–D9. Construct a mathematical model of a gear train consisting of two stages of two spur gears each and possessing an input capacity of T in.-lb. (Gear 1 contains the input shaft, gears 2 and 3 are compounded, and gear 4 carries the output shaft.)

6–D10. Construct a block diagram of a system of two water pipes (hot and cold) joining at a valve that can be adjusted to yield lukewarm water. The desired temperature T_d is controlled by an operator turning the valve in the needed direction. Include the control feedback in the diagram.

6–D11. Construct a block diagram of the automobile's speed control system —engine, accelerator, human sensor, auto speed, and desired speed.

6–D12. Construct a mathematical model of a centrifugal pump.

6–D13. Construct a mathematical model of a simple boiler.

7

Human Factors Engineering

Machines and systems need to be operated, directed, and thoughtfully "instructed." It takes people to supply such inputs, be it by direct contact, remote control, or symbol communication, and man is a most necessary and important component in the man–machine system; but, he is also the most difficult to design into the system, because he is individualistic and his reaction to any specific situation is not precisely predictable. If it were, the problem would be greatly simplified. Easy predictability is, of course, likely to remain impossible; and yet human beings will continue to be links in systems, because they and they alone can provide the qualitative ability, reasoning capacity, flexibility, and adaptability required in designing, fabricating, operating, and maintaining machines and systems.

7–1. HUMAN FACTORS

The full exploitation of modern engineering systems requires proper accounting of the inevitable and ever essential human link in the man–machine complex. Because of the nature of this link, the task is most difficult. Man is very much dependent upon his environment, yet, only he, of the man-machine combination, is capable of making decisions. He alone can reason, he alone can analyze and reach conclusions, he alone can think and rationalize. But his physical, mental, and physiological capacities are limited. Compared to modern speeds and machine complexities his reflexes can prove too slow and unsafe, unless properly planned for and supported.

Human factor problems are interdisciplinary. For example, the selection and training of a potential astronaut, who will participate in a space mission engulfed in unknowns, is an extremely complex matter; conceptualizing, designing, and constructing the space machine is critical, and certainly the man who will operate it must be carefully considered. Most engineering systems involve such human factor problems. Their solution demands the application of principles and knowledge found in many disciplines not normally defined as engineering sciences. Some of these are:

1. *Psychology:* Knowledge of the mind
2. *Physiology:* Knowledge of the body
3. *Anthropology:* The science of man
4. *Climatology:* The science of climates
5. *Environmentals:* The study of job performance
6. *Preventive therapy:* The study of medical values

These and others are too specialized, and extensive, for all engineers to master or even become sufficiently conversant with; but every designer must be fully aware of all aspects of his problem and must possess some feel for possible approaches to its solution. The designer has to consider not only the functional requirements, but the operational, environmental, utilitarian and maintenance features as well, if his man–machine creation is to be satisfactory, safe, and economical.

7-2. UTILITY DESIGN

Man, the user or operator, has been considered by the designer of products and machines from the beginning. Even the caveman found he had to allow himself the long end of the stick (fulcrum to hand) to move the heavy rock that blocked his cave. He fastened a stone to the end of another stick to multiply his hammering capacity; he swung on a vine to reach the opposite bank or cross a canyon; and he dressed himself in skins and searched for a cave to shield himself from a hostile environment. Man has been devising means to reinforce his kinesthetic ability, assist his senses, and improve his environment ever since.

There are numerous examples of design for utility, for easier operation, and for greater welfare. Most structures, devices and machines involve some consideration of human factors. The design of dials and displays must be suited to man's visual characteristics. Tonal signaling must consider man's ability to hear and discriminate sounds. Controls must be adjusted to the forces people can exert as well as to magnitudes they can discriminate. These are, of course, not easy matters because man differs from man in many ways, physically as well as psychologically. In the past the designer placed himself in the user's or operator's place and designed accordingly. Modern designs that require a more intimate relation between man and machine do not permit such simple substitutions. Some common examples will reveal the extent and variety of utility demands that have been, and still are, designer's problems.

The knob on the door must be located at such a height that the average person will have neither to reach up nor stoop down when turning it. Its size cannot be so small that it does not fill the hand, nor so large that it is difficult to grip comfortably. It must be placed at a distance from the end wherewith the fingers are not pinched between knob and door frame as it is turned.

The pencil you are writing with is likely of hexagonal section. This is not an accident, it has been so designed purposely to provide an easier grip and better writing control. The distance between opposite flats has been thoughtfully established so your fingers will cramp less when writing for longer periods.

The steering wheel in your automobile is of a size that holds your arms comfortably in front of you and requires a minimum of turning effort. The rear-view mirror is pivoted, so that you can adjust it for best observation. The braking system is mechanically and hydraulically boosted, so that the car can be stopped with relatively light foot pressure. The seat is so constructed and the car body and chassis so supported as to yield maximum riding comfort.

Boiler stokers were designed to overcome the human drudgery associated with continuous shoveling. A record of amazing ingenuity is revealed in the technical literature on how engineers designed to ease and eventually eliminate the chore. It probably all started with F. W. Taylor, who studied shoveling extensively in the attempt to establish compatibility between man and the density of material being moved.

The automation represented by the stoker was extended throughout the power station and many manufacturing plants. The design of automation arrangements and devices had to fit the limitations of the individuals who operate and maintain plants. Elaborate control systems that are complex and beyond reasonable comprehension can cause hazardous errors in time of emergency. On the other hand, inadequate systems can cause more work and human fatigue, physical as well as mental, than the absence of automation.

The numerosity of designs requiring consideration of human factors is extensive. That the designer is dealing with parameters difficult to fix, or even understand, has hopefully been made clear. Nevertheless, many utility problems are routine; the competent designer handles these with little but careful deliberation and judgment. When more complex situations arise, the design engineer must call upon the human factor specialist and even the psychologist for guidance and assistance.

Samples of the kind of human factor data becoming available in greater amounts daily are found throughout the chapter. Analysis, testing, and research of human behavior, reflexes, strength, fatigue and reaction are being conducted. The limitations of space do not permit inclusion of such data beyond what is contained in the text for illustrative purposes. The engineer concerned with such problem is urged to consult the latest references for the information.

7–3. SCOPE OF HUMAN FACTORS ENGINEERING

Human factors engineering has been dealt with to some extent in the previous utility design article. Designing for utility means designing so the user or operator can utilize the product as easily and effectively as possible. And this, of course, considers and accounts for human factors. But the more complex man–machine systems require much greater study and consideration.

Human factors engineering may be defined as the technology that considers the design of machines, operations, and environments so that human capabilities, needs, and limitations are matched. It concerns the engineering of machines for human use as well as the engineering of human tasks for better performance in operating the machines. It searches for compatibility between man and his technical environment.

Engineering systems and the machines within them become more complex daily; yet the human operator remains the same. The greater complexity of the machine places demands upon him that he cannot handle safely without additional assistance. Man's five senses are too slow in their response to stimuli to be capable, unaided, of the rapid reaction time so essential in modern systems. The designer must, therefore, take this into account, and design sensing instruments, controls, and manipulation devices accordingly. Furthermore, though man may be quite adaptable to usual terrestrial climatic variations, environmental demands of modern systems are often too excessive for, and even hostile to, his unaided physique. Thus the engineer must help surmount these differences by incorporating appropriate features in system design.

As an example, the need for proper human factors design of ground-support equipment, as well as of a space vehicle itself, was explained by V. Clark Roberts of the Apollo Support Department, the General Electric Company [1] as follows:

The importance of adequate human-factors engineering in space vehicles is evident. The success of any mission is dependent on the human operator and his ability to make decisions and to respond correctly and timely to routine

TABLE 7-1

Human Kinesthetic and Anthropometry Data

(Approximate, averaged from several sources)

(Use with care and factor of safety)

	Average	Standard Deviation
1. Lift capacity		
Lift to 1 foot	230 lb	47 lb
Lift to 5 feet	60	16
2. Right arm capacity—Pull on horizontal bar from sitting position		
With elbow straight	120	37
With elbow at 90°	88	30
3. Right arm capacity—Push on horizontal bar from sitting position		
With elbow straight	138	49
With elbow at 90°	86	37
4. Right arm capacity—Pull on vertical bar from sitting position		
With elbow straight	28	12
With elbow at 90°	32	13
5. Right arm capacity—Push on vertical bar from sitting position		
With elbow straight	32	12
With elbow at 90°	65	24
6. Right leg capacity—Push from sitting position		
With knee straight	300	
With knee at 130°	250	
7. Hand grip		
Right hand	100	18
Left hand	90	16
8. Suitable knob diameter	2 in. or more	
9. Arm reach		
Foward, from chest	32 in.	1.6 in.
Overhead, from floor	82	3.3
10. Working reach while sitting	15.5	
11. Comfortable working seat		
Length	18.5	
Width	17.5	
12. Neck rotation		
About vertical axis, to each side	79 deg	14 deg
About horizontal axis, front to back	41	7
About horizontal axis, right to left	60	18
13. Reaction time		
To sound	0.15 sec	
To sight	0.20	
To smell	0.30	
To touch	0.16	
14. Temperature		
Above which a physical worker is uncomfortable	70° F	
Below which dexterity drops	55	

TABLE 7–2

Statistical Data Describing the Average American

(Approximate only—gathered from several sources)

(Age in years, the rest in inches)

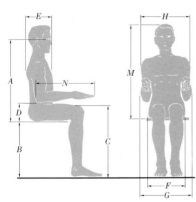

	Average	Standard Deviation
Age	28.0	10.4
Height	70.3	2.6
Eye height for normal sitting, A	30.9	2.0
Seat height, B	16.7	1.0
Knee height, C	22.7	1.0
Buttock-to-elbow height, D	9.7	1.6
Chest depth, E	9.7	1.2
Seat width, F	14.9	1.3
Elbow width, G	19.5	1.5
Shoulder width, H	18.3	0.9
Sitting height, M	35.7	1.9
Elbow-to-finger length, N	19.3	0.9
Hand length	7.9	0.5
Hand width	3.7	0.3

and emergency situations. There is no margin allowed for error, and therefore, the control/indicator panels must be designed to give every indication meaningfully, to give information which serves as system(s) recall and to impart confidence to the operator. The same requirements that are made for spacecraft should be made for GSE (ground-support equipment), for a mistake at this level can be as serious as a mistake at the spacecraft level. A human error, for example, in the operation of GSE used to check out spacecraft could eventually lead to mission shortcomings or possible failure. This type of error can be caused by poorly designed control panels.

What can the designer do about the situation? To begin with, the task of human factors design may be analyzed as to the extent it is based upon:

1. The five senses, primarily sight, hearing, and touch;
2. Body capabilities: movement, fatigue, strength, size;
3. Mental functions: thinking, reaction, nerve response; or
4. Environmental requirements: temperature, oxygen, moisture, radiation level, weightlessness.

One could easily argue that the designer has actually been doing these things right along, and he has; for example, when the first oar was developed centuries ago it had to be adapted in shape, size, length, and balance so that it could be effective as a man-operated propelling device. But the man–machine relationship is getting greatly more critical as system complexity increases. It is most important that the human factors involved not be compromised. Required reliability and high cost dictate complete and careful consideration of human factors. The designer can no longer use himself as a typical operator while designing. It is true that he is more familiar with the equipment being designed, but he is not the final field user. A psychologist pointed out, rightfully [2]: "Machines that are an engineer's dream are often a nightmare for the man who operates them." It is such consequences that human factors engineering attempts to eliminate.

It would very likely be quite impractical to try to train all engineers to be human factor specialists. However, all should acquire facility in recognizing the human component not only as a possible liability but also as a potential asset in system performance.

A brief discussion outlining the kind of knowledge that human factors engineering concerns itself with is presented below; Reference [3], from which much of it is derived, contains a great deal more of such information.

7–4. VISION

The eye is physiologically a well-developed and highly specialized sense organ that responds to radiant energy within a relatively narrow range of wavelengths, 4,000 to 8,000 Angstrom units. It consists of lenses, refracting media, and a light sensitive screen—the lens and iris, the aqueous and vitreous humor, and the retina as shown in Fig. 7–1. Over these lies the eyelid, which can exclude light when so directed and lubricates the eyeball by opening and closing periodically. Muscles change the shape of the lens so that it can focus on objects from a few inches to several miles away. The iris is a diaphragm that opens and closes to adjust the pupil, an opening in the cornea, to admit light rays

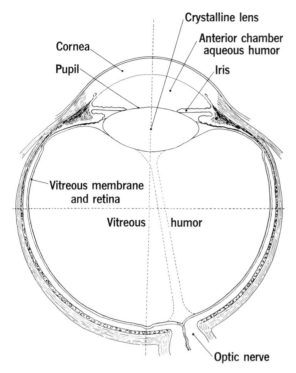

Fig. 7–1. The human eye.
From Roger C. Crafts, *A Textbook of Human Anatomy*. Copyright
© 1966, The Ronald Press Co., New York. Modified after Cunningham.

of proper intensity to the lens and on through to the retina. The
retina extends over the rear inner surface of the eyeball. It is photo-
sensitive, and picks up images and transfers them through the optic
nerve to the brain for interpretation.

The retina is visually not symmetrical with respect to its center.
Vision toward the nose (nasal) has about a 60° angle of vision, whereas
for vision to the outside (temporal) the angle is around 100°. The
retina seems, furthermore, to contain a blind spot, about 15° from the
center on the nasal side and about 7° wide by 5° high. A warning
light, for instance, placed on an instrument panel within the blind-spot
cone will never be seen by the operator unless the head is turned properly at the correct instant.

The retina contains two types of receptor cells, called cones and rods. The cones are denser toward the retina center, and can take the image in daylight when the pupil is quite small.   Rods, on the other hand, are more concentrated about 20° from the center, diminishing toward the outside; they provide night vision, when the pupil is larger.   Here, design must relate angle of vision to darkness and light.   Also, because the cones are more sensitive to yellow and green wavelengths and the rods respond better to the blue range and are quite insensitive to red, color choice must be closely related to intensity of light for best visibility.

It must be noted that vision depends not only on the eye, but as well upon the state of the object viewed, the medium through which it is being observed, and the intensity of its illumination.   Arrangements of work space, displays, controls, and other elements must be decided upon with regard for visibility.   Displays must somehow be arranged over the general field of vision, as well as specifically placed within that field, for minimization of required eye movements.

An indication, Fig. 7–2, of what eye movements are like when the display is well arranged is revealed in the analysis of an aircraft instrument panel while in use.   The percentage figures represent the average eye shifts of 36 pilots made during constant-heading climbing maneu-

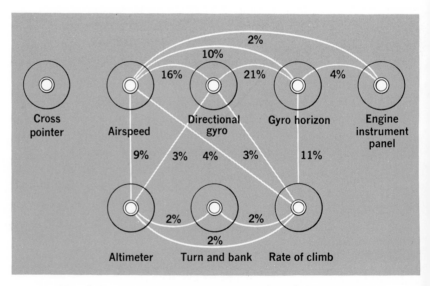

Fig. 7–2.   Eye movements among aircraft instruments.

vers. Movements of less than 2 per cent of the total number of shifts are not shown. This chart proves the effectiveness of the arrangement.

7–5. HEARING

Like the eye, the ear responds to energy impulses in the form of vibrations approximately at frequencies from 20 to 16,000 cycles per second and at pressures above 3.5×10^{-9} pounds per square inch [4]. When the pressure intensity reaches about 3.5×10^{-3} psi, the sound is not only heard but painfully felt. Frequency is what the human ear senses as pitch. Sound intensity is measured in decibels (db), which gives not an absolute dimension but rather a comparison with a standard reference intensity at some frequency. The intensity of an audible sound must be 10^6 times as strong at a frequency of 50 cps as at 1,000 cps, for example. The hearing threshold marks the lowest intensity at which sound can be heard. This threshold rises with age in both men and women, as depicted in Fig. 7–3, adapted from United

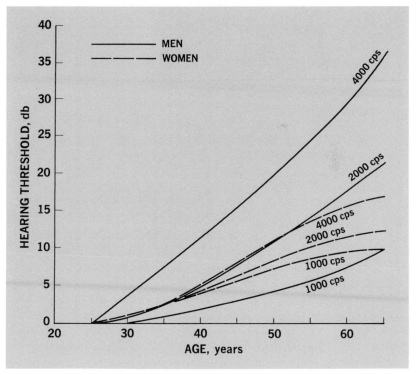

Fig. 7–3. Hearing threshold versus age.

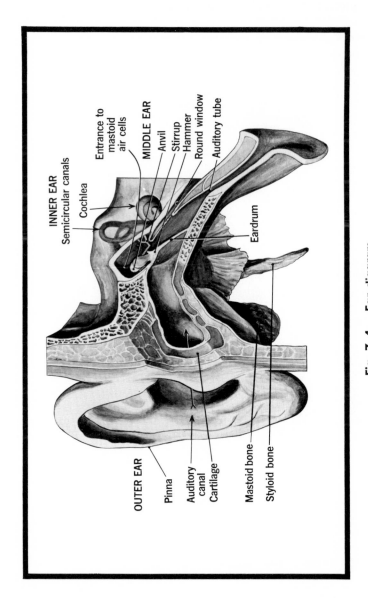

Fig. 7-4. Ear diagram.

Modified from Roger C. Crafts, A Textbook of Human Anatomy.
Copyright © 1966, The Ronald Press Co., New York.

States Standards Institute data. The rise in intensity threshold is apparently greater at the higher frequencies.

Sound, like light, is almost invariably a mixture of frequencies; few musical instruments can even approach emitting a pure tone. Sounds are some combination of a fundamental and harmonic frequencies; many probably contain as well non-harmonic vibrations that harshen them. When one adds that the ultimate judge is the unpredictable human ear, the complexity of the problem becomes fully evident. It is quite obvious that in any particular communication situation any unwanted sound or any complication of sound over the simplest possible pattern is technically undesirable. It is actually redundant because it is unrelated to the task at hand.

The human ear consists of three major parts (Fig. 7–4). The outer ear includes the auditory canal, which channels the sound collected by the external portion to the middle ear. The membranous eardrum separates the middle from the outer ear. Inside this section are three small bones, the ossicles. These are the hammer, the anvil, and the stirrup, which transmit the sound vibrations from the eardrum to the oval window of the inner ear. At the oval window the vibrations are picked up by the snail-like cochlea tube of the inner ear, which contains two canals full of liquid. The pressure-sensitive hair cells of the cochlea in turn transmit the impulses to the brain for interpretation.

The exact functioning of the human ear is not fully understood. The mechanical process of sound transmission through the ear is fairly clear, but how and why the vibrations are heard and discriminated is not. Fortunately the human ear can also analyze complex sound, differentiating its various components. The auditory system is known to serve the important function of the preservation of balance also. In some animal species this is the only function performed by the ear.

TABLE–7–3

Approximate Decimal Levels of
Various Sound Sources

Twelve-inch cannon at 12 feet	230
Pneumatic drill	150
Large jet motor	126
Threshold of feeling	120
Lathes	80
Average factory	75
Quiet automobile	50
Whispered conversation at 5 feet	25
Rustle of leaves	20
Hearing threshold	15

Initial exposure to noise can have many physiological effects. Among these are effects on heart rate, pulse rate, blood pressure, metabolism, and hearing. Man's wonderful adaptability, however, often permits adjustment following initial shock with apparently no permanent effect. The intensity of sound emanating from various typical sources is listed in Table 7–3.

The hearing mechanism can be afforded protection by several types of ear plugs. An example of this is plotted as in the threshold shift curves of Fig. 7–5. The data were obtained in a gunnery practice test with the participants wearing what are called *ear wardens*. Such data are not, however, conclusive in any way.

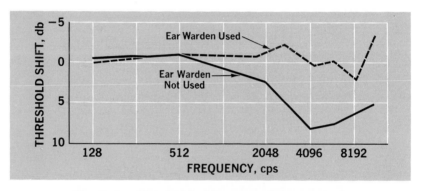

Fig. 7–5.   Threshold shift curves (approximate).

7–6. CUTANEOUS AND KINESTHETIC SENSES

The human nervous system extends into the several layers of the skin. When the detectors there are stimulated by some action or condition, the sensation of it is taken to the brain, where it is interpreted, as of heat or cold, for instance. One of the most frequently exercised senses is tactility, the sense of touch. And this is of particular importance to the designer; it is to this sense in the fingertips that the engineer refers when, for instance, he is coding control knobs by size, shape, and relative position.

The human's awareness, without visual or tactile perception, of the position and movement of his body and its extremities, such as arms, hands, fingers and legs, comes through his kinesthetic sense. The kinesthetic sensations are also of neural origin; nerves in the muscles, tendons, and joints, are the receptors for this kinesthesis. The movement, the human's motor activity, and these sensations as they are involved in its control, are important to the designer because they are an intimate part of what must be developed toward bringing about a desired end result.

Hand movements may be made more accurately in one direction than in another, a control might be manipulated more easily with the foot than with the hand, or its location in a particular position might be related to how quickly it must be reached in certain circumstances. Such are the considerations involving these senses. Problems may be classified as dealing with the selection, design, and location of control devices; with the selection and design of hand tools; and with work methods involving specific procedure and sequence of activity. Differences in motor-activity among individuals must be considered in establishing reasonable bounds for such factors as required operating force, and length of reach.

Involved in all this, is also the ability of an operator to perform a task for extended periods without loss of efficiency. Mental as well as physical fatigue can be of concern here. As man fatigues, waste products accumulate around his muscles, making them less responsive to stimulation.

7–7. EXAMPLES OF HUMAN FACTORS ENGINEERING

As already indicated, human factors engineering involves knowledge of human action and reaction. It is the application of the disciplines enumerated in the first article. Obviously, mastering the science, and the art, of human engineering requires an in-depth study of many subjects and much experience. No one engineer is likely to know it all well; it is rather a team effort that will be required whenever the problem is of more than secondary importance. An understanding may be gained by reviewing a few examples of design situations in which human factors must be considered.

Much has been done over the years to design safer automobiles. Many design features concerned vehicle control, that is, controls manipulated by the human operator. Braking system, steering mechanism, and panel arrangement were improved to take greater advantage of man's physiological and kinesthetic characteristics. Visibility, head lamps, and mirrors, features associated with driver aid and environmentals, were also refined. Vehicle-control standardization, exemplifying the consideration of driver learning, was instituted as well.

Whenever the automobile accident rate goes up, safety becomes an area of intensive study. The mechanism of vehicle accident and the relation between the first and second collisions become of primary importance. The second collision deals with the motion of the occupants after impact. A well known measure designed to prevent or at least minimize injury is the seat belt.

Analysis of the energy-absorption characteristics of the front end is another aspect of safety engineering. The typical car crushes some 25 inches during a 30 mile-per-hour flat barrier impact generating a force of around 50,000 pounds. Controlled-crush front ends, shock absorbing bumpers, and safety cell ideas are examples of what is being done toward improving energy absorption, which is now being studied by both automotive and human factors engineers.

The engine, of necessity very rigid, may shift injuriously to the passengers. Consideration is given to dropping it during the first collision. However, even if fully free it would drop only 2 inches of its own accord during the $\frac{1}{10}$ or so duration of the first collision [5]. Lowering the engine far enough and quickly enough to increase safety would require much force, so that even the problem of deflecting the engine downward creates a formidable task for the designer.

When one realizes that all this effort is directed towards a safer environment for the car occupants, one begins to understand the amount of human factors engineering that is involved in the automotive industry alone.

Acoustic fatigue in humans can render a person much less productive and efficient; misunderstanding and misinterpretation of information may cause a space mission to fail, an airplane to crash, or a ship to sink. The design engineer must so apply human factors principles that acoustic fatigue is reduced. Human fatigue is difficult to quantify, but it is claimed to be psychological as well as physiological. Studies seem to reveal that insofar as psychological effects are concerned, a sound signal should be systematically changeable, but not changed too abruptly, if it is to maintain attention. Many a listener has been fatigued to sleep by a speaker's monotone vocal output. Physiological parameters may be specified with a little more certainty; a little of this has been indicated in Article 7–4. Such physical factors as the frequency, wave form, duration, and intensity of sound can cause physiological deterioration of hearing ability. Tables 7–4 and 7–5 contain some information-transfer design hints currently being recommended by the Office of Naval Research [6].

The adaptability of the human system to weightlessness is another human factors problem of great concern in the planning of the exploration of space.　It is so much a matter of the astronaut's performance in the weightless state as of the gravity overstress environment upon his return to earth after a long stay in space.　The prolonged exposure to weightlessness affects the cardiovascular system, and bones assume a reduced mineral balance.　The physiological readjustment to the increased gravity stress on return is a long, troublesome process, and the question of what to do to ease the space worker's plight becomes a serious problem.

TABLE 7–4
Use of Auditory and Visual Presentation

Use auditory presentation if—	Use visual presentation if—
1. The message is simple	1. The message is complex
2. The message is short	2. The message is long
3. The message will not be referred to later	3. The message will be referred to later
4. The message deals with events in time	4. The message deals with location in space
5. The message calls for immediate action	5. The message does not call for immediate action
6. The visual system of the person is overburdened	6. The auditory system of the person is overburdened
7. The receiving location is too bright or dark-adaptation integrity is necessary	7. The receiving location is too noisy
8. The person's job requires him to move about continually	8. The person's job allows him to remain in one position

Practical methods of counteracting undesirable environmental adaptations that will not too severely compromise future manned-space-vehicle design are being investigated.　Techniques for exercising the affected systems to prevent atrophy is one possibility.　Tourniquets, periodically compressed, held, and relieved do exercise the cardiovascular system; but the devices and power required for this are undesirable to both astronauts and designers [7].

A more practical method seems to be to produce artificial gravity. This can be done by rotating the space vehicle so that the resulting

TABLE 7–5
Form of Auditory Presentation

Use tone or noise signals, rather than speech, if—	Use speech rather than tone or noise signals, if—
1. The message is extremely simple	1. Flexibility of communication is necessary
2. The listener has had adequate training in the meaning of the coded signal	2. It is necessary to quickly identify the source of the message
3. The message calls for immediate action, well rehearsed by the listener	3. The listener is not trained in coded signals
4. Speech signals are overloading the listener	4. Rapid two-way information exchange is necessary
5. Noise conditions are unfavorable for speech reception (tones can be detected in higher minus S/N ratios)	5. The message deals with a future time requiring listener preparation time to execute (example: countdown where number of beeps are hard to remember)
6. Security of the message is all important	6. The situation is so stressful that it could cause the listener to "forget" the code
7. Speech communication channels are overloaded	
8. Without extensive processing speech will mask other speech or will excessively annoy others than the intended listener	

centrifugal force provides a sufficient gravity vector. One drawback is Coriolis acceleration, the effect of which upon the astronauts is complicated because it varies with the direction of motion of the space vehicle and of the personnel within it. Other difficulties exist also. Under certain conditions of rotation and head movement the astronaut experiences a debilitating state termed *canal sickness*. Much more study remains to be performed before safe tolerances of operation are determined. Nevertheless, artificial gravity appears to promise the best solution even though adaptation to a rotating environment may be necessary.

7–8. LEARNING

Man has always had to cope with his environment, which has often proved hostile. To do this successfully he simulated environments and trained himself to work and survive in them. For instance, the Romans set up galleys on land to train the slaves how to row, sail, and even fight at sea. Often he has had to learn to adapt himself to changing conditions, to overcome fatigue and stress, to work with new tools, and to manipulate new machines.

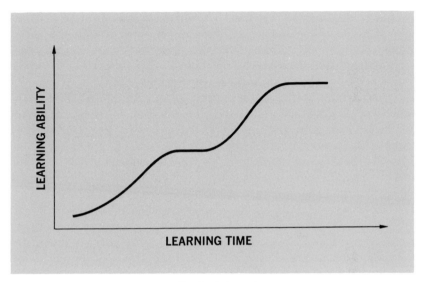

Fig. 7–6. Typical learning curve.

Modern man–machine systems require the services of highly trained and knowledgeable operators; astronauts are a prime example. The selection and training of such operators is a difficult task that falls within the province of human engineering. The learning itself is a complex process as well. No single direction can be given it. Typical learning curves contain plateaus during which learning seems to rest on its laurels. With more instruction, learning periods recur again and again, but over-all education efficiency has even been shown to increase when instruction was ceased during plateau periods. A typical learning curve is illustrated in Fig. 7–6.

7–9. CURRENT HUMAN FACTORS STUDIES

Much research is being conducted in the attempt to obtain more information concerning the man-factor in man–machine systems. A few such investigations are presented below.

The anatomy of the body is a complex combination of mass and elastic elements so assembled that small vibratory forces can easily disturb the rest or equilibrium state of an organ and in turn, so to speak, of the whole system. Vibrations stimulate sensory receptors, or excite other parts of the nervous system, with occasionally detrimental results. Fatigue is induced, alertness reduced, and work capacity diminished. Reactions occur of discomfort, fear, excitement, and anxiety. Pradko, Lee, and Greene [8] conclude that the entire human body responds linearly to random vibrations, and derive transfer functions describing human dynamics.

Heat stress is being investigated by Brouha, Smith, and Maxfield [9]. The human body must be in thermal equilibrium with its environment if life is to be maintained. Heat is continuously produced within the body chemically, and this heat must be lost to the atmosphere by radiation, convection, and evaporation of sweat. Evaporation of one liter of sweat removes approximately 660 kilo-calories of heat from the body. The effectiveness of the body in fighting off heat in its physiological adjustment seems to depend upon its ability to transfer the heat from the source site to the periphery plus its ability to form sweat. Heat balance is maintained only when the heat dissipated by the body equals the heat generated within the body. When not, body temperature will of course rise, and so will heart rate and cardiac output; dehydration will begin, and exhaustion set in.

Others are investigating the strength and other characteristics of skin, bones, and limbs. Such information also can be very useful in designing for conditions whereunder the human body is subjected to such dynamic conditions as in high-speed transportation, in space vehicles, and in rockets.

REFERENCES

1. V. C. Roberts, *Human Factors in Ground-Support Equipment*, ASME Paper No. 65-WA/HUF-16, Nov. 1965.
2. J. L. Seminara, and G. A. Peters, *Human Factors Responsibilities of Design Engineers*, ASME Paper No. 57-A-167, Dec. 1957.
3. A. Chapanis, W. R. Garner, and C. T. Morgan, *Applied Experimental Psychology*, John Wiley & Sons, Inc., New York, 1949.

4. J. N. Macduff, and J. R. Curreri, *Vibration Control*, McGraw-Hill Book Co., Inc., New York, 1958.

5. L. C. Lundstrom, *Safety Factor in Automotive Design*, SAE Paper No. 660539, August 1966.

6. G. C. Tolhurst, *Human Engineering and Acoustical Fatigue*, ASME Paper No. 66-MD-25, May, 1966.

7. A. B. Thompson, *Physiological Design Criteria for Artificial Gravity Environments in Manned Space Systems*, General Electric Co. Bulletin L-184, Jan. 1965, 19 pp.

8. F. Pradko, R. A. Lee, and J. D. Greene, *Human Vibration-Response Theory*, ASME Paper No. 65-WA/HUF-19, Nov. 1965.

9. L. Brouha, P. E. Smith, and Mary E. Maxfield, *Heat Stress and the Industrial Worker*, ASME Paper No. 59-A-213, Dec. 1959.

PROBLEMS

7-1. Which of man's senses are more likely to be used in system operation?

7-2. Identify five elements of the human eye and explain the function of each.

7-3. Identify the three major parts of the ear and explain the function of each.

7-4. What are some important physiological effects of exposure to noise?

7-5. Illustrate the ancientry of human factors engineering by an example.

7-6. Assuming that sound audibility varies linearly with intensity, compute how much more intense a sound would have to be at 600 cps than at 1,000 cps to be audible.

7-7. Compute the percentage difference in hearing-threshold rise between man and woman at age 50.

7-8. Compare the hearing loss of men from age 30 to age 60 at 1,000 and 4,000 cps.

7-9. The success of the human body in its fight against heat depends upon its ability to dissipate heat. Work requiring an oxygen consumption of 2 liters per minute above rest level produced 7.5 kilo-calories of excess heat per minute. To what temperature would the body of a 75-kilo man rise in 10-min, if his specific heat were 0.5 k-cal per kg per °C?

7-10. 600 k-c are removed on the average by the evaporation of each liter of perspiration from the body. Will the individual of Problem 7-9 retain thermal equilibrium in an environment in which he evaporates 0.75 l/hr?

7-11. Discuss why man is of as great importance as a system component.

7-12. Discuss the arrangement of the driver's panel in your car from the point of view of vision.

7-13. Discuss noise and its problems as these concern designers.

7-14. Analyze the situation and discuss any human factor that may be involved in the detail design of the casement window decided upon as the best alternate in Chapter 2.

7-15. Discuss the problem of training operators for modern engineering systems.

7-16. Search the technical literature for and discuss how human factors engineering was applied to some current design situation.

7-17. There are several ways in which kitchen stove controls can be arranged geometrically. Observe those on the stove in your home. Decide whether their arrangement is according to common sense or not in your opinion and discuss.

DESIGN PROBLEMS

7-D1. An experiment is to be set up in which the following must be accomplished: the reading of a strain indicator must be recorded every 3 min, the strain being a function of flow, which is changed by way of pressure and temperature. Thus the flow, temperature, and pressure meters, as well as the two knobs for controlling the pressure and temperature, are needed. Arrange a panel containing the meters and knobs and indicator needed to effectively conduct the experiment. Explain the reasons for your arrangement.

7-D2. An aircraft cockpit contains an instrument called an artificial horizon. A miniature airplane representation remains fixed while a white line representing the horizon rotates as the aircraft banks. During level flight the horizon line is level as well. But when the plane banks to the right the horizon line rotates counterclockwise. When banking left, the line rotates clockwise. The design was no doubt based on common sense because when one sits in the aircraft and the plane is banked to the right the actual horizon appears to lower on the left as though it were rotating counterclockwise. Research, however, indicates that the display is actually confusing and that interpretation would probably be easier were the rotation reversed. Consider the problem and decide whether it should be reversed or not. Explain why.

7-D3. Show schematically a possible design for a nut-tightening wrench intended for use in a weightless environment.

7-D4. A pedestal seat is to be designed for drill-press operators. The operator will be reaching for, locating, and drilling small components. Sketch a design for the seat, giving all critical dimensions.

7-D5. Sketch your idea of a satisfactory classroom seat. Indicate all critical dimensions and explain why it is a better seat.

7-D6. In a production set-up, a table must be power-moved in four orthogonal positions from a central station. The motion is to be controlled by an operator who must turn the correct knob for each motion. The table must be returned to the center position before going to a new station. Because of the nature of the process, the area can be only dimly illuminated. The knobs are *start, stop, center, forward, backward, right,* and *left.* Sketch an arrangement of a suitable panel and knobs. Show all critical dimensions.

7–D7. A seated operator is to manipulate the clutch, brake, and hold controls of a heavy-component positioning crawler. Sketch an arrangement of the three control extremities (lever, pedal, or handle) for effective operation of the crawler vehicle.

7–D8. A hand riveter of the plier or grip type, capable of applying up to 500 lb of pressure, is to be designed. Layout the mechanism giving all the kinematically critical dimensions.

8

Experimentation

As important to the engineer as any other tool he uses is experimentation. The engineer must be aware of the power of the experimental approach. He must have an understanding of the purpose of experimentation, of planning for experimentation, of the gathering and presentation of experimental data, and of the analysis, evaluation, and interpretation of results. To learn to so plan and conduct an experiment that sound conclusions and correct solutions are achieved is essential, if the engineer is to practice fully.

8–1. PURPOSE OF EXPERIMENTATION

Experimentation is used in testing to determine pertinent properties and accumulate data. It is also used to verify both theory and design. Finally, it is applied to problems that cannot, or at least not easily, be solved mathematically.

An important application of testing concerns material properties. Probably the most common example is the testing performed to obtain the stress–strain diagram and the essential material properties it reveals. Fatigue strength, dielectric constant, heat conductivity, creep rate, and damping coefficient are other examples of material properties found experimentally. It is possible that the time will come when the understanding of the fundamental nature of materials will be so complete that macroscopic-level properties will be predictable with assurance; but for now, bulk characteristics must be obtained by test.

Testing is used in other situations as well. The characteristic or performance curves of an electric motor, an indicator diagram, the proximate and ultimate analysis of coal, the superconductivity of metals at cryogenic temperatures, and many other tests, standard and otherwise, of materials, components, subassemblies and even systems

134

are examples. Most satellite flights are complex experiments conducted to gather space facts, information, and data.

It was some time in the sixteenth century that the experimental method was firmly established as a means of scientific inquiry. The development of physical theory up to then was practically nil, primarily because of the almost complete absence of experiment to test and verify what theory may have proposed.

Galileo suffered lifetime persecution because he dared to prove experimentally the error of the centuries-old claim of Aristotle that a heavy body falls more rapidly than a light one. Leonardo da Vinci wrote, "Experience never deceives; it is only our judgment which deceives us"; and, "Before making this case a general rule, test it by experiment, two or three times, and see if the experiment produces the same effect" [1]. Experimentation has been the positive means to knowledge ever since. In a real sense, then, all knowledge—data and theory—is empirical. But without it there would be little progress.

More recent experimental studies have, for instance, shown that fatigue consists of two independent stages, that of nucleation and that of crack growth [2, 3, 4]. Experimental studies by nuclear scientists have resulted in many new principles concerning the basic structure of matter. Space probes have revealed much valuable knowledge of the universe. And so, theory is developed, and principles and laws of nature uncovered and verified.

As pointed out in an earlier chapter, designs must be proven as well. No matter how experienced the design engineer is, trade-offs and incomplete information result in components, and equipment, and materials, and processes that must be checked out. Motors, boilers, space capsules, heat exchangers, and vehicles, all devices, are experimentally analyzed for function, capacity, and strength, to verify the soundness of the design before its production and use.

Solving problems experimentally is the third very important application of experimentation. There are many engineering situations that contain problems that cannot be solved wholly or in part by analytical means. An experimental solution becomes necessary.

Stress distribution and magnitude must be known, for example, if a sheet-metal structure is to be properly stiffened. Mathematically, the stress field is difficult to describe, and even if it were described the equation may not be explicitly solvable. The solution may be approximate, but this may not be accurate enough. A photoelastic polariscope or a few electric-strain gages will yield the answers experimentally. Spacecraft re-entry problems are best solved by studying experimentally the behavior of fluids at hypersonic speeds. The prob-

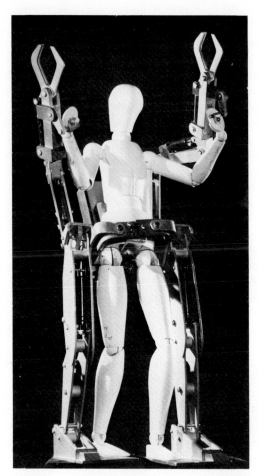

Fig. 8–1. The General Electric Hardi-Man.
Courtesy General Electric Research and Development Center.

lem of the self-welding of rubbing titanium parts has been solved by experimental studies of iodine lubricants. General Electric is developing "Hardi-Man" (Fig. 8–1), a device worn like an external skeleton of mechanical muscles to give ordinary man the strength of a giant.

As in many other situations, it is difficult to tell where testing stops and verification or solution starts. But then, the argument is academic and immaterial. The important point is that whether performed separately or in combination, experimentation deals with testing, verification, and solution.

8–2. MEASUREMENT

Measurement has been defined as the assignment of numerals to aspects of objects or events in accordance with a pre-established rule [5]. To put this in a way more appropriate to the present consideration, a measurement is almost invariably made when nature is being observed during an experiment. Thus a measurement is the statement of the result of an observation and hence is subject to all the deficiencies of the human observer.

An essential requirement, if reliability is to exist, is an accurate measuring instrument of high precision. The accuracy of an instrument, usually expressed as a percentage of its full scale, is how closely its readings come to actual input; whereas its precision is its ability to reproduce a reading, that is, yield the same output each time it is subjected to the same given input. These are functions of the design and fabrication of the instrument. Readability of its scale, its sensitivity, hysteresis, ambient condition effects, as well as the ease with which it can be calibrated are the important factors [6].

The instrumentation for an experiment may involve many measuring devices. These include means for measuring physical dimensions, mass, motion, time, thermal properties, pressure, radiation, electrical behavior, and many other parameters. Most modern measuring systems consist of three elements: a detector, a modifier, and a display device, often in rather sophisticated form. The first stage is usually a transducer capable of detecting a physical variable and converting it into a more easily handled mechanical or electrical signal. The second stage alters the detected signal by filtering, amplifying, or modifying it in some other way to make it a more useful output. The final stage displays the output in a convenient visual or graphic form. The output may also be used to control some other system variable.

Dynamic measurement, where the variable being observed is a function of time, requires instrumentation of low inertia, so that moving parts will respond rapidly and faithfully to the fluctuating variable. This is often accomplished by converting the variable signal into a proportional voltage, which becomes the measured quantity that is finally evaluated by means of a scale function. A very important characteristic of a dynamic-measurement device is its linear frequency response; that is, the device must react the same at all frequencies, so that the output-to-input ratio remains constant over the useful frequency range. Another feature, the phase shift, that is, the extent to which the output lags input, should be close to zero over the instrument's operating range.

There are many types of measuring instruments available in various grades of sophistication. The selection of the instrumentation for any experimental set-up must be carefully undertaken so that results will be consistent with requirements. Only some of the major considerations have been touched, and those but briefly. Much additional information can be found in the technical literature.

8–3. UNCERTAINTY OF MEASUREMENT

It has been indicated already that experimentation is subject to error, in set-up and in the selection of suitable instrumentation; inherent in the instruments; and present in the human frailties of the operator. Careful planning, selection, and training can practically eliminate some sources of error and minimize others. Where error cannot be eliminated to the desired extent, such as with accidental error arising from low precision, its magnitude must be at least predicted. In such situations the experimenter must revert to statistics and probability (see Chapter 4, and references given in the previous section).

When the variations among a series of readings is small, the data are considered more reliable, because each reading deviates little from the central value. Thus the probable error would appear to be a function of standard deviation. The probable error is generally a value having one half of the errors larger and the other half smaller than it. Using the Gaussian distribution this probable error, P_e, is

$$P_e = 0.6745D$$

The probable error applies to the average value that the standard deviation, D, was computed for. Thus the proper statement of the average reading is

$$N \pm P_e$$

Example 8-1. Compute the probable error for the data of Example 4-1.

Solution: Using the standard deviation already determined, the probable error is

$$P_e = 0.6745 \times 0.2523 = 0.170$$

Thus the rod length is 67.48 ± 0.17 in. Note the difference between the above value and that computed as the standard error.

There are many cases of indirect measurement, that is, where the quantity desired must be calculated from other observations or readings. The probable error, P_N, of the indirectly determined quantity, N, a function of $a, b, c, \ldots$, is determined as shown below. P_a, P_b, P_c, . . . are the probable errors of the measured quantities a, b, c, ...

$$P_N = \sqrt{\left(\frac{\partial N}{\partial a}\right)^2 P_a{}^2 + \left(\frac{\partial N}{\partial b}\right)^2 P_b{}^2 + \left(\frac{\partial N}{\partial c}\right)^2 P_c{}^2 + \cdots}$$

It is possible that requirements may arise where probabilities other than the above 50-50 grade are desired. In such case resort is made to confidence limit calculations [6]. The effect of population size or the number of readings can also be accounted for by the approach to confidence limits.

Example 8–2. The desired measurement N is a function of a and b:

$$N = \frac{a^2}{b}$$

The average value of readings a is 2.53, and of readings b, 1.67. Standard deviation D_a, calculated from the a readings, is 0.11, and D_b, from the b readings, is 0.08. Calculate the proper value of the arithmetic mean.

Solution:

$$N_A = 2.53^2/1.67 = 3.83$$
$$P_a = 0.6745 \times 0.11 = 0.07$$
$$P_b = 0.6745 \times 0.08 = 0.05$$

Differentiating the function as indicated above,

$$P_N = \sqrt{\left(\frac{2a}{b}\right)^2 P_a{}^2 + \left[\frac{(-a^2)}{b^2}\right]^2 P_b{}^2}$$

$$= \sqrt{\left(\frac{2 \times 2.53}{1.67}\right)^2 (0.07)^2 + \left(\frac{-2.53^2}{1.67^2}\right)^2 (0.05)^2}$$

$$= \sqrt{9.175 \times 0.0049 + 2.295 \times 0.0025}$$

$$= 0.051$$

$$N = 3.83 \pm 0.05$$

8–4. CONFIDENCE LIMITS

It is seldom practical to use large samples in experimental work. Yet, statistical mathematics is based on an infinite population. The accuracy of a sample value can therefore be justifiably questioned. Some measure of how closely the sample value approaches the true (population) value is often essential. Such a measure is identified as a confidence limit. Several statistical tests have been developed as indications of the probable extent to which sample values may differ from those for the entire (infinite) population. A few will be presented; others can be found in the literature.

The question whether an extreme reading should be rejected often arises. An arbitrary test based on the standard deviation has already been proposed. A better statistical method, however, is indicated below.

1. Observations are arranged in ascending order of magnitude.
2. Compute scale value γ using the equations below in which x_1 is the extreme reading, x_2 the next, and so on to the last reading x_k.

For 3 to 7 readings $\quad \gamma = \dfrac{x_2 - x_1}{x_k - x_1}$

For 8 to 10 $\quad \gamma = \dfrac{x_2 - x_1}{x_{k-1} - x_1}$

For 11 to 13 $\quad \gamma = \dfrac{x_3 - x_1}{x_{k-1} - x_1}$

For 14 to 30 $\quad \gamma = \dfrac{x_3 - x_1}{x_{k-2} - x_1}$

3. Decide upon one of the two probability levels given in Table 8–1. The probability that the computed value γ is larger than table γ is greater if the extreme reading is part of normal distribution.
4. Read γ value in Table 8–1.
5. If the computed magnitude is larger than table value, the extreme reading should be rejected.

Example 8–3. A set of mass moment of inertia readings are: 0.90, 0.96, 0.97, 0.99, 0.99, 1.00, 1.00, 1.01, and 1.01 lb-in-sec². Should the 0.90 reading be rejected?

Solution:

$$\gamma = \frac{x_2 - x_1}{x_{k-1} - x_1} = \frac{0.96 - 0.90}{1.01 - 0.90} = \frac{0.06}{0.11} = 0.545$$

From Table 8–1, $\gamma = 0.512$ for a 0.05 probability and 0.635 for 0.01 probability.

The 0.90 reading should, therefore, be rejected for a probability of 1 per cent and not for a probability of 5 per cent.

Confidence limits for the population mean $\bar{m}$ can be established from the sample mean $\bar{x}$ as follows.

$$\bar{m} = \bar{x} \pm \frac{D}{\sqrt{n}} t$$

where D is the standard deviation of the sample, n is the number of readings, and t is a statistical confidence factor given in Table 8–2. The degrees of freedom against which t is tabulated are $n - 1$. The probability value determines the level of confidence desired.

TABLE 8–1
Factor γ, Criteria for Testing Extreme Values

Number of means, k	Probability	
	.05	.01
3	.941	.988
4	.765	.889
5	.642	.780
6	.560	.698
7	.507	.637
8	.554	.683
9	.512	.635
10	.477	.597
11	.576	.679
12	.546	.642
13	.521	.615
14	.546	.641
15	.525	.616
16	.507	.595
17	.490	.577
18	.475	.561
19	.462	.547
20	.450	.535
21	.440	.524
22	.430	.514
23	.421	.505
24	.413	.497
25	.406	.489
26	.399	.486
27	.393	.475
28	.387	.469
29	.381	.463
30	376	.457

Example 8–4. Compute confidence limits for the mean of the data of Example 8–3, excluding the 0.90 reading, for a probability of 0.10.

Solution:

$$\bar{x} \equiv \frac{\Sigma\, x}{n} = \frac{7.93}{8} = 0.991$$

and

$$D = \sqrt{\frac{\Sigma\, (x - \bar{x})^2}{n}} = \sqrt{\frac{0.002288}{8}} = 0.0169$$

From Table 8–2, $t = 1.94$, for a probability of 0.10. Therefore

$$\bar{m} = \bar{x} \pm \frac{D}{\sqrt{n}} t = 0.991 \pm \frac{0.0169}{\sqrt{8}} \times 1.94$$
$$= 0.991 \pm 0.012.$$

The population mean thus lies between 1.003 and 0.979, with 90% confidence.

TABLE 8–2

Confidence Factor t^*

						P					
DF	0.90	0.80	0.70	0.60	0.50	0.25	0.10	0.05	0.025	0.010	0.005
1	0.158	0.325	0.510	0.727	1.000	2.414	6.314	12.71	25.45	63.66	127.3
2	0.142	0.289	0.445	0.617	0.817	1.604	2.920	4.303	6.205	9.925	14.09
3	0.137	0.277	0.424	0.584	0.765	1.423	2.353	3.183	4.177	5.841	7.453
4	0.134	0.271	0.414	0.569	0.741	1.344	2.132	2.776	3.495	4.604	5.598
5	0.132	0.267	0.408	0.559	0.727	1.301	2.015	2.571	3.163	4.032	4.773
6	0.131	0.265	0.404	0.553	0.718	1.273	1.943	2.447	2.969	3.707	4.317
7	0.130	0.263	0.402	0.549	0.711	1.254	1.895	2.365	2.841	3.500	4.029
8	0.130	0.262	0.399	0.546	0.706	1.240	1.860	2.306	2.752	3.355	3.833
9	0.129	0.261	0.398	0.543	0.703	1.230	1.833	2.262	2.685	3.250	3.690
10	0.129	0.260	0.397	0.542	0.700	1.221	1.813	2.228	2.634	3.169	3.581
11	0.129	0.260	0.396	0.540	0.697	1.215	1.796	2.201	2.593	3.106	3.500
12	0.128	0.259	0.395	0.539	0.695	1.209	1.782	2.179	2.560	3.055	3.428
13	0.128	0.259	0.394	0.538	0.694	1.204	1.771	2.160	2.533	3.012	3.373
14	0.128	0.258	0.393	0.537	0.692	1.200	1.761	2.145	2.510	2.977	3.326
15	0.128	0.258	0.393	0.536	0.691	1.197	1.753	2.132	2.490	2.947	3.286
20	0.127	0.257	0.391	0.533	0.687	1.185	1.725	2.086	2.423	2.845	3.153
25	0.127	0.256	0.390	0.531	0.684	1.178	1.708	2.060	2.385	2.787	3.078
30	0.127	0.256	0.389	0.530	0.683	1.173	1.697	2.042	2.360	2.750	3.030
40	0.126	0.255	0.388	0.529	0.681	1.167	1.684	2.021	2.329	2.705	2.971
60	0.126	0.254	0.387	0.527	0.679	1.162	1.671	2.000	2.299	2.660	2.915
120	0.126	0.254	0.386	0.526	0.677	1.156	1.658	1.980	2.270	2.617	2.860
∞	0.126	0.253	0.385	0.524	0.674	1.150	1.645	1.960	2.241	2.576	2.807

* Two-tailed probabilities P for given degrees of freedom, DF.

It is often necessary to determine from sample readings the limits within which the entire population will fall with some degree of confidence. Such limits can be determined using

$$\bar{x} \pm KD$$

TABLE 8–3
Tolerance Factor K for Normal Distributions

n	90% Confidence that percentage of population between limits is			95% Confidence that percentage of population between limits is			99% Confidence that percentage of population between limits is		
	90%	95%	99%	90%	95%	99%	90%	95%	99%
2	15.98	18.80	24.17	32.02	37.67	48.43	160.2	188.5	242.3
3	5.847	6.919	8.974	8.380	9.916	12.86	18.93	22.40	29.06
4	4.166	4.943	6.440	5.369	6.370	8.299	9.398	11.15	14.53
5	3.494	4.152	5.423	4.275	5.079	6.634	6.612	7.855	10.26
6	3.131	3.723	4.870	3.712	4.414	5.775	5.337	6.345	8.301
7	2.902	3.452	4.521	3.369	4.007	5.248	4.613	5.488	7.187
8	2.743	3.264	4.278	3.136	3.732	4.891	4.147	4.936	6.468
9	2.626	3.125	4.098	2.967	3.532	4.631	3.822	4.550	5.966
10	2.535	3.018	3.959	2.839	3.379	4.433	3.582	4.265	5.594
11	2.463	2.933	3.849	2.737	3.259	4.277	3.397	4.045	5.308
12	2.404	2.863	3.758	2.655	3.162	4.150	3.250	3.870	5.079
13	2.355	2.805	3.682	2.587	3.081	4.044	3.130	3.727	4.893
14	2.314	2.756	3.618	2.529	3.012	3.955	3.029	3.608	4.737
15	2.278	2.713	3.562	2.480	2.954	3.878	2.945	3.507	4.605
16	2.246	2.676	3.514	2.437	2.903	3.812	2.872	3.421	4.492
17	2.219	2.643	3.471	2.400	2.858	3.754	2.808	3.345	4.393
18	2.194	2.614	3.433	2.366	2.819	3.702	2.753	3.279	4.307
19	2.172	2.588	3.399	2.337	2.784	3.656	2.703	3.221	4.230
20	2.152	2.564	3.368	2.310	2.752	3.615	2.659	3.168	4.161
21	2.135	2.543	3.340	2.286	2.723	3.577	2.620	3.121	4.100
22	2.118	2.524	3.315	2.264	2.697	3.543	2.584	3.078	4.044
23	2.103	2.506	3.292	2.244	2.673	3.512	2.551	3.040	3.993
24	2.089	2.489	3.270	2.225	2.651	3.483	2.522	3.004	3.947
25	2.077	2.474	3.251	2.208	2.631	3.457	2.494	2.972	3.904
26	2.065	2.460	3.232	2.193	2.612	3.432	2.469	2.941	3.865
27	2.054	2.447	3.215	2.178	2.595	3.409	2.446	2.914	3.828
28	2.044	2.435	3.199	2.164	2.579	3.388	2.424	2.888	3.794
29	2.034	2.424	3.184	2.152	2.554	3.368	2.404	2.864	3.763
30	2.025	2.413	3.170	2.140	2.549	3.350	2.385	2.841	3.733
35	1.988	2.368	3.112	2.090	2.490	3.272	2.306	2.748	3.611
40	1.959	2.334	3.066	2.052	2.445	3.213	2.247	2.677	3.518
50	1.916	2.284	3.001	1.996	2.379	3.126	2.162	2.576	3.385
60	1.887	2.248	2.955	1.958	2.333	3.066	2.103	2.506	3.293
80	1.848	2.202	2.894	1.907	2.272	2.986	2.026	2.414	3.173
100	1.822	2.172	2.854	1.874	2.233	2.934	1.977	2.355	3.096
200	1.764	2.102	2.762	1.798	2.143	2.816	1.865	2.222	2.921
500	1.717	2.046	2.689	1.737	2.070	2.721	1.777	2.117	2.783
1000	1.695	2.019	2.654	1.709	2.036	2.676	1.736	2.068	2.718
∞	1.645	1.960	2.576	1.645	1.960	2.576	1.645	1.960	2.576

where K, the tolerance factor for the normal distribution, can be found in Table 8–3.

Example 8–5. The lengths of each of twenty-five random samples of a rod for an automobile steering mechanism have been measured. The mean value is 6.358 in., and the standard deviation is 0.056 in. Compute the limits within which 95% of the production can be expected to fall with 95% confidence.

Solution: Table 8–3 yields $K = 2.63$. Thus

$$\bar{x} \pm KD = 6.358 \pm 2.63 \times 0.056 = 6.358 \pm 0.147.$$

It can, therefore, be assumed with 95% confidence that 95% of the rods will be from 6.211 to 6.505 inches long.

8–5. EXPERIMENT PLANNING

An experiment must be so planned as to assure that when completed, the questions it was intended to resolve will be answered efficiently and unambiguously. No analysis of an investigation, no matter how ingenious, can compensate for poor planning. When designing an experiment, the purpose for experimentation and the analysis of results must be continually kept in mind. Furthermore, an experiment is not planned if the investigation can be better performed analytically. On the other hand, mathematics is not necessarily the best approach to a given problem.

The physical principle involved, the verification to be made, the property to be measured, or the problem to be solved, determines the form an experiment must take, the variables that must be measured, those that must be controlled, and the instrumentation needed. How accurate the instruments should be depends upon the purpose of the experiment and the use to which the results are to be put.

Where experimentation is under dynamic conditions, the frequency response of the instruments must be considered. Environmental conditions must often be controlled. In one instance absolute performance is to be measured, in another it becomes necessary to repeat tests under different conditions for comparison studies.

Another question that must be carefully decided on is the range of values each variable must be taken through. The volume of data required, and the size the intervals should take, are other important phases. Indicating instruments are satisfactory when exactly read and the data intelligibly recorded. To do this successfully, data sheets must be properly planned. When the situation is more critical, recording instruments provide permanent read-outs automatically. For computer data reduction, the record sheets should be so designed as to permit easy transfer.

A notebook should always be kept for a clear, chronological record of the experiment. Planning thoughts and decisions are recorded, the experimental procedure outlined, necessary computations performed, sketches drawn, and significant observations registered. Two examples of recorded observations are shown in Fig. 8–2. Not only will this

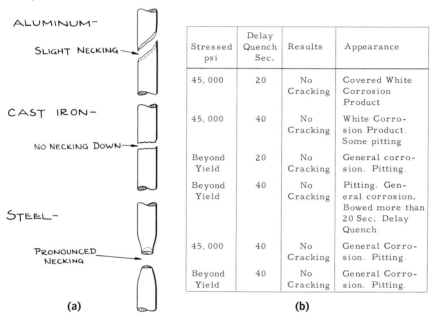

SKETCHES OF FAILURES:

ALUMINUM–

SLIGHT NECKING

CAST IRON–

NO NECKING DOWN

STEEL–

PRONOUNCED NECKING

Stressed psi	Delay Quench Sec.	Results	Appearance
45,000	20	No Cracking	Covered White Corrosion Product
45,000	40	No Cracking	White Corrosion Product. Some pitting
Beyond Yield	20	No Cracking	General corrosion. Pitting.
Beyond Yield	40	No Cracking	Pitting. General corrosion. Bowed more than 20 Sec. Delay Quench.
45,000	40	No Cracking	General Corrosion. Pitting.
Beyond Yield	40	No Cracking	General Corrosion. Pitting.

(a)   (b)

Fig. 8–2.   Recording test observations.

provide all the information needed to complete the analysis, but it will also provide a record of discoveries and priority of ideas.

An enumeration of the steps taken in planning an experiment may be as follows.

1. Analyze the purpose and objectives of the experiment to understand the problem completely.

2. Investigate the problem to decide what principles and variables are involved and how best to proceed; keep economics in mind.

3. Design the experimental set-up.

4. Decide the quality of apparatus and instruments needed, and select these accordingly.

5. Consider carefully all variables and parameters involved to decide upon those that must be controlled and those that will be permitted to vary.

6. Investigate to decide upon the range the variables should take and the number of readings that should be made within the range.

7. Design and prepare all necessary data sheets.

You are now ready to set up the experiment, check it out, and proceed with the investigation. Of course, money is a consideration in experimental work, too. How extensive the experimentation can be, therefore, depends not only on what is most desirable, but on the time–cost factor as well. One time, for a particular end use, the experiment must be thorough and highly accurate regardless of cost; whereas the next time a reasonable indication, quickly determined, is all that is needed.

As an example of planning, an elementary experiment is used to illustrate the process.

Example 8–6. A special lead-alloy piece is used to close a circuit at room temperature approximately 1 hr after it is set. The lead member lengthens under stress to complete the circuit.

The Analysis: Since the stress to which the lead member is subjected is tension and since the closing time is long, activation must depend upon creep. Creep characteristics of the lead alloy at room temperature need therefore be investigated.

The Plan: Creep at room temperature will be measured at several stress levels in order to establish the creep rate at each stress level.

The approximate nature of the time requirement indicates that the application is such that costly tests of high accuracy are unnecessary.

The lead alloy was found to possess a tensile strength of around 3,500 psi in a preliminary test.

Since the exact design of the member itself is not known (actually its dimensions will be based on the creep properties yet to be found), it is assumed that a stress range of 500 to 2,500 psi, in around 500 psi intervals, is appropriate.

A specimen cross section of $\frac{1}{4}$ in. by $\frac{1}{8}$ in. will be used so that relatively low dead weights are required for creep loading.

Six specimens at each stress level should provide a reasonable average; thirty specimens are needed.

Increase in gauge length will be measured with dividers and scale. The initial gauge length is decided upon as 5 in. The specimens will be cut as shown in Fig. 8–3, and the test set-up will be as in Fig. 8–4.

Gauge length readings will be taken every 10 sec until the length remains unchanged or the elongation rate becomes constant. Then readings will be

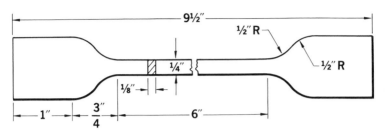

Fig. 8–3.　Lead alloy test specimen.

taken every 30 sec until the elongation speeds up again, whereupon 10-sec intervals will again be resumed to fracture or no further elongation.

Data sheets will be prepared as in Fig. 8–5.

Elongation vs. time curves will be plotted at each stress from which creep rates in in./in.-min will be determined.　The creep rates will then be plotted against stress for use in designing the switch part.

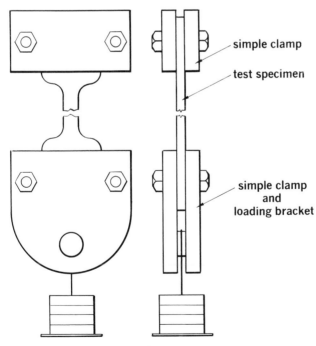

Fig. 8–4.　Creep test set-up.

LOAD (lb)	STRESS (psi)	TIME (sec)	GAGE LENGTH (in.)
15	480	0	5.000

Fig. 8–5. Data sheet.

8–6. DATA PRESENTATION AND ANALYSIS

Graphs, charts, and tables are indispensible in experimentation. A graphical presentation of experimental data can prove the validity of the experiment, scatter points can reveal uncertainties in observations, graphs can ease calculations of answers to the problem in question, and tabled data can portray a panorama of understanding not visible in the single point. Qualitative as well as quantitative graphs are commonly used. Like everything else, graphs have limitations, and so must be drawn, used, and interpreted with knowledgeable care.

Qualitative graphs and charts, such as those in Fig. 8–6, are usually used only to illustrate or emphasize some particular point or notion.

Quantitative charts or graphs must be developed accurately. The graph paper should be appropriate to the problem—rectangular, polar, log-log, etc. Coordinate scales should be such as to permit precise plotting and easy reading of any point; division lines should preferably be multiples of ten. The coordinates, curves, and graphs should be clearly marked and identified. An example of a readable chart, representing solutions to the Watt approximate straight-line four-bar linkage is shown in Fig. 8–7. Note how completely the chart is labeled and illustrated.

The independent variable must be selected for proper significance. Curves should be precisely fitted to the plotted points. When a curve is extrapolated to depict future trends, the extension is dotted to prevent confusion. Experimental points are often emphasized on a graph by circles as shown in Fig. 8–8. In such cases, curves are drawn to and not through the markings. When more than one curve is plotted on the same coordinates and a differentiation may be helpful, other figures such as squares and triangles are used on individual curves (Fig. 8-9).

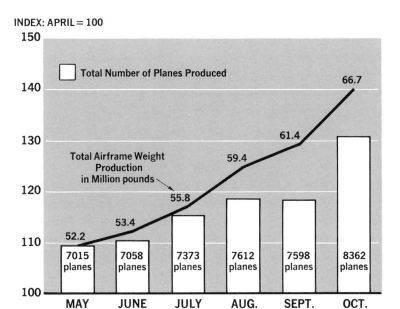

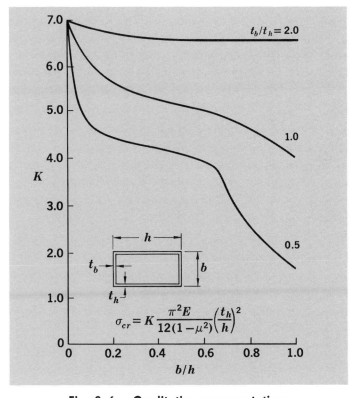

Fig. 8–6.   Qualitative representation.

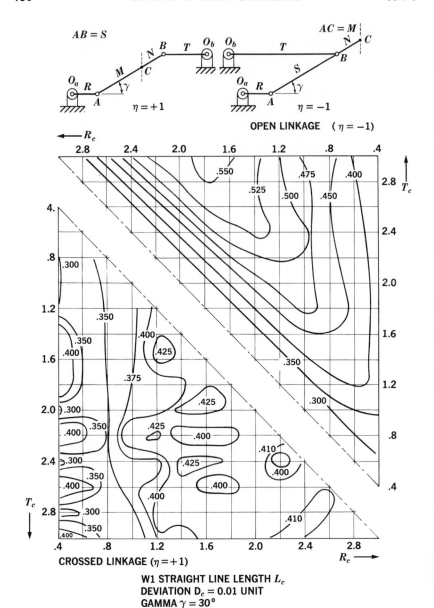

W1 STRAIGHT LINE LENGTH L_c
DEVIATION $D_c = 0.01$ UNIT
GAMMA $\gamma = 30°$

Fig. 8–7. Watt mechanism solution chart.

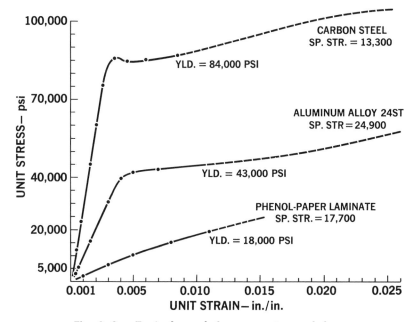

Fig. 8–8.   Typical graph from experimental data.
From J. P. Vidosic, *Machine Design Projects*.   Copyright © 1957,
The Ronald Press Co., New York.

There are many cases where it is necessary to determine how two
variables or parameters are related.   A clue may be obtained by plotting the two variables, y vs x, and observing whether a reasonably
smooth curve of some kind passes through the points.   If the curve
appears to be a straight line, the relation $y = f(x)$ is established by com-

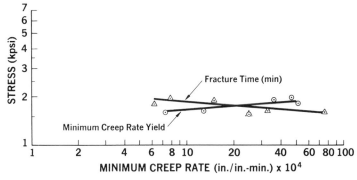

Fig. 8–9.   Graph with symbols identifying points of different curves.

puting the best value for m and b in the straight-line equation

$$y = mx + b$$

The criterion of least squares yields as the best values

$$m = \frac{n \Sigma (x_i y_i) - \Sigma x_i \Sigma y_i}{n \Sigma x_i^2 - (\Sigma x_i)^2}$$

and

$$b = \frac{\Sigma x_i^2 \Sigma y_i - \Sigma x_i \Sigma (x_i y_i)}{n \Sigma x_i^2 - (\Sigma x_i)^2}$$

where n is the number of points and the other terms refer to individual readings.

If the curve is not a straight line, more complicated procedures become necessary. Suppose it appears to be a power relation; the constant m in the following relation must be established.

$$y = x^m$$

Since $\log y = m \log x$, the data will plot as a straight line on log-log paper. The slope of the line yields m.

If the relation is exponential,

$$y = b e^{mx}$$

applies.

Then $\log y = \log b + mx$ and a plot of $\log y$ vs x on semi-log paper becomes a straight line. Constant m is the slope of the line and b is the y intercept.

Other such reductions to straight-line plots are possible and sometime used when evident. However, if the power or exponential laws do not apply, it is probably preferable to fit a polynomial relation to the test results. The general polynomial equation is

$$y = a_0 + a_1 x + a_2 x^2 + a_3 x^3 + \cdots + a_n x^n$$

One can write as many equations, using pairs of variables, as there are test points and solve the n linear equations simultaneously for the constants a_i. Where many test pairs are available, a decision, based on the precision required, is made with regard to the number of constants desired. Solving more than three simultaneous equations, however, becomes cumbersome unless a computer is used. Other methods for finding the constants are also available.

Before final acceptance, the derived equation should be checked in every case by substitution of readings not used in its derivations. When the check proves unsatisfactory, the equation may be rederived, using one or more of the remaining points. The equation can thus be made acceptable to whatever degree desired or required.

Example 8–7. Test data involving two variables measure as listed.

x	1	2	3	4	5	6
y	6	11	18	27	38	51

Determine the y vs x relation.

Solution: A preliminary plot reveals no particular type of relation. The polynomial fit is therefore decided upon.

(a) Only the first two terms will be used. Thus $y = a_0 + a_1 x$ and, using the first and fourth points,

$$6 = a_0 + a_1$$
$$27 = a_0 + 4a_1$$

Solving simultaneously yields $a_0 = -1$, and $a_1 = 7$, giving the relation

$$y = -1 + 7x$$

A check of the equation for each value of x produces the y values tabulated in column 4 of the table below.

Except for the points used in the derivation, very poor agreement exists.

(b) Continuing with only two terms, but using first and last points,

$$6 = a_0 + a_1$$
$$51 = a_0 + 6a_1$$

Solving yields $a_0 = -3$, and $a_1 = 9$. Thus the equation is $y = -3 + 9x$. Checking produces the ordinates as shown in column 5. Still a very poor fit.

(c) Three terms or $y = a_0 + a_1 x + a_2 x^2$ will be tried, using the first, fourth, and last points.

$$6 = a_0 + a_1 + a_2$$
$$27 = a_0 + 4a_1 + 16a_2$$
$$51 = a_0 + 6a_1 + 36a_2$$

A determinant solution yields $a_0 = 3$, $a_1 = 2$, and $a_2 = 1$, making the equation

$$y = 3 + 2x + x^2$$

The check now yields the ordinates shown in column 6, which is the same as column 2, or a perfect fit.

(1) x	(2) y	(3) x^2	(4) y	(5) y	(6) y
1	6	1	6	6	6
2	11	4	13	15	11
3	18	9	20	24	18
4	27	16	27	33	27
5	38	25	34	42	38
6	51	36	41	51	51

REFERENCES

1. Ivor B. Hart, *The Mechanical Investigation of Leonardo da Vinci*, The Open Court Publ. Co., Chicago.
2. W. A. Wood, "Some Basic Studies of Fatigue of Metals," *Conf. on Fracture*, Nat. Acad. of Sci., Apr. 1959.
3. A. K. Head, "The Propagation of Fatigue Cracks," *Trans. ASME*, v. 78 (1956), p. 407.
4. N. E. Frost and D. S. Dugdale, "The Propagation of Fatigue Cracks in Sheet Specimens," *J. Mech. and Phys. Solids*, v. 6, n. 2 (1958), p. 92.
5. J. P. Vidosic, *Metal Machining and Forming Technology*, The Ronald Press Co., New York, 1964.
6. E. E. Ambrosius, R. D. Fellows, and A. D. Brickman, *Mechanical Measurement and Instrumentation*, The Ronald Press Co., New York, 1966.

PROBLEMS

8–1. Identify at least three types of engineering applications for experimentation.

8–2. Define measurement and measurements.

8–3. Identify clearly a motion-, time-, pressure-, and mass-measuring device.

8–4. Illustrate a measuring system; identify and describe its three major elements.

8–5. Identify three types of errors that experimentation may be subject to.

8–6. Identify and describe three cases of your personal use of experimentation as the data-gathering tool.

8–7. Describe how an astronaut walking in space may be performing each major type of experimentation.

8–8. Determine the proper average value for the data of Problem 4–7.

8–9. A technician measures a $\frac{1}{2}$-in. bolt to the nearest thousandth of an inch, and another measures a 12-ft long shaft to the nearest $\frac{1}{8}$ in. Which is the more accurate measurement?

8–10. The power available from a stream is expressed by $P = whQ/550$ hp. The weight of water is 62.4 lb/ft^3, the average head h is 17.2 ft, and the average discharge Q is 523 ft^3/sec. From a series of readings it is determined that standard deviations of 0.150, 0.00742, and 0.750 apply, respectively. Determine completely the average stream horse power.

8–11. A set of frequency readings taken in a vibration experiment are: 51.62, 51.33, 49.75, 53.48, 50.89, 51.58, 50.21, 49.63, 47.45, 50.68, 50.36, 51.11, and 50.73 cps. Should any of the readings be rejected if a probability level of 0.05 is desired?

8–12. What percentage of the frequencies of an infinite number of readings would fall below 50.5 cps if the sample readings are those given in Problem 8–11?

8–13. Compute the limits within which 99% of the frequencies of Problem 8–11 can be expected to fall with 90% confidence. How do the limits for 90% of the population at 99% confidence compare with the previous figures?

8–14. Portray the distribution established in the solution of Problem 1–3 on an effective chart suitable to the data.

8–15. Determine the relation between the variables of the carbon steel stress-strain curve in Fig. 8–8.

8–16. Determine the K-vs.-section ratio for one of the curves of the accompanying crescent beam graph.

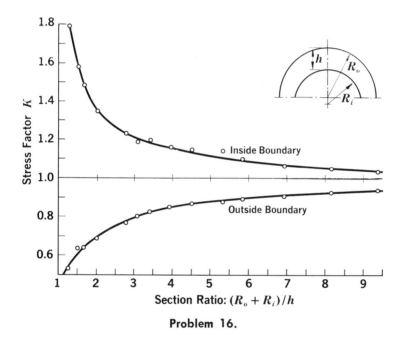

Problem 16.

8–17. From the experimental point of view, how would you classify the moon mission of Surveyor I? Give reasons for your answer, and discuss.

8–18. From the point of view of experimentation, how would you classify the first satelite, Explorer I, launched by the United States? Give reasons for your answer, and discuss.

8–19. Discuss the reasons why recording instruments may be preferable to the indicating type.

DESIGN PROBLEMS

8–D1. Select the instruments needed to investigate the performance of a pump.

8–D2. How can the weight of solid objects be determined at the bottom of the ocean? Describe the arrangement and method completely.

8–D3. Develop the plan for an experiment to be conducted to determine the penetration of sunlight energy through water.

8–D4. Plan an experiment conducted to investigate the flatness of a 5-ft by 3-ft surface plate.

8–D5. Develop the plan for an experiment to determine the air pollution situation in city X occupying an area of approximately 100 mi².

8–D6. You possess six rods, each of a different and unknown metal; each rod is of $\frac{1}{4}$-in. diam and trimmed to a length of 16 in. In a home application you have in mind, you must use the rod having the greatest thermal conductivity. Plan an experiment you could easily conduct at home, using ordinary home materials, to determine which rod to use.

8–D7. Plan an experiment that will establish the most effective (learn more) 3-hr, continuous study period (homework and reading) during the 24-hr day, excluding scheduled class and laboratory hours.

8–D8. You have just designed a gear-type speed reducer. Plan an experimental test procedure that will yield all the reducer data needed to properly advertise its qualities and market the device.

8–D9. As city engineer you have been requested to investigate the possible pollution of air in your community. Formulate a plan of attack designed to establish its existence, its sources, and the best scheme for its elimination.

9

Reliability Engineering

Quality control has been a systematic effort that industry has applied to its products for a long time. It is the method by which conformance to specifications and workmanship is maintained. It does not, however, involve the element of time. It is, on the other hand, a major ingredient in high reliability. Superior workmanship does tend to lengthen the life of a device and thus improve its reliability to perform as intended for as long as expected.

Consider, for instance, the automobile. Fifty years or so ago the automobile's operation was casual and troublesome. Today millions of people ride automobiles with little if any concern over its ability to get them to destination regularly. And how about electric power? In its early decades it was quite undependable; voltage fluctuations were large, and power failures frequent.

In the past reliability was largely a matter of redesign based on gained experience and larger factors of safety. Such approaches are no longer practical. Weight is critical, innovation cannot wait for prior experience, and modern engineering systems are a complex, interdependent combination of numerous and varied components. The basic elements of reliability are briefly presented here; many good textbooks are available and recommended for further study.

9–1. MEASURES OF RELIABILITY

When equipment works well every time it is called upon to perform its function, it is said to be reliable. The ideal situation would of course exist were the mission completely accomplished one hundred per cent of the time. Because of many design, fabrication, operation and even cost factors, the ideal is seldom achieved in actual situations. Design is only optimum, depending upon trade-offs among the many factors, and never perfect.

157

The Electronic Industries Association defines reliability as " . . . the probability of a device performing its purpose adequately for the period of time intended under the operating conditions encountered." And, it must be clearly noted that a machine or a system is made of many components each of which contributes to the over-all reliability. That is, the over-all reliability is dependent upon the reliability of each component composing the system. The more extensive the system, the greater the reliability problem.

Because of the very lack of an exact and even practical mathematical definition, the measure of reliability depends upon the specific situation —the function being performed, the economics of failure, the nature of the mission, the operating environment. In today's world of science and exact requirements, too much is at stake in terms of human life, security, safety, speed and cost to take risks with equipment; a high degree of reliability is essential. Mature design is the only answer, and reliability prediction the necessary assessment. A measurement, an index, a numeric expression of reliability, is therefore essential to good design.

Reliability might be the fraction of the total quantity of equipment operating satisfactorily for a given period of time.

Reliability might just be a function of time, the duration of satisfactory operation compared to total expected operating time.

Reliability might be the average number of hours of maintenance per hour of satisfactory operation.

Reliability might also be the actual performance compared to ideal performance (the actual as well as the ideal must be defined for each particular situation).

There are three more specific measures of reliability or statistical parameters. The first is the rate of failure, r, expressed as the number of failures per a convenient unit of time (1, 100, 1000, 10^6 hr). Next is the probability of survival, P_s, which indicates, usually as a percentage, the number of units of a kind expected to operate for a given period of time. Thus, the rating life of ball bearings guarantees that 90 per cent of a group will not fail for a given number of hours of operation at the design speed and load. The last measure is that of mean time between failures, m, or mean life, usually expressed in hours. Note that the failure rate (per hour) is the reciprocal of mean life (hour). In general then high reliability goes with a small failure rate, a high probability of survival, and a high value of mean life.

9–2. RELIABILITY AND PROBABILITY

The limits of satisfactory performance are quite obvious; the equipment is either totally operative or totally inoperative. Total inoperativeness, however, is beyond consideration, and total operativeness can only be a goal at which to aim. It is the in-between performance that needs attention.

An attempt must be made to define mathematically the level at which satisfactory performance is maintained for every component and for all aspects of operation of equipment in question.

Since an exact determination of reliability cannot be made, experimental data and statistics are used. The theory of probability can provide an answer or, at least, a close approximation.

Probability is likelihood, the likelihood that the one particular event will occur where several various events are possible. In tossing a coin, the probability that heads (H) or tails (T) will turn up is $\frac{1}{2}$ or 0.5. In some cases, as above, the result can be predicted from prior knowledge of the very nature of the event; this is a priori probability. For instance, as already shown, if standing on edge is excluded, a coin must evidently rest on either heads or tails. Empirical probability, on the other hand, is, must be, based on measured data. As an example, five coins are tossed simultaneously. The chances that all five will turn up heads is $\frac{1}{32}$ or 0.03125. If they are tossed 1,000 times, heads should show 31.25 times, meaning that on one toss 5×0.25 or 1.25 heads should show. But a fractional part of a head is not possible. If the coins are tossed 800 times, 25 tosses could result in all heads. Is this likely? Well, the distribution, at least, would group around 25. As the number of tosses is increased, the 0.03125 is more and more likely to hold. This empirical probability is

$$P = \frac{\text{Total occurrences}}{\text{Total trials}}$$

An experiment can only yield the empirical probability, which in turn approaches the true probability, $\bar{P}$, as the number of trials, N, becomes infinite. That is,

$$\bar{P} = \int_{N \to \infty} P = \int_{N \to \infty} \frac{n}{N}$$

An infinite number of trials is of course impossible, and so the selection of a sufficient sample is essential. To assist us in probability calculations the probability theorems given in Art. 4–7 are useful.

Example 9–1.   Compute the a priori probabilities of getting, in tosses of five coins:

(a) All heads
(b) All tails
(c) Either all heads or all tails
(d) At least one head and one tail.

Solution: The probability of any coin turning head (or tail) is $\frac{1}{2}$.

(a) By the multiplication law,

$$P(5 \text{ H}) = \tfrac{1}{2} \times \tfrac{1}{2} \times \tfrac{1}{2} \times \tfrac{1}{2} \times \tfrac{1}{2} = \tfrac{1}{32}$$
$$= 0.03125$$

(b) $P_{(5T)} = P_{(5H)} = \tfrac{1}{32} = 0.03125$
(c) By the addition law,

$$P_{(5H\text{ or }5T)} = \tfrac{1}{32} + \tfrac{1}{32} = \tfrac{1}{16} = 0.0625$$

(d) By the complementary law,

$$P_{(1H+1T)} = 1 - P_{(5H\text{ or }5T)} = 1 - \tfrac{1}{16}$$
$$= \tfrac{15}{16} = 0.9375$$

Permutations and combinations are useful in reliability considerations. Each of the ways that a group of n items can be arranged, with attention to the order in which the items are arranged, is called a permutation. If, from n items, subgroups of r items are taken then the total possible permutations $_nP_r$ (read "n items taken r at a time") can be calculated.

$$_nP_r = \frac{n!}{(n - r)!}$$

When it is only a matter of the items involved appearing in the arrangement, regardless of order, the sequence is called a combination and is determined by

$$_nC_r = \frac{n!}{r!(n - r)!}$$

Note that the relation between the two is

$$_nC_r = \frac{_nP_r}{r!}$$

Example 9–2.   How many permutations, and how many combinations of three letters each, are possible using the letters M–E–T–A–L.

Solution: The number of permutations is

$$_5P_3 = \frac{5!}{(5 - 3)!} = \frac{5!}{2!} = 60$$

and the number of combinations is

$$_nC_r = \frac{5!}{3!(5-3)!} = \frac{5!}{3!\,2!} = 10$$

9–3. RELIABILITY MATHEMATICS

Reliability was defined as the probability that equipment will perform its intended function satisfactorily for the intended time in the intended environment. The problem is to define it mathematically.

If N_o units are started with, and N_f failures are experienced in a given time t, the reliability R for time t is

$$R = \frac{N_o - N_f}{N_o} = \frac{N_s}{N_o} = 1 - \frac{N_f}{N_o} \tag{1}$$

The rate of failure is the time rate of change of reliability, or

$$r = \frac{dR}{dt} \tag{2}$$

Substituting Eq. (1) in Eq. (2) and differentiating,

$$\frac{dR}{dt} = \frac{d}{dt}\left(1 - \frac{N_f}{N_o}\right) = -\frac{1}{N_o} \times \frac{dN_f}{dt}$$

Thus the rate at which units fail and/or survive is

$$\frac{dN_f}{dt} = -N_o\frac{dR}{dt} = \frac{d}{dt}(N_o - N_s) = -\frac{dN_s}{dt}$$

The instantaneous probability of failure per hour, ρ, can be found by dividing the above rate by the number of units surviving at that instant;

$$\rho = \frac{1}{N_s}\frac{dN_f}{dt} = -\frac{N_o}{N_s}\frac{dR}{dt} = -\frac{1}{R}\frac{dR}{dt} \tag{3}$$

Thus

$$\rho\,dt = -\frac{dR}{R}$$

and

$$\ln R = -\int_0^t \rho\,dt$$

but at $t = 0$, $R = 1$; and

$$R(t) = e^{-\int_0^t \rho\,dt}$$

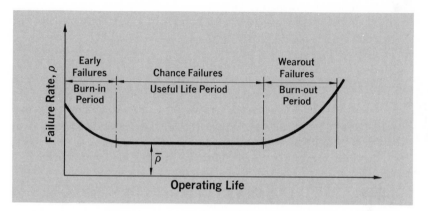

Fig. 9–1.   Failure rate versus operating time for large sample.

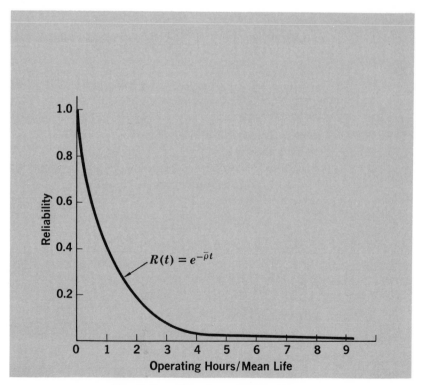

Fig. 9–2.   The Law of Reliability.

Also, by combining Eqs. (2) and (3),

$$r = \frac{dR}{dt} = -\rho R$$

The instantaneous probability of failure ρ, often called *hazard rate*, varies with time as indicated. This tends to greatly complicate the computation. To simplify this, and fortunately with little error, ρ is assumed time invariant $(\bar{\rho})$. For the mid-life period, between the rapid burn-in and burn-out intervals (Fig. 9–1) this is quite practical. Then the law of reliability simplifies to (Fig. 9–2):

$$R = e^{-\bar{\rho}t}$$

The hazard rate can be deduced from Eq. (3) to be the number of failures occurring per hour for each survived unit. Therefore, its reciprocal σ is the number of survival hours to the next failure or the mean time to failure. Thus

$$\sigma = \frac{1}{\bar{\rho}}$$

and

$$R = e^{-t/\sigma}$$

9–4. RELIABILITY OF COMPLEX SYSTEMS

Reliability has been defined and mathematically expressed for a single component. But systems are made of many components, all inter-related and most of them contributing to the unreliability of the system as a unit. Since it is rather difficult and uneconomical to obtain the failure rate for a system experimentally, the joint reliability must be predicted from individual component probabilities. It must be remembered that most systems, like components, contain potential early (burn-in) failures, which make for very low reliabilities until the system is debugged. Poor repair techniques also affect system reliability. Therefore, if reliability computations are to be relied upon, good debugging and fully effective repair must be practiced. It must be clearly understood that, whereas probabilities can be considered without reference to time, reliability is a function of time and always refers to a properly specified period.

Series Systems

Systems consisting of several components so connected and inter-dependent that if one part fails the entire system fails, are series sys-

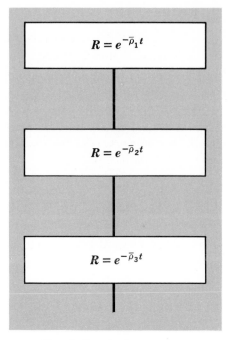

Fig. 9–3.   Series system.

tems (Fig. 9–3).   In such a system the reliability is the product of the reliabilities of each component.   The system's reliability is thus computed by the product rule as follows:

$$R_s = R_1 \times R_2 \times \cdots \times R_n = \prod_1^n R_i$$

$$= e^{-(\bar{\rho}_1 + \bar{\rho}_2 + \cdots + \bar{\rho}_n)t} = e^{-\sum_1^n \bar{\rho}\, t}$$

The unreliability of probability of failure of such a system is

$$Q_s = 1 - e^{-\sum_1^n \bar{\rho}_i t}$$

It is quite evident that a minimum number of series components plus a maximum reliability per individual component tend to provide optimum system reliability.

Parallel Redundant Systems

When very high system reliabilities are required, duplicate components and even entire duplicate circuits become desirable, so that if the first fails, the second will carry on (Fig. 9–4). This parallel reliability is referred to as parallel redundancy, because all units operate

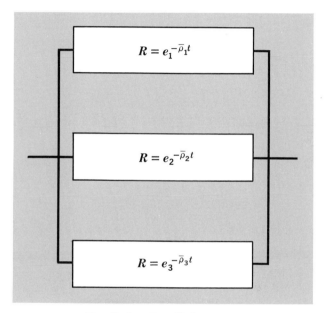

Fig. 9–4.   Parallel system.

simultaneously. The probability that one of two parallel components will survive is the sum of the probabilities of three outcomes; neither of components A and B fails, A fails but not B, and B fails but not A. According to the probability addition law, the reliability equation becomes

$$R_p = e^{-\bar{\rho}_1 t} + e^{-\bar{\rho}_2 t} - e^{-(\bar{\rho}_1 + \bar{\rho}_2)t} = R_1 + R_2 - R_1 R_2$$

Since both components might fail, the unreliability or probability of failure becomes, according to the multiplication and complementary laws,

$$Q_p = (1 - e^{-\bar{\rho}_1 t})(1 - e^{-\bar{\rho}_2 t})$$

There may be more than two parallel components. The probability of survival for n components is determined by expanding the addition equation as evidenced in its expansion for three components:

$$R_p = e^{-\bar{\rho}_1 t} + e^{-\bar{\rho}_2 t} + e^{-\bar{\rho}_3 t} - e^{-(\bar{\rho}_1 + \bar{\rho}_2)t} - e^{-(\bar{\rho}_1 + \bar{\rho}_3)t} - e^{-(\bar{\rho}_2 + \bar{\rho}_3)t} + e^{-(\bar{\rho}_1 + \bar{\rho}_2 + \bar{\rho}_3)t}$$

However, it is simpler to compute the reliability via unreliability and the multiplication plus complementary laws:

$$Q_p = Q_{p1} \times Q_{p2} \times \cdots Q_{pn} = \prod_{i=1}^{n} Q_i$$

and

$$R_p = 1 - Q_p = 1 - \prod_{1}^{n} Q_i$$

Stand-by Systems

When it is impractical to operate a system with parallel branches, and yet some assurance of continued operation is necessary, stand-by units become advisable (Fig. 9–5). The additional units stand idle

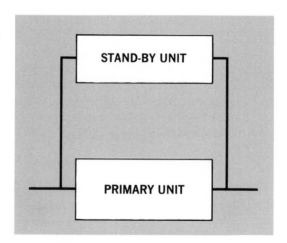

STAND-BY UNIT

PRIMARY UNIT

Fig. 9–5.   Stand-by system.

until activated by the failure of operating units.   Such a system may be regarded as a single system with multiple lives.   That is, if n stand-by units are involved, $n + 1$ units are available, and so n failures can occur without system failure.   The $(n + 1)^{\text{th}}$ failure finally stops the system.   Appropriate probability theory, including a principle known as Poisson's distribution, yields the identity

$$e^{-\bar{\rho}t}\left[1 + \bar{\rho}t + \frac{(\bar{\rho}t)^2}{2!} + \cdots + \frac{(\bar{\rho}t)^n}{n!}\right] = 1$$

The term $e^{-\bar{\rho}t}$ indicates no failure will occur; $e^{-\bar{\rho}t}(\bar{\rho}t)$ represents the probability that the system will not fail if one failure does occur; $e^{-\bar{\rho}t}\dfrac{(\bar{\rho}t)^2}{2!}$, two; etc. Thus, the reliability of a system with one stand-by unit is

$$R_B = e^{-\bar{\rho}t}(1 + \bar{\rho}t)$$

and with two stand-by units

$$R_B = e^{-\bar{\rho}t}\left[1 + \bar{\rho}t + \frac{(\bar{\rho}t)^2}{2!}\right]$$

In general then, for n equal units,

$$R_B = e^{-\bar{\rho}t}\left[1 + \bar{\rho}t + \frac{(\bar{\rho}t)^2}{2!} + \cdots + \frac{(\bar{\rho}t)^n}{n!}\right]$$

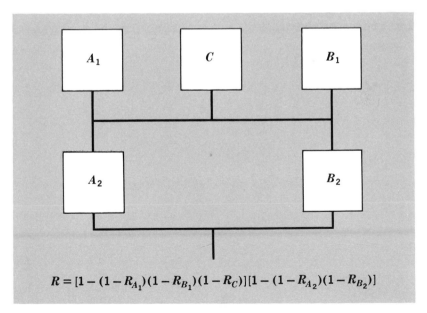

$$R = [1 - (1 - R_{A_1})(1 - R_{B_1})(1 - R_C)][1 - (1 - R_{A_2})(1 - R_{B_2})]$$

Fig. 9–6. Two parallel reliabilities in series.

Systems other than series, parallel, and stand-by are used as well. These, however, can not be all enumerated (as one example, see Fig. 9–6).

Example 9–3. A series–parallel system is made of components as depicted below. The probabilities for each component, all for the same period of time, is as indicated in the box. Compute the reliability of the system.

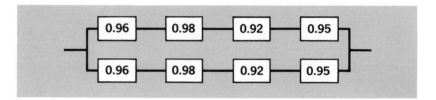

Example 9–3.

Solution: The reliability of each series branch is

$$R_s = 0.96 \times 0.98 \times 0.92 \times 0.95 = 0.82$$

The reliability of the two parallel branches, and therefore for the system, is

$$R_p = 2R_s - R_sR_s = 2 \times 0.82 - 0.82 \times 0.82 = 0.97.$$

9–5. WEIBULL DISTRIBUTION

Weibull's extensive study of the fatigue of metals prompted him to propose a statistical distribution that has been named for him. Mathematically, the cumulative form of the Weibull distribution [1] is

$$F(x) = 1 - e^{-(x-x_u)^m/x_0}$$

where x_u is a location parameter
x_0 is a scale parameter and
m is a shape parameter

Investigation shows that at $m = 1$ the equation reduces to the probability–density function, while for larger values of the shape parameter the Weibull function approaches the normal or gaussian distribution. It therefore seems that the Weibull function has a wider range of usefulness than either of the other two. The function is shown in Fig. 9–7. Its first derivative or the probability–density function, a general plot of which appears in Fig. 9–8, is

$$f(x) = \frac{m(x - x_u)^{m-1}}{x_0} e^{-(x-x_u)^m/x_0}$$

for $x > x_u \geq 0$.

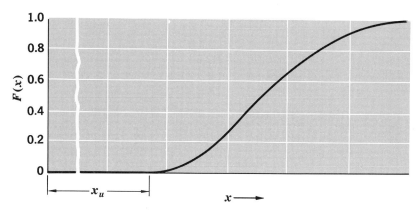

Fig. 9–7.   Weibull cumulative distribution function.

The application of the Weibull distribution to reliability calculations was proposed by J. H. K. Kao [2], who was studying failure
histories of electron tubes.   In such calculations, the location parameter x_u can be assumed zero, because the item is exposed to the risk of
failure with the beginning of test or service.   The scale parameter x_0
is a measure of the time interval between failures and so is sometimes
taken as the mean time to failure, denoted in this book as σ.   The independent variable x becomes time t measured from start of service.
When the Weibull function is converted as implied (it is actually an
unreliability) and subtracted from one, according to the complimentary

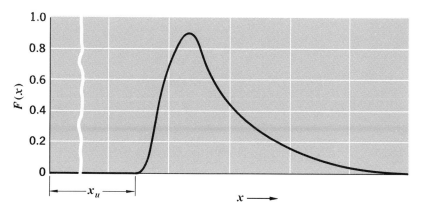

Fig. 9–8.   Weibull probability–density function.

law of probability, it yields the reliability relation

$$R(t) = 1 - F(t) = 1 - (1 - e^{-t^m/x_0}) = e^{-t^m/x_0}$$

The problem still existing is that of finding the shape and scale parameters. Kao proposed several techniques [3, 4, 5] for evaluating m and x_0, each of which is of necessity cumbersome and can best be carried out using a computer. In failure tests the times to failure t_j of each of r_j units out of a total of n are recorded. The mathematical relation involved is

$$F(t_j) = 1 - e^{-t_j^m/x_0}$$

and taking the natural logarithm of it twice results in

$$\ln \ln \frac{1}{1 - F(t_j)} = - \ln x_0 + m \ln t_j$$

where t_j is time to each failure from first to r^{th}. The above expression is a straight line on log–vs.–log-log paper. The intercept of the line on the log-log axis provides the scale parameter x_0, while the slope of the line yields the shape parameter m.

Other mathematical and logic manipulations result in

$$x_0 = \frac{1}{r} \left[\sum_{j=1}^{r} t_j^m + (n - r)t_j^m \right]$$

and

$$x_0 = \frac{\displaystyle\sum_{j=1}^{r} t_j^m \ln t_j + (n - r)t_j^m}{\dfrac{r}{m} + \displaystyle\sum_{j=1}^{r} \ln t_j}$$

The simultaneous solution of the equations yields m and x_0.

It must be noted that because of intricacies involved in the determination, the scale parameter and t are substituted in kilo-hours or hr/1,000 in the reliability equation. It should also be noted that all determinations are statistical rather than explicit.

Example 9–4. Kao established the scale parameter at 19,700 hours and the shape parameter at 1.7 for certain electron tubes. Determine the reliability at the end of the first 500 hr.

Solution:

$$R(t) = e^{-t^m/x_0} = e^{-0.5^{1.7}/19.7} = e^{-0.308/19.7} = 2.718^{-0.0156}$$
$$= 1/1.015 = 0.985$$

9–6. RELIABILITY AND DESIGN

Though probability and reliability are, in a strict sense, sciences, formulation for actual systems is not precisely feasible. The data, and hazard rates, are experimentally established. The predictions are only statistical in nature, and one cannot claim full compliance by any particular component. Furthermore, the unpredictable human factor is usually involved in the operation of the system. As in all of engineering, however, careful analyses, good judgments, sound decisions, and wise compromises always result in more satisfactory performance and better products.

Systems requiring reliability consideration pose the designer a double problem. Not only must he design equipments for performance, but he must also design failure endurance into it. The best design now becomes narrowed down, because it must be reliable as well.

To provide quantitative reliability, designs require effective reliability control in every stage of the design of a system and of its components. Reliability analysis must be applied during the preliminary design phase, and during detail design, as well as during the prototype testing and modification phase. The engineer needs to give continuous consideration to many items during the design, particularly the following:

1. A minimum of parts without loss in performance.
2. Understanding of environmental as well as functional requirements of equipment.
3. Awareness of the interplay among components and the effect of this upon system reliability.
4. Reflection of human limitations in operating requirements.
5. Reduction of operating temperatures and provision for heat sinks, cooling, and appropriate packaging.
6. Protection for equipment against shock, resonant vibration, and corrosion.
7. Specification of proper manufacture and quality control.
8. Correct application of sound statistical failure data for components and subsystems.
9. Specification of run-in or burn-in requirements.
10. Specification of debugging procedures, schedule, and extent.

9–7. RELIABILITY DEMONSTRATION

The quantitative or numerical proof of system reliability is not an easy matter. A frequent approach is to set aside some number of the devices contained in the system for simulated testing and evaluating. Eventually several systems must be tested as a whole to realistically establish the reliability of the system. Such procedure can be prohibitively costly and often too late to significantly influence development. A more timely and less expensive approach is most desirable. Many short cuts have been, and are being, tried and used. Described, as an

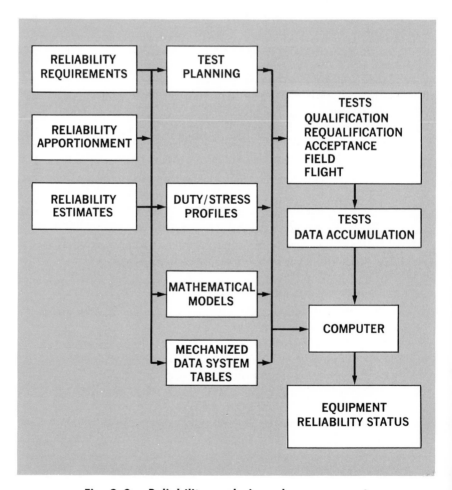

Fig. 9–9. Reliability analysis and measurement.

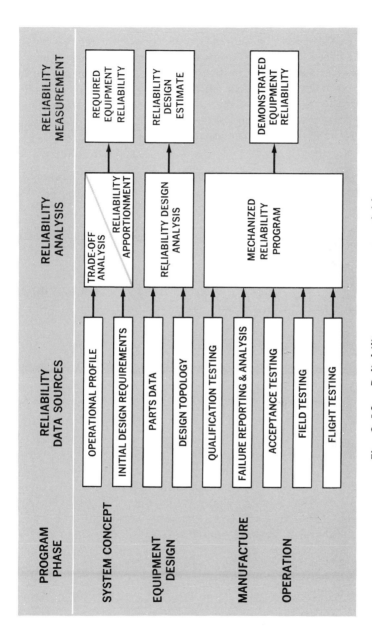

Fig. 9–10.   Reliability measurement activities.

example of what might be done, is the Reliability Measurement/ Demonstration method developed by the General Electric Company [6]. The problem is not only one of establishing and designing satisfactory reliability into the equipment, but measuring and demonstrating it as well.

A system development program requires that three key reliabilities— required equipment reliability, reliability design estimate, and demonstrated equipment reliability—be carefully considered. The reliability analysis and measurement program is depicted in Fig. 9–9. The data

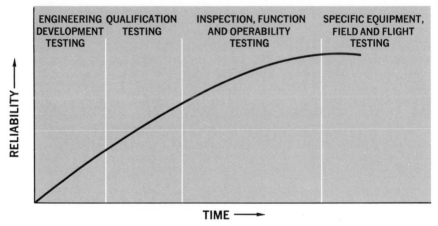

Fig. 9–11.   Reliability growth versus test activities.

sources, analysis and measurement phases and their interlocking nature are illustrated in Fig. 9-10. The operational profile provides for all environmental conditions such as temperature, pressure, acceleration, humidity, and even radiation and fungus growth when necessary.

The required system reliability is established from an analysis of mission requirements. Apportionment is then affected by assigning reliabilities to individual components composing the system so as to realize the required reliability for the entire system. As shown in Fig. 9–11, test activity must accompany every step of the process until the complete system is finally "flight" tested.

An illustration of how a system with a reliability objective of 0.995 can be apportioned is contained in Fig. 9–12. The initial apportionment is, as depicted, at the functional levels, such as attitude control, and by way of significant characteristics, such as system complexity. Eventually the apportionment becomes hardware oriented; necessary

HYPOTHETICAL SUBSYSTEM	SYSTEM COMPLEXITY	STATE OF ART	OPER PROFILE	CRITICALITY	SUBTOTAL
ATTITUDE CONTROL	5	2	1	8	16
SEPARATION	3	1	1	1	6
DECOY EJECTION	6	3	3	10	22
ECM	10	5	3	10	28
STRUCTURAL	1	1	5	1	8
A & F	9	4	5	2	20
TOTAL					100

HYPOTHETICAL SUBSYSTEM	RATIO SUB-TOTAL/TOTAL	RATIO X SYSTEM FAILURE PROBABILITY	RELIABILITY * DESIGN OBJECTIVE
ATTITUDE CONTROL	16/100	.16 x .005 = .0008	.9992
SEPARATION	6/100	.06 x .005 = .0003	.9997
DECOY EJECTION	22/100	.22 x .005 = .0011	.9989
ECM	28/100	.28 x .005 = .0014	.9986
STRUCTURAL	8/100	.08 x .005 = .0004	.9996
A & F	20/100	.20 x .005 = .0010	.9990

*THE PRODUCT OF THESE NUMBERS EQUALS THE RE-ENTRY SYSTEM RELIABILITY DESIGN OBJECTIVE OF 0.995.
R = 0.9992 x 0.9997 x 0.9989 x 0.9986 x 0.9996 = 0.995

Fig. 9–12.   Reliability apportionment.

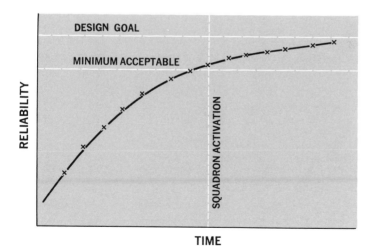

TIME

Fig. 9–13.   Demonstrated reliability.

reliabilities for individual components become specified. As the program progresses from conceptualization to testing, of course, the ability to estimate reliabilities improves.

To further improve the process and to speed it up so that information can be fed back early enough, the estimation and reliability determination can be mechanized. Test data, failure rates, and environmental factors, are quickly analyzed and processed. Reliability reports and indices define the status and afford the design engineer an opportunity to refine components as needed. Thus parts, subsystems, and systems are systematically evaluated, and reliabilities measured and demonstrated. Program dollars can be concentrated where the most good can be done in improving the system reliability. An illustration of what actually happens is presented in Fig. 9–13, where the reliability demonstration curve shows how the contractural requirement was well met.

REFERENCES

1. W. Weibull, "A Statistical Distribution Function of Wide Applicability," *J. Appl. Mech.*, v. 18 (1951), pp. 293–97.
2. J. H. K. Kao, *Electron Tube Research for Reliability Statistical Studies*, Research Report EE 410, Sch. of Elec. Eng., Cornell U., May, 1958.
3. J. H. K. Kao, "A New Life-Quality Measure for Electron Tubes," *Trans. IRE*, Part 4 (April 1956), pp. 1–11.
4. J. H. K. Kao, "Computer Methods for Estimating Weibull Parameters in Reliability Studies," *Trans. IRE*, Part 4 (July 1958), pp. 15–22.
5. J. H. K. Kao, "A Graphical Estimation of Mixed Weibull Parameters in Life-Testing of Electron Tubes," *Technometrics*, v. 1, n. 4 (Nov. 1959), pp. 389–407.
6. E. D. Karmiol, W. T. Weir, and J. S. Youtcheff, *A Practical Method of Reliability Demonstration*, General Electric Co., 1954, 15 pp.

PROBLEMS

9–1. Ten ball-point pens are tested to failure (failure is the pen's running dry). The times to failure in minutes were measured at 1,830, 2,100, 1,512, 1,975, 1,364, 1,834, 1,960, 1,796, 2,067, and 1,839, respectively. Compute the mean life and the rate of failure.

9–2. A firm owning a fleet of trucks has 86 tires in stock. It is known that 9.3% of these are slightly defective. Compute the probability that four tires, picked at random, will be perfect.

9–3. A subassembly consists of a shaft-gear combination. In a bin of 40 shafts, 20 are known to be of proper tolerance. The batch of 40 gears, on the other hand, is known to contain 10 gears of incorrect tolerance. Compute the probability of obtaining 20 satisfactory subassemblies.

9–4. Compute the reliability for a ten-hour period of the ball-point pens of Problem 9–1.

9–5. Assuming an individual component reliability of 0.98, compute and plot the system reliability as the number of series components increases from 5 to 100.

9–6. A series system is made of 3 motors each having a hazard rate of 0.000002, 5 speed reducers at 0.00001 each, 2 pumps at 0.00005 each, and 3 alternators at 0.000006 each. Compute the system reliability for an operation of 10 hr. What is the mean time between failures?

9–7. Write the reliability equation for a system having four parallel components.

9–8. Compute the reliability of a system having parallel branches each of which is made of two components in series, the first of which is characterized by a hazard rate of 0.00003 and the second by 0.000007. How does this compare with the reliability, if only one branch is present?

9–9. The hazard rate of a circuit is 0.01. Thus for a 10-hr operation period the reliability computes at 90.48%. How much will the reliability be improved if three such circuits are operated in parallel?

9–10. Each of 100 units have a reliability of 0.92. Determine by how much the reliability of the equipment would increase when the units are connected in two parallel branches of 50 each in series, as compared to with all 100 connected in series.

9–11. The probabilities of 3 units are e^{-at}, e^{-bt} and e^{-ct}, respectively. Derive the probability of failure when two of the units are connected in parallel with the third in series with the two parallel branches.

9–12. Show how the Weibull distribution approaches the probability–density function as one limit, and the normal gaussian distribution as the other.

9–13. How may the reliability of a single rocket be measured? May this measure apply to several rockets of the same kind? Discuss.

9–14. Discuss the reliability measure that may be applied to the operation of a newly developed device in the laboratory, as compared to in-field operation.

9–15. Hydrofluoric acid fumes are recommended for etching macroscopic designs on glass reticules. The chemist who developed the technique and used it in his laboratory claims it works easily and well. Discuss the probability of the method's being a reliable commercial process.

DESIGN PROBLEMS

9–D1. Sketch block diagrams depicting all possible systems you can visualize that consist of the components specified in Problem 9–6. What might each combination do?

9–D2. Calculate the reliability of a system with two stand-by units, if each has a hazard rate of 0.01 for a period of 10 hr. Compare this with the reliability for the system after one stand-by unit is removed; after both stand-by units are removed.

9–D3. Hydraulic pressure is applied to the brakes of an aircraft by pumps driven by the aircraft engines. It is found that the reliability of the pressure supply, which is 0.9957 for a 10-hr period, is too low. Therefore, a parallel hydraulic system powered by an electric motor is to be tied in. The reliability of the auxiliary system is computed at 0.9948 for the same period. Determine the new probability of normal pressure availability.

9–D4. A manufacturer has beads of 30 different colors. He proposes to produce abacuses, each of three rows with 10 beads per row. How many different color-combination abacuses can he market?

9–D5. A board has been set up that will be used to decide upon the most effective arrangement of hand knobs. Knob shapes will be used to help distinguish the various controls in the application under consideration. How many possible arrangements must be experimented with to assure that all possibilities have been tried?

9–D6. In an evaluation of the use of a straight-line, four-bar linkage on a printing press it is found that the mean time to failure is 1,500 hr. In order to thoroughly investigate its reliability potential, it becomes necessary to analyze the Weibull distribution for shape parameters 1, 2, and 4. Plot the distributions for up to 5,000 hr of service.

9–D7. What life expectancy can be warranted for a special rolling bearing, if it is found previously that the mean time to failure is 90,000 hr and its shape parameter using the Weibull reliability approach is 1.7?

10

Materials and Processes

Everything from man to machine, from sustenance to system, from toy to tool is made from materials. Every technical advance, every engineering design must eventually find its form in a material structure. Matter exists in the gaseous, liquid, and solid states, but for present purposes the last only is of major concern. If the engineer is to fulfill his responsibility well, he must possess, among other qualifications, an understanding of the nature, behavior, and technology of materials.

A study of its nature informs of the elements, basic structure, and chemical combination of matter. Knowledge of its behavior enables proper application of its nature to conditions of engineering practice. And familiarity with phenomenological properties is essential, if handling, fabrication and appearance are to be economically accomplished [1].

10–1. ENGINEERING MATERIALS

Although man has made use of materials since time immemorial, significant developments in the area of metallic materials have occurred only during about the last century; those in the non-metallic area are even more recent. The engineer in general, and the designer in particular must keep abreast of the diverse improvements in a multitude of material categories. He must evaluate and properly adapt them to his needs. To develop effective low-cost products, from critical system components to everyday items, a good deal of creative imagination must be used in the selection and application of materials.

In a basic sense, solid-state materials can be classified as crystalline and amorphous. The solid state can be defined as a state of aggregation of atoms or molecules forming a substance possessing both definite volume and definite shape. Crystalline materials—metals—are characterized by regularity in the arrangement of atoms or molecules;

whereas amorphous materials—many non-metallics—contain a random arrangement of atoms or molecules. Metals, the larger in volume consumption, are opaque, have a characteristic lustre, possess relatively high electrical and heat conductivity, and manifest some plasticity.

There are many materials of engineering value in both the metallic and the non-metallic groups. These can vary in physical, chemical, mechanical, and technical properties. They can satisfy many economic situations, serve various functions, present numerous appearances, behave distinctively in service, and provide exceptional life expectancies. Some of the more common members in each category are:

METALLICS

Ferrous

Gray irons	Low-alloy steels (wrought)
Ductile irons	Corrosion-resistant steels
Malleable irons	Heat-resistant steels
Carbon steels (cast)	Stainless steels
Carbon steels (wrought)	Super-strength steels
Low-alloy steels (cast)	High-temperature steels

Non-Ferrous

Aluminum alloys (wrought)	Titanium alloys
Aluminum alloys (cast)	Beryllium and its alloys
Copper alloys (brasses & bronzes)	Zirconium and its alloys
Magnesium alloys	Refractory metals (tungsten, tantalum,
Nickel and its alloys	molybdenum, columbium)
Zinc alloys	Precious metals (platinum, gold, silver)

NON-METALLICS

Ceramics

Glass	Structural clays
Refractories	Abrasives
Cermets	Whitewares
Crystalline materials	

Rubbers

Natural	Synthetic (neoprene, buna, butyl, silicone, thiokol)

Organics

Wood	Plastics
Leather	Fibers (natural, synthetic)
Cork	

10–2. STRUCTURES

A metal is a chemical element existing in the solid form as an aggregation of crystals.   The industrially important metals are further characterized by two properties: plasticity, the ability to undergo deformation before fracture, and conductivity, both electrical and thermal.   A few metal elements exhibit little, if any, plasticity or conductivity, but these are only alloying elements used in small percentages.   Crystals are composed of a regular arrangement of unit cells, repetitive in each of three directions.   Of the fourteen space lattices or unit cells, five are of particular importance in connection with the major elements contained in alloys.

(a) Body-centered cubic (bcc)
(b) Face-centered cubic (fcc)
(c) Close-packed hexagonal (cph)
(d) Simple cubic (c)
(e) Tetragonal (tetrag., simple, or fc)

These are shown in Fig. 10–1.

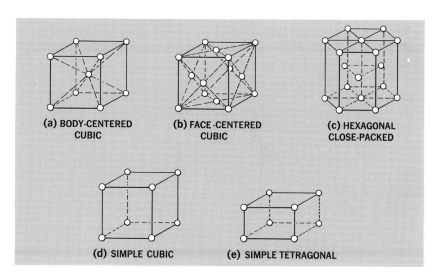

(a) BODY-CENTERED CUBIC

(b) FACE-CENTERED CUBIC

(c) HEXAGONAL CLOSE-PACKED

(d) SIMPLE CUBIC

(e) SIMPLE TETRAGONAL

Fig. 10–1. Metal space lattices.

Each sphere in the lattice is an atom that in its equilibrium state is of such size that it touches its nearest neighbors.   Thus represented, the face-centered cube might appear as in Fig. 10–2.   Of course, in

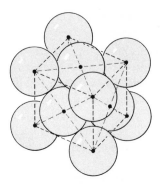

Fig. 10–2.   A face-centered cubic crystal structure showing ions as spheres in contact.
From Stephen M. Edelglass, *Engineering Materials Science—Structure and Mechanical Behavior of Solids.*   Copyright © 1966, The Ronald Press Co., New York.

reality the atoms and in turn the unit cells are sub-microscopically small.   The body-centered cubic cell of iron is about 2.86×10^{-8} centimeters on each side and the face-centered cubic aluminum cell is 4.04×10^{-8} centimeters per side.

The commercial processing of ores produces metallic elements that always contain small amounts—up to 2 per cent by weight, at maximum—of foreign elements, called impurities.   To improve desired properties, however, other foreign elements are intentionally added to the major constituent; thus alloys are formed.   If the two or more elements are soluble in each other, a solid solution is formed.   The element present in greatest amount is generally referred to as the solvent and the others as solutes.   When solute atoms go into solution by replacing one or more of the solvent atoms, a substitutional solid solution is formed.   On the other hand, the solute atom may be small enough to fit into the interspace between solvent atoms, in which case an interstitial solution forms.   In substitutional and interstitial solutions the solute does not normally change the structural pattern of the solvent.

When elements are insoluble in each other, mechanical mixtures are formed; eutectics are mechanical mixtures.   In this case more than one structural pattern is present in the solid.   Finally, various elements may react chemically with each other.   Thus solute atoms will combine with solvent atoms to form more complex space lattices with definite compositions.   Such combinations are correctly called intermetallic compounds.   Like other chemical compounds, these melt at definite temperatures, but unlike other chemical compounds they do not follow valence rules.   Intermetallic compounds also exhibit lower conductivity, ductility, and plasticity and are generally harder as well as stronger than simpler structures.

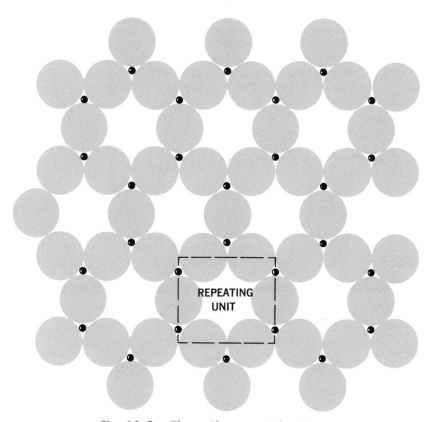

Fig. 10–3.   The uniform crystal pattern.

Whatever the structure formed, one or more solute elements are added to solvent elements in the attempt to achieve desired physical, mechanical, or technological properties.

Like the metals, many ceramics consist of an orderly arrangement of atom species forming the repeating pattern or unit cell.   The body-centered, face-centered, and hexagonal cells are found among the ceramics.   The crystal is a large combination of the repeating unit cells.   Such a repeating pattern is shown in Fig. 10–3.   In contrast the somewhat random arrangement of the glassy state is shown in Fig. 10–4. The fundamental properties of both the cell and the crystal depend largely upon the size and valance of individual atoms.

Solid solutions are substitutional, interstitial, and omission types. Substitutional solutions form when the solvent and solute ions have

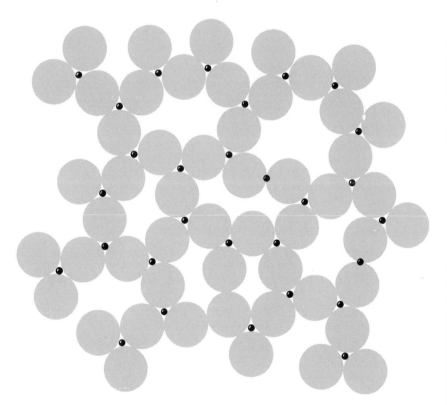

Fig. 10–4. The irregular glassy state.

the same valance and nearly the same radius. When the solute ion is small compared to the solvent ion, the interstitial solution is likely to form. At times some of the ions do not assume their proper positions in the lattice pattern, in which case the structure is referred to as an omission solid solution.

Rubber has a polymeric structure like other organic materials. It is a long continuous chain of carbon and hydrogen, a hydrocarbon. Other elements may be attached as well. The rubber state is characterized by an arrangement of molecules possessing favorable intermolecular forces.

Plastics are compounds of hydrogen and carbon as already indicated, that is, long complex chains. The smallest chain is that of methane, CH_4, while others are much longer. Carried on indefinitely, the chain takes the form

$$C_nH_{2n+2}$$

Molecules of this type possess strong intermolecular, covalent bonds as well as the weaker van der Waal forces. When each carbon atom is surrounded by a full compliment of hydrogen (or other atoms), the molecule is saturated. The saturated molecule is called the polymer, and the unsaturated a monomer.

Plastic resins may be classified as thermoplastic or thermosetting, depending upon their behavior under heat. Thermoplastic resins have long aligned chains such as depicted in Fig. 10–5, which are easily

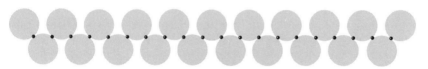

Fig. 10–5. Long aligned hydrocarbon chains.

deformed under pressure, particularly at elevated temperatures. Thermosetting resins are characterized by three-dimensional chains that cannot be deformed readily once cured (polymerized). These do not soften with temperature.

The resin itself is often too weak for engineering use. It is, therefore, reinforced, strengthened, or otherwise improved with fillers, such as paper, pulp, fibers, and macerations.

10–3. PROPERTIES OF MATERIALS

A study of the properties of materials depends upon the level of aggregation of the structural elements being considered.

1. The atomic or molecular level, which considers an aggregate of discrete particles of the dimensional order of around 10^{-6} inch.
2. The phenomenological level, which is more or less continuous and homogeneous and is characterized by forces that represent the average effects of atomic bonds and of forces determined by imperfections in the atomic structure.

No definite correlations are known to exist between the atomic and phenomenological properties because of the apparent structure sensitivity.

The ideal crystal is a simplification of the real crystal, because the lattices contain structural imperfections as well as impurities. The imperfections can be a matter of vacancies, dislocations, and boundary blocks (arrays of dislocations). Such imperfections probably occur because of accidents of growth during solidification, from thermal agitation, or from slip motion. Our basic knowledge of materials is thus unfortunately limited. A better understanding will be possible only after much more is known about the force interaction of atomic structure and the mechanism of growth to bulk size. For the present, designers must depend upon bulk properties determined by test, which are a sort of statistical average of millions of bonded atoms.

The designer must, therefore, realize that a given material has a range of property values, rather than the single value given in a table or chart. Knowledge and appreciation of the scatter and of the shape of the probability curve for the particular material lot in question may be necessary in many situations. Intelligent use of materials requires also sound engineering judgment in matching the property range to the degree of admissibility of possible modes of failure.

Despite the above limitations, the practical utility of properties data cannot be denied. The wide use is completely justified because of its standardized form and relative availability. The material properties which the engineer uses in various situations that arise in his work may be categorized as follows:

Mechanical	*Physical*
Ultimate strength	Specific strength
Yield strength	Thermal expansion
Modulus of elasticity	Heat fatigue
Compressive strength	Creep characteristics
Shear strength	Age hardening
Shear modulus	Strain hardening
Bearing strength	Electrical conductivity
Poisson's ratio	Stress corrosion
Per cent elongation	Rate of shrinkage
Hardness	Thermal conductivity
Impact strength	Specific heat
Fatigue strength	Plasticity
Notch sensitivity	Melting point

Technological	*Chemical*
Machining	Composition
Casting	Chemical affinity
Forging	Microscopic structure
Swaging	Weldability
Forming	Brazing
Drawing	Surface treatment
	Paint adhesion
	Heat treatment

The most common material test is the conventional static tension test that provides data that are converted into stress–strain diagrams such as shown in Fig. 8–8.   The ideal stress–strain diagram depicted in Fig. 10–6 identifies features that possess engineering significance. There are, however, very few materials that more than approach such well defined characteristics.   Arbitrary but rational definitions are used to establish needed properties in such cases.

Loads vary in most cases either in magnitude or direction or both during repeating cycles of operation.   Static properties, though sometimes used, are usually unsuitable for such conditions.   Instead, reversed stress tests resulting in stress-number-of-cycle (S-N) diagrams provide the fatigue properties needed.   Surface conditions, corrosion pitting, stress raisers, grain size, decarburization, internal stress, and even previous stress history are among the factors that can greatly influence fatigue behavior.

The designer must always consider the possibility of sudden load application, because stresses are thereby multiplied many times over. A force application is considered an impact when the application is accomplished in somewhat less time than one-half the natural period of vibration of the member to which applied.   The Charpy and Izod tests have been developed to investigate impact behavior.   Such test data, however, must be used cautiously, because results are easily misjudged and misused.   Some widely used steels, for instance, may be very tough at room temperature and shift to extreme brittleness at only slightly lower temperatures.

Temperature influences the properties of materials so that what is satisfactory under standard conditions can become inadequate at low and high temperatures.   Low temperatures increase strength, but appreciably reduce ductility.   Elevated temperatures cause, on the other hand, progressive changes in the design-important properties.

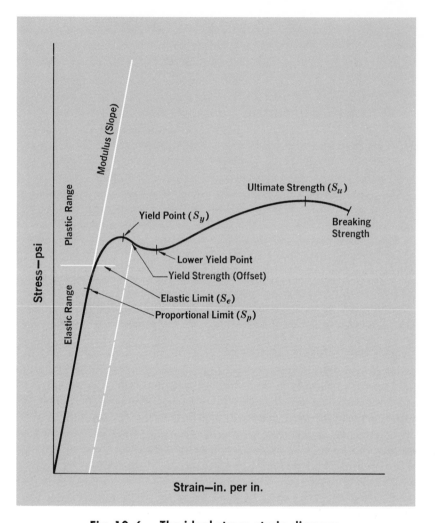

Fig. 10–6.   The ideal stress–strain diagram.
From J. P. Vidosic, *Machine Design Projects.*   Copyright © 1957, The
Ronald Press Co., New York.

Conventional tensile testing, even though performed at the operating
temperature, is of little value for high-temperature service. For
extended-duration, elevated-temperature service refined creep tests,
conducted under controlled temperature and stress conditions for thousands of hours, are essential. Creep, a continuous deformation, is
accounted for by the selection of a maximum stress that will not cause

a total deformation in excess of a specified amount during the estimated life span at the operating temperature.

Materials that do not behave as purely elastic bodies or are stressed beyond elastic limits must be approached with plasticity consideration. Theories developed for such situations normally assume ideal materials. In a viscous material the shearing strain is proportional to the shearing stress. On the other hand, the purely plastic material yields indefinitely after a yield stress is reached. Elastico-viscous and elastico-plastic materials suffer additional elastic properties. Engineering materials are never ideal, hence plasticity design involves much empiricism.

There are many other factors that affect material properties and the behavior of bodies under varied operating environments. Residual stress, size effect, high-temperature fatigue, strain rate, vibration, combined stress, thermal stress, cold working, hardening mechanism phenomena and other variables can each require its measure of consideration when available material properties are used in the solution of engineering situations.

10–4. SELECTION OF MATERIALS

The selection of an engineering material for a specific application is a matter of intelligent trade-offs. Compromises, such as between the cost of the finished part and the hazard of its possible failure, are always necessary. The hazard of failure must take into account the purpose for which the part is intended, the condition of service, the kind and intensity of stress, and the potential danger to life. The designer must match the capacity, strength, and life requirements of the equipment to the expected performance of the material as indicated by its properties.

In selecting the material a full effort is made to obtain the best balance among the properties that affect manufacture as well as performance. The material selected must be strong enough to transmit forces economically, tough enough to withstand wear, soft enough to be machinable, inert enough to resist the environment, and light enough to provide no excess of weight. Cost consciousness as well as awareness of availability of materials, of standard sizes, and of special shapes must exist. It is of little value to design a component using an ideal material, if purchasing is unable to obtain the material in sufficient quantity when needed.

If the design engineer can answer the following questions affirmatively, he has probably made the appropriate material selection

1. Will the material satisfy the functional, strength, and rigidity requirements?
2. Can the material be fabricated into the part?
3. Will the part, made of the selected material, be able to perform its task during the expected life in the environment in which it may have to function?
4. Will the material be available in sufficient quantity when needed?
5. Is the cost of making the part from this material as low as that of any other material that also meets requirements?

The second question is quite significant and yet often neglected, particularly by beginners. The choice of a material can well be based on the facility with which it can be given form; that is, based on its technological rather than mechanical properties. The choice among processing methods is largely predicated upon the number of pieces to be made and upon the economics of amortization of the cost of special equipment. The requirement of dimensional precision is another important consideration. Competing processes should always be carefully examined, and new processing developments noted.

Many of the above implied or stated characteristics of materials cannot be expressed quantitatively. Hence it is necessary to have the judgments of the materials, design, and production engineers if correct design is to be ensured. The importance of such judgments cannot be overemphasized, because, as previously indicated, the properties measured by standard tests do not define the inherent characteristics of a material. This is due to the fact that the test situation employed rarely corresponds to actual service conditions or to actual part configurations. Simulated and even full-scale service testing is often undertaken when it is essential to ascertain the precise behavior of a material under operational conditions.

10-5. MATERIAL PROCESSING

The ability to convert materials economically into needed products has much to do with the standard of living of a country. Countries are underdeveloped because they possess little ability to fabricate even the simplest tools with which basic food can be produced more abundantly. A very important part of manufacturing is the casting, shaping and forming of materials. This is closely related to the development of machine tools, forming equipment, and measurement apparatus. A design engineer must be sufficiently knowledgeable in this area if he is to succeed.

Probably the oldest and most basic manufacturing process is casting. It is the production of desired shapes by pouring molten material into a previously prepared mold or cavity. Casting possesses some clear production advantages. It permits production of intricate shapes of almost unlimited size, with thin as well as thick sections, of any material that can be melted. Sand-casting utilizes molding sand—a mixture of silica, clay and water—for the mold material. Patterns used to form the mold cavity in a container, called the flask, must be expertly made to allow for shrinkage and draft. Jolt and squeeze machines are often used to assist in mold making. Large castings are usually poured in pit molds.

Specialized casting techniques, used when particular requirements are to be met, are die, permanent-mold, centrifugal, investment, and shell casting. Such processes present advantages of better dimensional accuracy, considerable automation, and greater economy in the case of smaller, more delicate parts.

A power-driven machine, designed to cut or otherwise shape materials, is generally referred to as a machine tool. The essential elements are the tool that does the cutting, the device that holds the work, the speed and feed control mechanism, the prime mover, and the bed or frame that holds the rest together. All products useful to man are made with either machine tools or other machines manufactured with machine tools. Among the more common machine tools are the lathe, drill press, shaper, planer, miller, and grinder. Among the important machining operations are turning, shaping, milling, grinding, threading, boring, reaming, broaching, sawing, and filing; machine-tool operations are shown in Figures 10–7, 10–8 and 10–9. In mass production, much of this is done on automatic machine tools, on transfer machines, and on tape-operated, numerical-control, machines. Some special machine tools, such as gear hobbers and screw machines, are available as well. Much detail instruction is contained in many good books dealing with such material.

Some modern high-strength alloys defy ordinary machining. Intricate profiles and irregular cavities are difficult to generate even in soft materials. Electromachining and ultrasonic machining techniques become useful in such situations. Chemical milling, plasma-jet machining, and laser cutting are other such chipless processes. Further information is to be found in Reference [2].

Other important shaping processes are those based on plastic flow, hot and cold. Such methods are fast, accurate, and economical. Press forming, rolling, forging, extruding, deep drawing, cold spinning, and stamping are among these. References [2] and [3] present the

MOTIONS	OPERATION	MACHINE
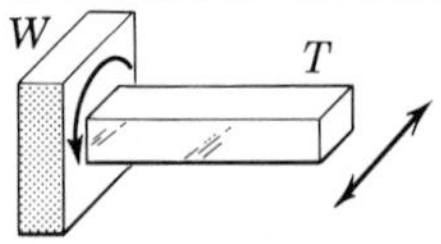	Facing	Lathe
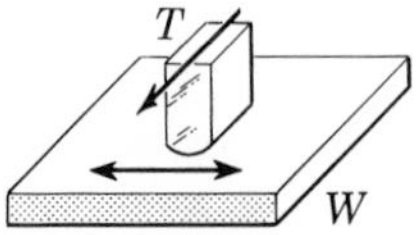	Shaping	Shaper
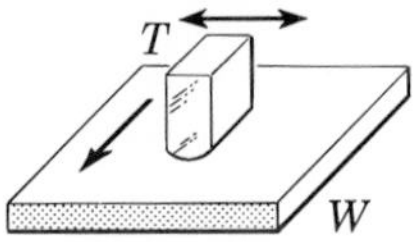	Planing	Planer
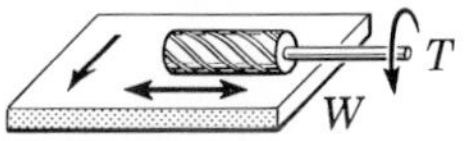	Peripheral milling	Horizontal spindle miller
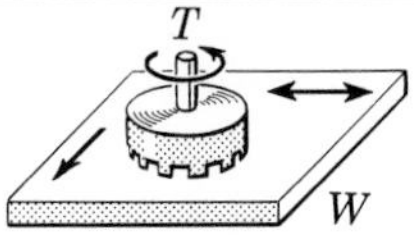	Face milling	Miller
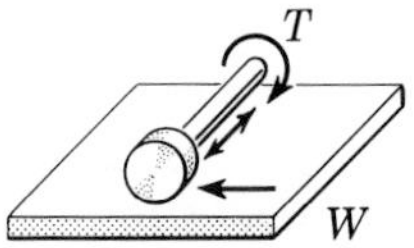	Grinding	Surface grinder
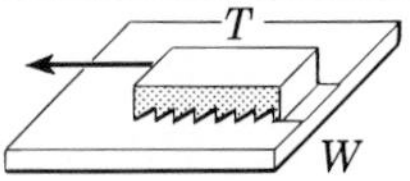	Broaching	Broacher
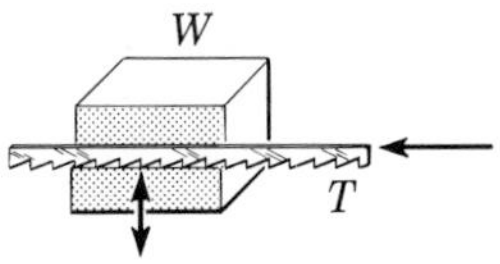	Sawing	Saw
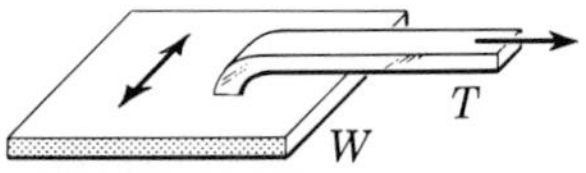	Slotting	Vertical shaper

Legend:
    Work $= W$ Tool $= T$ Speed $= \longrightarrow$ Feed $= \longleftrightarrow$

Fig. 10–7.   Machine tool motions, flat surfaces.
From J. P. Vidosic, *Metal Machining and Forming Technology.*   Copyright © 1964, The Ronald Press Co., New York.

MOTIONS	OPERATION	MACHINE
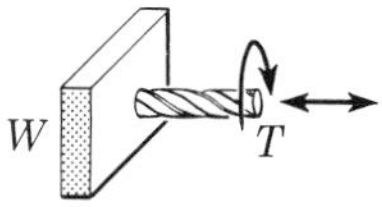	Drilling	Drill press
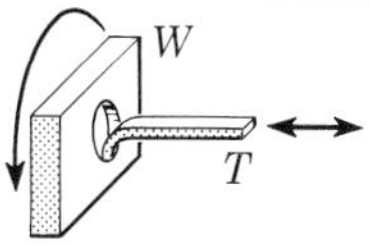	Boring	Lathe or boring mill
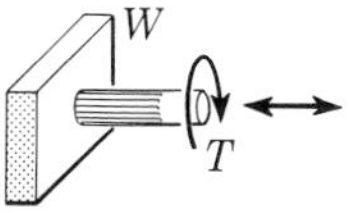	Reaming	Lathe or boring mill
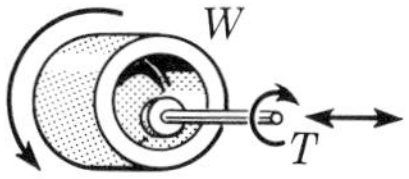	Grinding	Cylindrical grinder
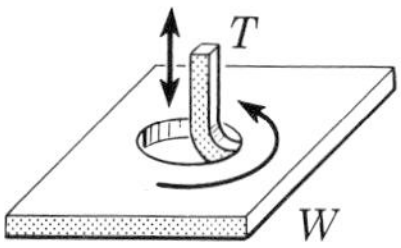	Slotter boring	Vertical shaper
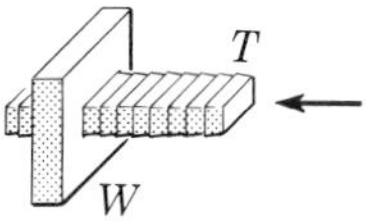	Broaching	Broacher

Legend:
  Work $= W$ Tool $= T$ Speed $= \longrightarrow$ Feed $= \longleftrightarrow$

Fig. 10–8.   Machine tool motions, internal surfaces.
From J. P. Vidosic, *Metal Machining and Forming Technology.*   Copyright © 1964, The Ronald Press Co., New York.

theory and techniques, and Fig. 10–10 portrays the operations schematically.

Joining processes accomplish localized coalescence between the materials being welded, by the application of temperature and pressure. Theoretically all that is necessary is to bring perfectly clean surfaces an atomic distance apart.   Practically, of course, neither a perfectly clean surface nor the atomic distance have yet been made possible.   The human mind has, however, developed many different ways of overcoming the difficulties and accomplishing the union.   Welding tech-

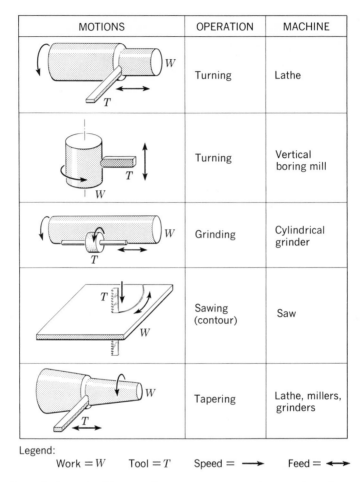

MOTIONS	OPERATION	MACHINE
	Turning	Lathe
	Turning	Vertical boring mill
	Grinding	Cylindrical grinder
	Sawing (contour)	Saw
	Tapering	Lathe, millers, grinders

Legend:
Work $= W$ Tool $= T$ Speed $= \longrightarrow$ Feed $= \longleftrightarrow$

Fig. 10–9.   Machine tool motions, external curved surfaces.
From J. P. Vidosic, *Metal Machining and Forming Technology.*   Copyright © 1964, The Ronald Press Co., New York.

niques can be categorized as non-pressure and pressure welding, or as heat and resistance welding.   Gas and electric-arc welding are the most important non-pressure processes.   Combustion of a gas in union with oxygen in a torch provides the energy needed to bring the workpieces to fusion temperature in gas welding.   In arc welding, the heat source becomes an electric arc maintained between the work and the electrode, or in some cases between two electrodes.   In both gas and

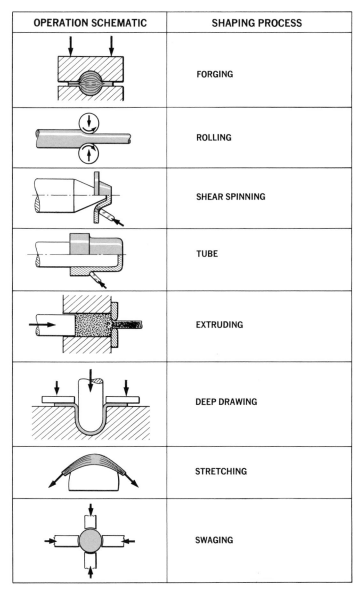

OPERATION SCHEMATIC	SHAPING PROCESS
	FORGING
	ROLLING
	SHEAR SPINNING
	TUBE
	EXTRUDING
	DEEP DRAWING
	STRETCHING
	SWAGING

Fig. 10–10.   Forming processes schematically portrayed.

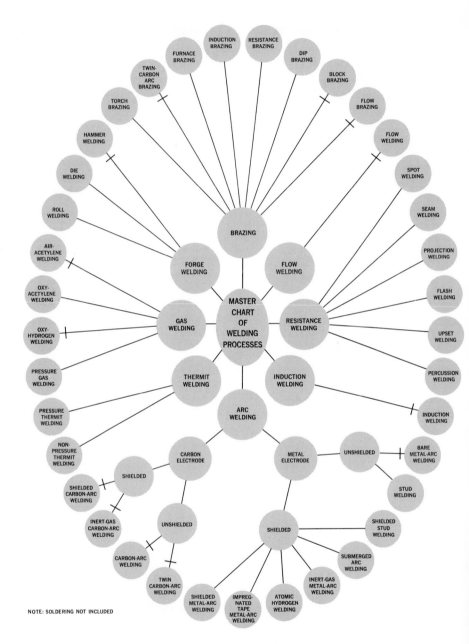

Fig. 10–11. Welding processes chart.
Courtesy American Welding Society.

arc welding, cleanliness of surface can be optimized by the incorporation of fluxes and shielding media. The gas torch and the arc can also be used to cut metals.

The older method of pressure welding is forging, in which heated pieces are hammered until fused together. A more modern method of pressure welding is the resistance technique. The necessary fusion temperature is obtained because of the resistance to passage of electric current through the work as well as the workpiece interface. When the proper temperature is reached, pressure is applied to force the pieces together. Spot, seam, and stud joining are examples of resistance welding.

Thermit, electron beam, friction, laser, and metallizing are some of the special welding techniques. Brazing and soldering are joining processes in which joining by capillary attraction and adhesion between parent metal and fusible metal alloy (the solder) are the respective phenomena.

Thermosetting as well as thermoplastic adhesives provide another joining method. Much development in recent years has produced very effective adhesive bonding agents for both metallic and non-metallic parts.

The master welding chart in Fig. 10–11 symbolizes the many basic processes used to produce welds. The short cross line on some of the rays identifies processes of no present industrial importance. The Welding Handbook [4] contains every kind of welding information for those wishing a more extensive review.

10–6. METROLOGY

Mass production and interchangeability, economical manufacture and conformity gaging, precise functional requirements and microscopic tolerances, have each placed greater demands upon design, production, and operation engineers. It is essential that dimensions be carefully specified, accurately measured and precisely controlled. The specification of dimensions not only affects proper functioning of manufactured products, but also determines the quality of the machine, process and skill needed, and therefore the cost of production. Measurement and dimensional control must be exercised at every step of the production process, if close dimensional specification is to be satisfied. Each component must be of extreme precision in order that the system be near-perfect as sometime required (a space ship for instance).

Measurement is defined as the assignment of numerals to aspects of objects or events in accordance with a pre-established rule. A foot, the fundamental unit of length, is defined as exactly $\frac{1}{3}$ yard. Congress (in 1866), set the U. S. yard at $\frac{3600}{3937}$ meter. Finally, the meter is defined as 1,650,763.73 wavelengths of the light emitted by Krypton 86. Measurement is of particular importance to the designer, because in establishing such aspects, either by reason or calculation, he must fully appreciate the need for and significance of his decisions.

Gaging determines conformity of product to specification. Gaging therefore differs from measurement in that it aims at dimensional accuracy with reference to specified size, and not the determination of actual size. It is the responsibility of the production engineer.

The engineer, whose design must be fabricated to be of service, must possess knowledge of measurement theory, acquaintance with primary standards, and familiarity with measuring instruments, their limita-

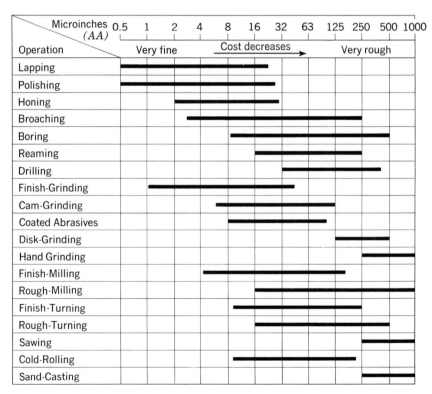

Fig. 10–12. Range of roughness values expected from common cutting operations.

From J. P. Vidosic, *Metal Machining and Forming Technology.* Copyright © 1964, The Ronald Press Co., New York.

tions as well as capability [2]. Linear and angular measurements can be made to great accuracy with several precise tools as well as with optical, pneumatic, and electrical measuring instruments. Straightness, flatness, and surface texture are other important and often critical measurements. The optical flat along with the application of the interference principle is the most precise method of measuring flatness.

Surface quality is often of great significance in the operation and life of a device, machine, or system. A microfinish not only reduces friction and thereby wear, but assures the desired life under severe conditions when dynamic stresses are present. The roughness of a surface depends upon how it has been produced. Figure 10–12 depicts the range of roughness values that may be expected from common cutting operations. It is important to notice the statistical nature of surface finish that results, because of the span of values probable in any one operation. Extreme care and most sensitive instrumentation must be used in the measurement of these tiny surface irregularities. Such instruments are fortunately available.

REFERENCES

1. S. M. Edelglass, *Engineering Materials Science—Structure and Mechanical Behavior of Solids*, The Ronald Press Co., New York, 1966.
2. J. P. Vidosic, *Metal Machining and Forming Technology*, The Ronald Press Co., New York, 1964.
3. C. R. Hine, *Machine Tools for Engineers*, 2nd Ed., McGraw-Hill Book Co., Inc., New York, 1959.
4. A. L. Phillips, Editor, *Welding Handbook*, American Welding Society, New York, 1961.

PROBLEMS

10–1. Identify two particular aspects that characterize industrially important metals.

10–2. What is a mechanical-mixture alloy?

10–3. Define the group of materials known as *plastics*.

10–4. Identify three household items that contain ceramic parts. Describe what function the ceramic component performs.

10–5. Are all plastic chains made up of carbon and hydrogen?

10–6. Why can thermoplastics be easily deformed upon application of heat while thermosetting resins cannot?

10–7. State five questions that a designer should be able to answer affirmatively if the appropriate material has been selected.

10–8. Why does sound engineering judgment enter the selection of materials?

10-9. Identify the five major component complexes of a lathe.

10-10. What is measurement, and how does gaging differ from it?

10-11. How and why is the designer concerned with metrology?

10-12. Which principle does precise flatness measurement depend upon?

10-13. Compute the contraction a 5-in.-long bar of aluminum will undergo when subjected to a compressive stress of 100,000 psi. Compare with steel.

10-14. Seek and identify five engineering applications where plastics have successfully replaced metals.

10-15. Are butane, C_4H_{10}, acetylene, C_2H_2, and styrene, C_8H_8 saturated chains, and why?

10-16. A simply supported square beam 4 ft long carries a concentrated load of 800 lb at its midpoint. Compare the cross sections required for beams made of SAE-1020 steel, aluminum alloy 2024, and a CA-16065 plastic having a flexure strength of 7,800 psi.

10-17. One dial gage designed to measure 0.1 in. per pointer revolution contains 200 equal divisions on its 360° scale. Another measures 0.5 in. per two revolutions and contains 100 divisions. Which gage has the better discrimination and why?

10-18. Discuss the basic differences between crystalline and amorphous structures.

10-19. Discuss the correlation between the atomic and phenomenological properties of metallic materials.

10-20. Discuss the statistical nature of the properties of metallic materials.

10-21. Discuss the importance of considering the technological properties in the selection of materials for engineering applications.

10-22. Discuss the importance of surface quality in engineering applications of materials.

DESIGN PROBLEMS

10-D1. Identify the three material properties that are most likely needed when designing a steel beam; explain why.

10-D2. A metallic material is being considered for a high-temperature application. What properties should you take into consideration and why?

10-D3. Explain fatigue loading and what is involved in designing for its action.

10-D4. Sketch the stress-strain diagram of a typical metallic material, and identify whatever properties can be obtained therefrom that are most essential in design.

10-D5. The capsule re-entry material problem has been a troublesome one because of the short-time loading and high-temperature situation involved. Ordinarily determined mechanical properties are insufficient, because of the dynamic nature of the application. An important property needed in the design for such situations, is the modulus of elasticity. What are two possible methods that could be used to experimentally determine the modulus of elasticity under dynamic loading conditions? Briefly explain the theory underlying the techniques suggested.

10–D6. Select the type of steel that could be used in spindles 1 in. in diam, if the torsional deflection is to be minimized.

10–D7. A first-class job shop makes a series of replacement parts as needed. Requirements are such parts as gears, cams, special bolts, and lead screws. Which material would you recommend be stocked as a general purpose, machinable steel alloy? Give your reasons for the selection.

10–D8. AISI–2330 steel bolts are being used for the connecting rod of small engines. These bolts serve well except they tend to stretch in service, which causes loosening of nuts. What do you suggest be done to solve this problem safely?

10–D9. You have designed a heavy steel plate for the base of a special machine. It contains six holes. Hole number 1 is cored 3 in. in diam and 4 in. deep. It is to be used to support a $3\frac{1}{4}$-in. diam steel column. Holes 2 to 5 are drilled $\frac{1}{2}$ in. through for hold-down studs. Hole number 6 is a 1-in. hole, through which a 1-in. shaft is to reciprocate. Specify whether the holes should be bored or reamed, and indicate why.

10–D10. Turbine blades are cast from a high-temperature-resistant alloy. Specify the casting process you recommend be used to mass produce the blades. Prepare some valid reasons for your choice so that management can be convinced of the correctness of the selection.

10–D11. Would you recommend a connecting-rod made of nickel steel round bars be cold or hot shaped? Explain your decision carefully.

10–D12. An automobile water jacket has been burst by freezing. How would you recommend it be welded for satisfactory repair?

11

Design Economics

Money has time and most-return value. The effectiveness–cost ratio is an important economic criterion that every engineer must consider when making design decisions. All products and services must be rendered within cost limitations. A difficult and yet essential adjustment that every engineer must make to be successful is in the recognition that money is another important material in every product he designs.

Is the material the most economical that can be used? Has the product been so designed that it can be economically produced? Is material being wasted where not needed? Will the available fabrication method permit most economical manufacture? Are the controls so designed that operators can be easily trained? Would automation of production be more economical? Such questions—and even: Is the project necessary? Is now the most opportune time to market the product?—arise throughout all stages of design. And the larger the project, the more critical its economical solution. To best handle such problems, the design engineer must have an understanding and appreciation of the principles of economy. What follows can only briefly point out some of the more basic concepts.

11-1. WEALTH AND INCOME

Wealth can be briefly defined as material items that are useful and relatively scarce. It is, more exactly, the total stock of items or objects owned by an individual, organization, or nation that are economically significant. There can, however, be a legitimate argument as to what items are economically significant. This classification depends upon the point of view, that is, upon the nature of the particular item under consideration. For instance, air is certainly useful; yet it could not be included, because it is so plentiful that it exceeds demand. Change

202

the natural state of some of it, however, and the acted-upon amount becomes a part of wealth because a restrictive value has been added (the value-added concept). Military weapons have no value except as scrap or salvage; or do they in war? The good will that a corporation earns by its reputation and dependability is usually given a value, though this is not often very large.

Wealth can be natural, such as the minerals in the ground, the chemicals in water, and the fruit on the trees. Wealth is also man-made, such as when ore is reduced to iron, the iron is cast into a part, and the part is assembled with other components to form a machine. Man-made wealth is thus the value added by an effort to make an item more useful; it is the difference between the total cost of a product and the competitive price at which it can be sold. Anything, then, to which the common denominator, the market-price yardstick, can be applied constitutes wealth. The real, tangible commodities that are wealth fall into the following categories.

1. Land, the minerals within it, and the expendable plants on it.
2. Water, for its specialized real-estate use and for the chemicals it contains.
3. Man-made land improvements, such as buildings, roads, and gardens.
4. Durable goods, such as machines, engines, and transportation equipment.
5. Consumer goods, such as wheat, fabrics, and hand tools.
6. Productive stocks in the hands of business, such as metals, paper, and transistors.
7. The net balance of foreign claims.

Income is the gross earnings per unit of time (usually one year) received. An individual earns some for the physical and mental services (work) he renders. Another earns some as rent or interest in payment for the use of property or other assets. A firm earns income for the sale of its products or services in the marketplace. Even a nation may earn income in the form of rentals, toll charges or for the sale of power, water, or transportation. Income depends upon the sale price per unit product or service, and the quantity of units sold.

The term National Income does not refer only to the above, but rather to the aggregate value of all—the goods and services that become available to the population over the period of time considered (usually one year). The real National Income per person measures the standard of living of the Nation. The higher this parameter the better the living conditions. Since National Income figures are essential to the planning of the economy, it is important to note that the National Income total actually arises from a circular flow of money between the various sectors of the economy. That is, the payment of each sector is the income of another. The questions of fair income distribution, of sound local and federal use, of the share invested, and of international trade are each answered and investigated via National Income statistics.

11–2. MONEY AND CAPITAL

Money has been defined as "anything that is acceptable in payment of a debt." Over the years many items have been used as money in payment by one individual for a desired item made or acquired by another. In the economy of two small groups, business is simple to conduct. There need only occur an exchange of goods between the two groups. But as groups grow, such a barter system becomes extremely cumbersome. It becomes essential that the means of exchange, the monetary system, be more convenient. To be this, the exchange medium should be portable, easy to recognize, and divisible in simple, distinguishable units. The paper money and coins used today meet these requirements.

Thus money is only a medium through which wealth can be readily exchanged. It is not wealth per se; it cannot be used as food, clothing or shelter, but it can be used to buy these. Thus, because it can easily be changed into any other needed asset, money is referred to as liquid asset. It can be used to pay for services as well, as when the engineer needs legal advice. The liquidity of money offers the advantages of universal transaction, of easy storage (savings) for a later transaction, and of the ease in which it can be invested or speculated with.

It is the last characteristic that relates money to capital. Capital refers to the money invested in an enterprise or business. In a capitalistic or free economy, capital derives out of the savings of private individuals, from corporations out of profits, and from government out of taxes. Funds owned by the corporation are called equity capital. When advantageous, a firm borrows money to expand its operations; such monies are called borrowed capital. On the other hand, when cash is converted via purchase into material commodities, real estate, durable goods, or productive stock, the properties are considered fixed assets.

11–3. INTEREST AND PROFIT

When one invests his savings he gives up command over his money. He denies himself the ability to buy whatever goods or services may provide immediate satisfaction, or whatever an emergency may demand. Naturally no one will assume the disadvantages unless the investment risk promises a reasonable return. The most common type of return is interest. Rent is an alternate form of interest (and so is a dividend). Since both a loan and a rental are for a period of time, money is said to possess time value. In order that the payment of interest be possible, the borrower must make a profit. Interest and profit are thus inseparable.

Interest can be defined as the periodic compensation for the lending of money; it is the financial share for participation in an enterprise. Expressed as a percentage of the principal or loan to which it applies, it is called interest rate. Interest can be simple; that is, it is paid in one sum at the end of the loan period, which may or may not be the same length of time as that upon which the interest rate is based (usually one year). Compound interest is paid when the loan period consists of several interest periods.

If r is the interest rate (annual basis), C the principal and n the number of interest periods, the total simple interest, I_s, earned is

$$I_s = rnC$$

The compound interest, I_c, on the other hand, is

$$I_c = C[(1 + r_p)^n - 1]$$

where r_p is the interest rate per period.

Example 11–1. One thousand dollars ($1,000) are loaned at 4% interest for three years. How much simple interest will be earned? What will be earned if compounded quarterly?

Solution:

$$I_s = rnC = 0.04 \times 3 \times 1000 = \$120.00$$

for quarterly compounding $r_p = r/4 = 0.04/4 = 0.01$, $n = 3 \times 4$,

$$I_c = C[(1 + r_p)^n - 1] = 1000[1.01^{12} - 1] = \$126.82$$

Profits must be earned in a competitive economy, if needed capital is to be available, or more realistically, if the organization is to remain in business. Profit is the excess of income over expenses. Expenses consist of operation, O, and maintenance, M, expenses; of depreciation, D, of real estate, buildings and equipment; of interest, I, paid for the use of borrowed money; and even corporation income taxes, T, paid on profit. Thus, if gross income is indicated as G, the net profit after taxes, P, can be expressed symbolically as follows.

$$P = G - (O + M + D + I) - T$$

Profit by itself is not a complete measure of the success of a business. It should be compared with the investment from which it results, or possibly even with total cost or sales volume. The word *yield* is used to denote the better measure of financial success. It is

$$\text{Yield} = \frac{\text{Profit}}{\text{Total investment}}$$

Business transactions and economics are a very complex and subjective situation. The terms above have been defined and used in only the very simplest sense. A much lengthier analysis and study is essential for full understanding and sound application of income, profit, and yield concepts.

11–4. SUPPLY AND DEMAND

In a perfectly competitive economy, market price is a direct function of demand, as shown in Fig. 11–1(a). Price is also a function of supply, an inverse function, as shown in Fig. 11–1(b). When both functions are plotted on the same coordinates, as in Fig. 11–1(c), it becomes obvious that S units of supply will just meet the demand at the price P. That is, the best price occurs at the value at which supply just equals demand. This is the important law of supply and demand.

In the real human world though, price is not influenced solely by the law. Trade strategy, social factors, tastes, and government controls, as well as other factors, can and do influence the price also. Besides, the engineer influences the cost and therefore the price at which his design can be sold at a profit. Thus he must be conscious of cost, because the cost, and thus the price, designed into the product can drop the demand much below the given capacity to produce. The price for maximum immediate gain is one thing, and for long-term production quite something else.

The law of diminishing returns is another bit of economics the engineer must observe. The law points out that the benefit gained by changing one of a series of influencing variables is likely to proportionately decrease after the factor reaches some value. For instance, closer tolerances are likely to improve the quality and possibly the functional ability of a product, but simultaneously increase its cost. A tolerance will therefore be reached beyond which cost will become too high to permit sale at market price; the tolerance has reached the point of diminishing returns. Obviously the engineer must observe the law in some of the design decisions he has to make.

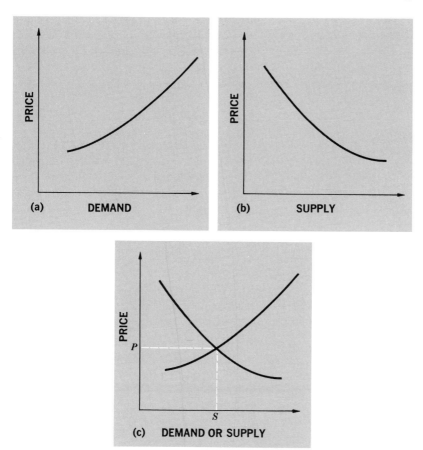

Fig. 11–1.　Law of supply and demand.

11–5. VALUE AND DEPRECIATION

A machine or product in service loses some of its value because wear and deterioration make it less capable of performing its intended function.　Other causes, such as new improved equipment that reduces fabrication costs, changes in taste, and even intended style modifications, exist and reduce value.　Such decreases in value are called depreciation.

There are several kinds of value as well as several methods for computing depreciation.　Probably the most common measure of value is the price that a willing buyer will pay a willing seller, or market value.

The book value is what is reflected in accounting records, the original value minus depreciation. The salvage or resale value is what can be obtained for the item second-hand; it usually implies the product still possesses some utility. Salvage value is often equal to book value. Scrap value is what is obtained when the product loses its utility and can only be treated as junk.

Depreciation must be computed to provide for recovery of invested capital and to add the amount of depreciation to the cost of the product or service obtained therefrom. There is no absolute way of computing depreciation; therefore several rational but more or less arbitrary methods are used.

Simple straight-line depreciation assumes that the loss in value is directionally proportional to age. It is computed

$$D_a = (C - S) \frac{a}{L}$$

where C is original value
S is salvage value
L is the useful life of the property in years
a is the age in question

When physical deterioration is due primarily to how long the device has been operated, another straight-line expression, machine-hour, is computed. The method is particularly applicable when operation is irregular.

$$D_a = (C - S) \frac{a}{H}$$

where H denotes the total number of life hours of available operation. Fixed-percentage depreciation is computed as follows:

$$D_a = C \left[1 - \left(\frac{S}{C} \right)^{a/L} \right]$$

The sinking-fund method, in which cumulated periodic deposits are soundly invested, formulates as

$$D_a = (C - S) \left[\frac{(1 + r_p)^a - 1}{(1 + r_p)^L - 1} \right]$$

Example 11–2. A piece of equipment costs \$60,000 initially and is expected to salvage at \$10,000 at the end of its 10-yr life.

(a) How much straight-line depreciation will occur in its first two years?
(b) What would the sinking-fund depreciation be if the interest rate available were 4%?

(c) How much is the machine-hour depreciation, assuming a fixed-hour day?

Solution:

(a) $\quad D_a = (C - S) \left(\dfrac{a}{L} \right)$

$\qquad = (60,000 - 10,000) \dfrac{2}{10}$

$\qquad = 50,000 \times 0.2$

$\qquad = \$10,000$

(b) $\quad D_a = (C - S) \left[\dfrac{(1 + r_p)^a - 1}{(1 + r_p)^L - 1} \right]$

$\qquad = (60,000 - 10,000) \left[\dfrac{(1 + 0.04)^2 - 1}{(1 + 0.04)^{10} - 1} \right]$

$\qquad = 50,000 \left[\dfrac{1.0816 - 1}{1.4802 - 1} \right] = 50,000[0.1699]$

$\qquad = \$8,495$

(c) $\quad D_a = (C - S) \dfrac{a}{H}$

$\qquad = (60,000 - 10,000) \dfrac{2 \times 365 \times 8}{10 \times 365 \times 8}$

$\qquad = 50,000 \times 0.2$

$\qquad = \$10,000$

11–6. COST CONSIDERATIONS

It has been indicated already that the total cost of producing a physical product must be somewhat less than the price for which it can be sold in a free, competitive market. It is therefore necessary to estimate as soundly as possible the market price that will likely be prevailing, and to then design and manufacture the item at a cost somewhat less. In a more favorable business situation, it may be possible to take the total cost and add profit, to establish the price at which it must and will be sold. In either case, cost estimating and cost analysis have to be undertaken. For success the design engineer must be cost conscious and must ascertain that the design of the device, machine, or system is performed as economically as safely possible and the product so designed that it can be physically realized at as low a cost as possible.

Cost is total expenditure for a product or service. It includes the salary paid the engineer for developing, designing, and producing it; wages paid labor for its fabrication; the cost of marketing and maintaining it; the overhead cost allocated for its management; the cost of the materials it is made of; interest on the investment in facilities, machines, and real estate used in its manufacture; the cost of its packaging and transportation; and even the cost of fringe benefits to personnel involved in the foregoing.

Determining the total cost is obviously not a simple matter. It is the function of accounting to gather the cost data and analyze the engineering, production, and marketing activities toward prediction of cost. Insofar as the individual designer is concerned, it is his duty to see that the work is directed to result in the lowest possible cost-to-effectiveness ratio. He must assure that he is selecting the most economical material; that his engineering endeavors—talent used, extent of development insisted on, accuracy required, testing demanded, and extras decided upon—are consistent with the need that is to be satisfied; that fabrication costs are not in excess of what is needed to safely meet functional requirements; that the design is marketable; and that obsolescence is not a major problem and depreciation is reasonable.

The designer is not so much concerned with the actual cost as he is with minimizing it wherever size, capacity, configuration, production, processing, and finish permit. He must appreciate the difference between design for custom fabrication and design for mass production. He must understand the ability and status of the ultimate consumer. He must be familiar with the scope, goals and policies of the business for which he is designing. And he must be conscious of such fixed costs as taxes and insurance, as well as the variable costs of labor, material, and overhead.

A listing of the elements of total cost that the design engineer has an effect upon includes the following:

1. Cost of research incurred when it must be performed, particularly in innovation situations, to provide needed knowledge.
2. Development and design costs.
3. Direct product costs, including material, manufacturing equipment, and fabrication of components.
4. Assembly of component costs.
5. Equipment installation costs, where applicable.
6. Cost of spare parts that have to be stocked.
7. Maintenance costs (these can be quite high when systems are improperly designed).
8. Operating costs for such items as fuel and operating labor.
9. Training costs, for complex systems requiring particular operating skills.

In a study [1] conducted at Bradley University it was reported that decisions affecting cost were ranked in the following order by practicing engineers.

1. Selection of an over-all design concept for a product.
2. Definition and analysis of customer requirements for a product.
3. Selection of specific parts for a design.
4. Design analysis (selection of safety factors, etc.)
5. Selection and/or development of manufacturing processes.
6. Selection of materials.
7. Selection of new equipment.
8. Analysis to determine the need for equipment replacement.
9. Cost analysis of current products.
10. Cost analysis of current processes.
11. Analysis and selection of manufacturing areas for potential cost reduction.

Item 8 above needs a brief explanation. Deterioration and obsolescence gradually befall machines. The inevitable penalty is in higher operating costs, less competitive product, lower earnings, and wasted manpower. A systematic, economically determined replacement of machines is thus essential. The Machinery and Allied Products Institute [2, 3] has developed formulas and charts that enable machine replacement determination even where precise cost records are not available.

The name *defender* is assigned the machine in use that is up for replacement. The *challenger* is a better machine available as replacement for the defender. The adverse minimum is the sum of the operating inferiority and capital cost (the average yearly cost of the machine plus the annual interest on the capital). Whenever the adverse minimum, L_a, of the defender exceeds that of the challenger, replacement is economically dictated.

$$L_a \approx \frac{g(n-1)}{2} + \frac{C-S}{2} + \frac{i(C+S)}{2}$$

where L_a = life average operating inferiority plus capital cost in dollars
g = annual operating inferiority rate in dollars
n = remaining life of machine
C = present salvage value (and installation cost) in dollars
S = next year's salvage value of machine in dollars
i = interest rate

The bar chart in Fig. 11–2 illustrates the replacement situation. Portion A represents the adverse minimum of the defender; B is the adverse minimum of challenger; C represents revenue lost to defender because of greater productivity, or operation elimination, or worker morale improvement of challenger. Note that in order to establish the

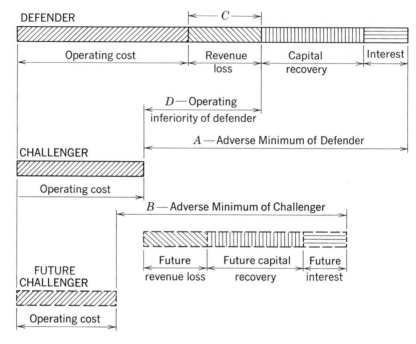

Fig. 11–2.   Machine replacement chart.
From J. P. Vidosic, *Metal Machining and Forming Technology.*   Copyright © 1964, The Ronald Press Co., New York.

challenger's adverse minimum it becomes necessary to estimate future challenger factors shown as broken lines.

Example 11–3.   The yearly deterioration and obsolescence of a certain machine is estimated at $6,720.   Present machine value is $7,500, and its value next year is expected to be $4,500; its remaining expected life is 3.5 yr. Compute the defender's adverse minimum if current interest rate is 7%.

Solution:

$$L_a = \frac{g(n-1)}{2} + \frac{C-S}{2} + \frac{i(C+S)}{2}$$
$$= \frac{6720(3.5-1)}{2} + \frac{7500-4500}{2} + \frac{0.07(7500+4500)}{2}$$
$$= 8400 + 1500 + 420$$
$$= \$10,320$$

11–7. ECONOMICS IN DESIGN

The subject of economics is very extensive, and most critical, particularly in a capitalistic community. Problems in investment, expansion, plant location, labor costs, overhead charges, and pension plans are serious matters that occupy much of management's time. It is not the purpose here to investigate such questions; our concern is rather for the many possible minor but economically contributing decisions that the design engineer must make in his everyday work. This has already been mentioned. The chapter on optimum design, for instance, points out that cost of material is an undesirable factor that must be minimized. This is typical of the type of economic questions that concern the design engineer.

The actual problem of establishing cost data is a function of accounting. Of course the engineer must assist accounting if the cost facts he needs are to be forthcoming. Without substantial cost records, engineering can do little but make the best estimates possible. Extensive experience with the particular raw materials and equipment involved, as well as judgment and decision-making, become essential constituents.

Engineers are often required to conduct economy studies of products, engineering services, and production processes that they design or are otherwise involved with. It is therefore necessary to give at least brief consideration to the subject. Such studies are used to decide upon a more economical yet just as satisfactory design, to establish budgets, and to arrive at standards in size, model, quality, practice, or policy. These studies often require the engineer to look beyond the accounting figure. It is quite possible that a fact or figure needed is hidden under another heading or possibly not entered at all; for instance, the cost of inspection may be included in testing costs, or part of the material cost may be called storage charges.

The matter of detail vs. economy plagues accountants, too. To what detail should accounting records be carried in a particular situation? How does the cost of better accounting records compare with the value of the greater cost information thus made available? Is it more economical to generally maintain more detailed cost records than it is to conduct cost analyses when particular information is required? It is certainly obvious that, the greater the amount expended for accounting, the greater the cost of the product being designed. Experimental studies are sometime the best way of obtaining operational costs. Time and motion studies will reveal the cost of an assembly detail, the difficulty of machining a rib that could be satisfactorily welded on at a lower price, or possibly even that a change to automatic control would remove the need for highly trained operators. Study of the locally applicable characteristics of a new piece of equipment may provide cost figures not otherwise available.

One must also consider the effect that changes in price levels of materials and purchased components may have upon alternate designs. This may require estimation of cost under more than one set of assumptions or conditions. For instance, oranges are to be waxed by dipping in a wax–water solution and then dried by an air-conditioning system. If the temperature of the oranges is raised a few degrees above the cold-storage temperature, the drying load will be noticeably lower. This appears to be currently the more economical procedure. An increase in the price of the heating fuel seems imminent; should the heating cycle be eliminated and a larger, costlier air-conditioning system, that will handle the heavier load because of lower fruit temperature, be selected instead?

Such then are the types of economic studies and cost considerations the design engineer is often involved in. Such are the cost questions he must analyze, the cost estimates he must undertake, and the economy decisions he must make, if his product or process is to be marketable. Some examples will better reveal what these tasks may be like.

Example 11–4. A small shop having an available electric load of 37 hp purchases its electricity at the following rates:

kw-hr/month	@¢/kw-hr
First 1,500	2.5
Next 1,250	1.5
Next 3,000	0.9
All over 5,750	0.8

The current monthly consumption of electric power averages 3,200 kw-hr. A bid is to be made on some new business that would require an additional 3,500 kw-hr per month. What is the lowest possible amount that should be added for the cost of the additional energy?

Study: Cost of present energy is

kw-hr	@$/kw-hr	
1,500	0.025	= $37.50
1,250	0.015	= 18.75
450	0.009	= 4.05
3,200		$60.30

or the equivalent of $6,030/3,200 = 1.885$¢/kw-hr.

The new average cost is

kw-hr	@ $/kw-hr	
1,500	0.025	= $37.50
1,250	0.015	= 18.75
3,000	0.009	= 27.00
950	0.008	= 7.60
6,700		$90.86

or $9,085/6,700 = 1.356 ¢/\text{kw-hr}$.

The lowest possible amount to be added for the extra cost of electric energy is, of course, $90.85 − $60.30 = $30.55, or $3,055/3,500 = 0.865 ¢/\text{extra kw-hr}$.

Example 11–5. A base plate for an air metering device that is to be mass-produced contains ten pierced holes that must be reamed. As the designer of the plate, you are asked to conduct an economic study comparing the use of existing drill presses (five single-spindle presses or one six-spindle press) with the purchase of a special ten-spindle press that would ream the holes simultaneously, and recommend appropriate action.

Study: It is necessary to first gather the following pertinent cost data. Accounting, and the manufacturer of the new machine, help supply the information.

a. Existing equipment is fully depreciated. Total normal maintenance, however, is $30/yr on the single-spindle presses, and $80/yr for the six-spindle machine.

b. Total set-up time for the five single-spindle presses is 0.90 hr, and reaming time is 0.050 hr/base plate. The six-spindle set-up time is 0.80 hr, and running time reduces to 0.030 hr/plate.

c. Existing machines require operator-skill labor of a level being paid $2.25/hr.

d. The installed cost of the new ten-spindle press is $2,350. It can be depreciated over 15 yr, and its maintenance cost is estimated at $120/yr.

e. Set-up time on new machine is estimated at 1.25 hr, and running at 0.015 hr/plate. Slightly lower level operating labor being paid $2.10 per hour can be used.

f. Insurance and tax costs are $1.45/$100 of initial investment for both new and old equipment. The initial cost of single-spindle equipment was $600, and of six-spindle $2,800.

g. Fixture costs are about the same for all set-ups, as is the electric power used.

h. It is estimated that 2,500 base plates will be produced per year.

Annual cost to ream with existing single-spindle drill presses:

Maintenance	$ 30.00
Setup (0.90 × 2.25)	2.03
Reaming (2,500 × 0.05 × 2.25)	281.25
Insurance plus tax (1.45 × 600/100)	8.70
Total	$321.98

or 32,198/2,500 = 12.88¢/plate.

Annual cost to ream with existing six-spindle drill press:

Maintenance	$ 80.00
Setup (0.80 × 2.25)	1.80
Reaming (2,500 × 0.03 × 2.25)	168.75
Insurance plus tax (1.45 × 2,800/100)	40.60
Total	$291.15

or 29,115/2,500 = 11.65¢/plate.

Annual cost to ream with new ten-spindle drill press:

Maintenance	$120.00
Setup (1.25 × 2.10)	2.63
Reaming (2,500 × 0.015 × 2.10)	78.75
Insurance plus tax (1.45 × 2,350/100)	34.08
Total	$235.46

or 23,546/2,500 = 9.42¢/plate.

Reaming cost per plate can be reduced by at least (11.65 − 9.42) or 2.23 cents. This will not pay for the new drill press even during the 15-yr depreciation life at the 2,500-piece annual production. Notice, however, that the press would be used only 1.25 + 2500 × 0.015 = 38.75 hr/yr. It is, therefore, available for other use as well. Thus the plate job alone may not warrant purchase, but additional work could well do so. Management should probably give above cost figures consideration from the point of view of the total business of the company. It could well be that, if deterioration and obsolescence were considered, a defender–challenger analysis may dictate the opposite conclusion.

Example 11-6. A concern having an annual demand of 12,000 feet of a section asks for bids from two fabricators. Fabricator A proposes to supply a solid section weighing 60.7 lb/ft at 1.4¢/lb at his factory, which is 70 mi from the using firm. Fabricator B, on the other hand, proposes a hollow section of another material weighing 19.4 lb/ft at 3.4¢/lb at his factory door, which is 8 mi from the user. The designer has checked and is certain either section will serve the purpose well, both functionally and structurally. You are asked to make an economic study to uncover the section costing less delivered.

Study: The following facts and figures are first obtained from accounting and trucking department.

a. A closed 10-ton truck can be made available to haul the section to the plant.
b. Truck cost, including depreciation, is 10¢/mi for trips up to 25 mi and 8¢/mile for trips over 25 mi.
c. The driver of the truck is paid $3.50/hr, and his helper $2.50/hr.
d. Test runs reveal loading, unloading, and round trip take 4 hr with the closer supplier, and 7 hr with the other.
e. Production decides it must have a 1-wk reserve supply of the section that is 8 mi away, and a 1-mo reserve supply of the other. Accounting estimates an annual storage cost of 3¢/ft of either section.

Cost using fabricator A section:

Feet of section carried per trip (20,000/60.7 = 329.4)	330 ft
Trips required (12,000/330 = 36.4)	37 trips
Material (12,000 × 60.7 × 0.014)	$10,197.60
Truck (37 × 140 × 0.08)	414.40
Driver (37 × 7 × 3.50)	906.50
Helper (37 × 7 × 2.50)	647.50
Storage ([12,000/12]0.03)	30.00
Total	$12,196.00

or 12,196/12,000 = $1.02/ft.

Cost using fabricator B section:

Feet of section carried per trip (20,000/19.4)	1031 ft
Trips required (12,000/1,031 = 11.7)	12 trips
Material (12,000 × 19.4 × 0.034)	$7,915.20
Truck (12 × 16 × 0.10)	19.20
Driver (12 × 4 × 3.50)	168.00
Helper (12 × 4 × 2.50)	120.00
Storage ([12,000/52]0.03)	6.92
Total	$8,229.32

or 8,229.32/12,000 = 68.5¢/ft.

Thus fabricator B section will cost much less delivered. Unless handling and cutting the hollow section to length is expensive or too troublesome, section B should be used.

REFERENCES

1. F. M. Gryna, Jr., "Engineering Economy in Product Design," Annual Meeting of American Society for Engineering Education, June 22–26, 1964, U. of Maine.
2. The Machinery and Allied Products Institute, MAPI Replacement Manual, 1950.
3. J. P. Vidosic, Metal Machining and Forming Technology, The Ronald Press Co., New York, 1964.

PROBLEMS

11-1. Distinguish between fixed assets and capital.

11-2. Explain the law of diminishing returns.

11-3. What is a good measure of value?

11-4. Identify five elements of total cost that the designer has an effect upon.

11-5. If $100 are deposited each year for 5 yr at 5% interest compounded semiannually, how much cash will be available at the end of the period?

11-6. How much must be invested today at 4.5% interest, compounded annually, to secure a perpetual yearly income of $1,000?

11-7. Two machines are being considered for purchase at a difference of $2,000 in price. The more expensive machine will yield an estimated saving of $300 a year in operating costs. Is the extra investment justified, if the expected life of both machines is 10 yr and money is worth 6%?

11-8. A proposed product modification that will eliminate certain fabrication difficulties costs $6,000 in new dies. How much should be realized in annual saving because of the change, if the extra expenditure is to be realized in 5 yr at 7% interest compounded annually?

11-9. A machine tool is bought for $26,000 installed. Its life is estimated at 12 yr, with a salvage value of $1,500 at the end of the period. Compute the straight-line depreciation that will occur in the first 4 yr.

11-10. What would the sinking-fund depreciation of Problem 11-9 be if money is worth 8%?

11-11. A machine is bought for $42,000; its expected life is 15 yr and salvage value is $3,000. Using straight-line depreciation, determine the book value of the machine at the end of 7 yr.

11-12. Compute the adverse minimum for a defender machine described by the following data: the annual operating inferiority rate is $3,053, present value is $5,300, and next year's expected value is $3,500; life left is 4 yr, and the interest rate is 10%.

11-13. Discuss *wealth* and *value added*.

11-14. Discuss the phrase *economically significant* as applied to wealth.

11-15. Discuss the need and convenience of money in the economy of a country and its business.

11-16. Discuss *profit* and *yield*.

11-17. Does the law of supply and demand always work? Discuss.

11-18. Discuss the responsibility a designer assumes with regard to cost of product.

11-19. Discuss how a designer may reduce the maintenance costs of a product.

DESIGN PROBLEMS

11–D1. The following figures are established for a defender machine: annual operating inferiority is $10,347, present salvage value is $3,650, and next year's salvage value is $2,800; the interest rate is 12%. Two challenger machines are being considered. Using MAPI charts, challenger A's adverse minimum is found to be $7,830, and that of challenger B $12,150. Would you recommend defender be replaced by either challenger and why?

11–D2. Assuming the 6-spindle drill press of Example 11–5 has a remaining expected life of 3 yr, and current interest rate is 9%, estimate the remaining values needed, using your best judgment. Then compute the adverse minimums and decide if the new 10-spindle press should be obtained to replace the old 6-spindle.

11–D3. A rectangular box section is to be used to house certain tubes in a new house appliance. The outside box dimensions required are 4 in. by 6 in. Two extruded sections made of the same material have been proposed. One is a hollow section having a 0.102-in. wall, the other is a 2-piece section of 0.064-in. wall thickness. The two pieces forming the second section snap together, the snap ears on each end of one of the two pieces require an additional length of 1 in. at each end. In either case the section is available at 45¢/lb plus the cost of dies needed to extrude the section. Extrusion dies, having a life of 6,000 ft of draw, cost $80 for the 1-piece section and $340 for the 2-piece section (each half is extruded separately). Labor cost is the same in either case. Appliance assembly labor is paid $4.50/hr and assembling the 1-piece section adds 15 min/appliance. The yearly output of the appliance is expected to reach 8,000 units, each of which requires 4 ft of section. Conduct an economic investigation and recommend the section that should be contracted for.

11–D4. You have contracted to provide some engineering consulting on the detail design and manufacture of a new product by a concern 65 miles from your home. Trips to the plant to discuss matters with engineers and management will be necessary in your own automobile. Compute the appropriate charge that you should make per mile of travel.

11–D5. A small shop is going into the production of 10-ft flag poles for home use. The poles are to be made of two 5-ft lengths of $1\frac{1}{4}$-in. standard pipe with 3 in. of one end of the upper piece symmetrically offset to fit firmly inside the other. The finial with a rope slideway is to be inserted and riveted to the upper end of the top pipe length. Three materials are found functionally suitable: WX-5, XY-8, and YZ-3. The WX-5 pipe sells at 5¢/ft and its processing (cutting to length, offsetting and riveting) is estimated at 12¢/pole. The XY-8 pipe can be purchased at 6¢/ft and its fabrication will cost 8¢/pole. The third or YZ-3 pipe costs 4.5¢/ft and adds 14¢/pole for processing. Which pipe should you select if a market survey indicates around a 25,000-pole demand within the area you hope to supply each year?

11–D6. You are entering the leather-softener business with a rubbing solution made of four constituents. The composition of the softener is 76% by volume of constituent A, 12% of B, 7% of C and the balance constituent D. A standard drum of A wholesales at $2.50, B is 15¢/gal, C is 11¢/gal and D costs 23¢/gal. An investment of $25,000 is required for vats, mixers and bottlers, which are expected to depreciate to $6,000 in five years; the sum is now invested at 6%. Suitable production space is available in your plant at a cost of about $15/mo. To supply the annual 45,000-gal demand, two operators will be required a total of 4 mo the first year and 3 mo each during the remaining years. You figure you can use them on other projects the rest of the time. Their combined wages average $225/wk; about $45/mo is expected as the additional overhead and power cost insofar as production only is concerned. Determine the minimum production cost per gallon of the leather softener.

12

Optimum Design

Since any given set of product and system specifications could be satisfied by more than one design, there are several solutions to every real engineering problem. All such designs, except as incorrect for evident reasons, may be adequate; and one of the adequate designs may for certain applicable logical reasons be decided best. But even then, improvements may still be possible. It could possibly be made a little lighter or a little less expensive, a little faster or a little less hazardous. One way to accomplish the improvement is to test and modify; another is to iterate towards a more exact solution by cut-and-try procedures. Such methods for refining to the best design have been used for a long time. The growing need for optimal designs in recent years has, however, resulted in more critical requirements, and optimization has of necessity been given more attention. The mathematical concepts of maxima and minima have been seriously applied to the problem, and optimum-seeking techniques developed.

12–1. GENERAL CONCEPTS

The solution of a design problem involves the transformation of given input variables into a desired output by means of applicable design parameters. The value of the accomplished design depends upon the selection of a criterion appropriate to the design objective. Often more than one criterion is effective, and it becomes necessary to establish a composite criterion that generally is not possible except by compromise. Trade-offs are almost always involved, and thus even this ultimate refinement is not optimum but really only an approach to it, an optimal design.

The output parameters are the requirements that the component assembly or the system must satisfy to perform its function optimally. Some of these are positive, others are negative. For example, capacity, life, reliability, and efficiency are desirable effects; others such as stress, heat loss, weight, and cost are undesirable effects. In a particular design, some desirable effect, or possibly some undesirable effect, is of greatest significance.

In optimum-design procedures, the significant desirable effect is explicitly maximized, or the significant undesirable effect minimized. When only one such significant effect exists, the design is easily optimized. When several features are critical, however, optimum design is much more complicated, and even numerical methods become most difficult.

Though it might appear contradictory at first, it must be understood that even optimum design is not absolute. Models are still idealized, average properties used, and approximations made even though the consequent manipulations may be mathematically direct. In making approximations and arriving at compromises, good judgment on the part of the designer is essential. Both simplicity of computation and accuracy of result are desirable; yet these are mutually exclusive. The engineer must establish appropriate balance if his design is to be optimal.

Engineering design generally attempts to satisfy functional or value requirements, under unavoidable limitations, without creating intolerable effects. The three general parametric groups common to all designs are the functional, material, and geometrical. Functional requirements are usually interdependent and influenced by factors external to the element being designed, and they may have to be satisfactory over a range of values. Material parameters can occasionally be defined uniquely, at least on a statistical basis. Usually they are difficult to express mathematically, are independent of the functional requirements, and are discrete rather than continuous in nature. The geometry can be specified by series of dimensions. Unless standard sizes are available and preferable, geometric parameters are continuous and, if properly selected, independent of each other. The geometry is, however, dependent upon the functional and material group.

The design is generally a functional aggregate of the parameter groups. The groups are related by natural laws or empirical relations, which form the *criterion function* or, in other words, the primary design equation

$$U = f(u, v, w, x, \ldots)$$

Other expressions will generally exist involving variables that specify additional design requirements. These are the *functional constraints* distinguished by equalities:

$$F_i(u, v, w, x, \ldots) = 0$$

As indicated, limits are often imposed upon some or all of the parameters, establishing regions of usefulness. These are the *regional constraints* distinguished by inequalities:

$$R_i(u, v, w, x, \ldots) \leq L_i$$

12–2. OPTIMIZING TECHNIQUES

The ingenious engineer uses many approaches to the optimization of his designs. His decision as to what might be best in a particular case may be purely subjective. An approximate layout, a rough sketch, the plot of a curve, or a quick graphical computation may afford him the information he needs to select the optimum parameter value. Intuition is often used as well by the knowledgeable engineer when he applies general principles and experience in deciding upon the optimum answer. He avoids, for instance, sharp corners, to minimize stress; he coats an external surface, to protect it and thereby maximize life; he designs a large boiler rather than combine two smaller ones, to optimize volume requirements; and he stamps disks, to reduce cost.

There are times, however, when the value must be more exact; times when subjectivity alone will not yield the result needed. In such cases explicit mathematical methods are the only feasible approach. Differential calculus provides one direct approach. When separate constraint equations exist, Lagrangian multipliers may permit solution. Where the criterion function and constraint equations are linear relations, linear programming is the method to use. On the other hand, where multistage optimization is required, dynamic programming [1] permits a sequence of single-stage decisions. Mulligan of General Electric suggested [2] the scheme presented in Fig. 12–1 as a systematic probe for the proper approach. It should be noted that many optimization methods, the above and others, have been developed primarily to assist managers in making the right decisions.

The more general techniques for designers are maximum–minimum differentiation, use of dual variables [3], and numerical search. These methods are explained in the following articles. Probably the most useful approach to the optimum design of mechanical elements, however, is the one developed by Johnson [4]. It will be explained as well.

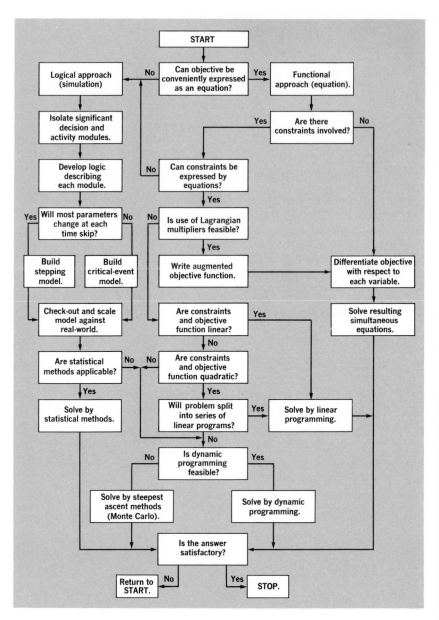

Fig. 12–1.   Optimum design probe scheme.

12–3. OPTIMIZING BY DIFFERENTIATION

When all functional constraints can be involved in a single criterion function (or when no functional constraints exist), the parameters are readily optimized. The derivative of the criterion function with respect to each parameter is set to zero. The n equations are then solved simultaneously for the optimum parametric values. Of course, these must be established consistent with any regional limitations that may apply.

If the criterion function is expressible in terms of a single significant parameter, the mathematical problem reduces to finding where the slope is zero. Examples will best illustrate the procedure.

Example 12–1. A rectangular tank with its base twice as long as wide is to have a volume of 12 ft³. Determine the most economical dimensions, if the bottom sheet material costs 20¢/ft² and the sides 10¢/ft.²

Solution: Let a represent the width of the base, and b the height of tank. Then

$$\text{Cost of bottom} = a \times 2a \times 20 = 40a^2 \text{¢}$$

and of the four sides the cost is

$$2 \times ab \times 10 + 2 \times 2ab \times 10 = 60ab\text{¢}$$

Thus

$$\text{Total cost} = C = 40a^2 + 60ab$$

But

$$V = 2a \times a \times b = 12 \quad \text{or} \quad b = \frac{6}{a^2}$$

and

$$C = 40a^2 + \frac{360}{a}$$

Differentiating,

$$\frac{dC}{da} = 80a - \frac{360}{a^2} = 0$$

From which $a = 1.65$ ft, and $b = 2.20$ ft, and most economical tank is

$$1.65 \text{ ft} \times 3.30 \text{ ft} \times 2.20 \text{ ft.}$$

Example 12–2. Suppose the tank in Example 12–1 is to have another degree of freedom; that is, the long side of base is not necessarily twice the short side, everything else remaining the same. What are the most economical dimensions in this case?

Solution:

Cost of base $= 20ac$, if c is length of base
Cost of sides $= 20ab + 20bc$

Total cost $= C = 20ac + 20ab + 20bc$

and $V = abc = 12$, or $c = 12/ab$

Thus, $C = 240/b + 20ab + 240/a$

$$\partial C/\partial a = 20b - 240/a^2 = 0$$
$$\partial C/\partial b = -240/b^2 + 20a = 0$$

from which $a = 2.29$ ft

$b = 2.29$ ft

$c = 2.29$ ft

12-4. OPTIMIZATION BY DUAL VARIABLES

This method, by Dr. C. Zener [3], consists of the replacement of the generalized function by a dual problem that results in the simultaneous solution of a system of linear equations. If the number of unknowns exceeds the number of equations that can be written, the method will not yield a solution. The dual problem derives from a particular treatment of arithmetic and geometric mean expressions.

If $a_1 + a_2 + a_3 + \cdots a_n = 1$, the expression concerned with the weighted arithmetic mean is $(a_1 x_1 + a_2 x_2 + \cdots a_n x_n)$ and that for the weighted geometric mean is $(x_1^{a_1} \times x_2^{a_2} \times \cdots x_n^{a_n})$. The inequality—the arithmetic average is greater than the geometric—becomes an equality only if all the x-terms are, in addition to the above, equal. The inequality is best written in the following form for present purposes. If $a_i x_i = u_i$, then

$$u_1 + u_2 + \cdots u_n \geq \left(\frac{u_1}{a_1}\right)^{a_1} \left(\frac{u_2}{a_2}\right)^{a_2} \cdots \left(\frac{u_n}{a_n}\right)^{a_n}$$

Again an example will best illustrate the procedure.

Example 12-3. Four hundred (400) yd^3 of sand must be ferried across a river. The sand is to be shipped across in open containers of length l, width w, and height h. The bottom and sides of the container cost \$10/yd^2 and the ends \$20/yd^2. Each round trip on the ferry costs 10¢. The containers are assumed to have no salvage value after the transfer. Minimize the transportation cost.

Solution: The total transportation cost is

$$C = 10lw + 20lh + 40wh + \left(\frac{400}{lwh}\right)\left(\frac{10}{100}\right)$$

The dual function is

$$C(a) = \left(\frac{10lw}{a_1}\right)^{a_1} \left(\frac{20lh}{a_2}\right)^{a_2} \left(\frac{40wh}{a_3}\right)^{a_3} \left(\frac{40}{lwha_4}\right)^{a_4}$$

To satisfy a minimum C, the dual variables must conform to

$$(lw)^{a_1}(lh)^{a_2}(wh)^{a_3}\left(\frac{1}{lwh}\right)^{a_4} = 1$$

and eliminating the variables the dual function becomes

$$C(a) = \left(\frac{10}{a_1}\right)^{a_1}\left(\frac{20}{a_2}\right)^{a_2}\left(\frac{40}{a_3}\right)^{a_3}\left(\frac{40}{a_4}\right)^{a_4}$$

In order that the dual variables relation be satisfied, the sum of the exponents for each variable must equal zero. Thus,

For l, $a_1 + a_2 + 0\ + a_4 = 0$
For w, $a_1 + 0\ + a_3 + a_4 = 0$
For h, $0 + a_2 + a_3 + a_4 = 0$

and $a_1 + a_2 + a_3 + a_4 = 1$ for the inequality to become an equality. Solving simultaneously,

$$a_1 = \tfrac{1}{5}, a_2 = \tfrac{1}{5}, a_3 = \tfrac{1}{5}\ \text{ and }\ a_4 = \tfrac{2}{5}$$

Thus,

$$C(a) = \left(\frac{10}{\frac{1}{5}}\right)^{\frac{1}{5}}\left(\frac{20}{\frac{1}{5}}\right)^{\frac{1}{5}}\left(\frac{40}{\frac{1}{5}}\right)^{\frac{1}{5}}\left(\frac{40}{\frac{2}{5}}\right)^{\frac{2}{5}} = 100$$

The minimum cost is, therefore, \$100. (Note the cost is obtained before the parameter values.)

To obtain the design parameters, observe that the exponent values yield the proportionate cost of each contributing cost. Thus for

$$a_1 \quad 10lw \ = \frac{\frac{1}{5}}{\frac{5}{5}} \times 100 = 20$$

$$a_2 \quad 20lh \ = \frac{\frac{1}{5}}{\frac{5}{5}} \times 100 = 20$$

$$a_3 \quad 40wh = \frac{\frac{1}{5}}{\frac{5}{5}} \times 100 = 20$$

$$a_4 \quad \frac{40}{lwh} \ = \frac{\frac{2}{5}}{\frac{5}{5}} \times 100 = 40$$

And solving the above, the optimum parameter values are

$$l = 2\ \text{yd} \qquad w = 1\ \text{yd}\ \text{ and }\ h = \tfrac{1}{2}\ \text{yd}$$

12–5. NUMERICAL SEARCH METHOD

A general surface may possess hills and valleys. The highest hill constitutes a maximum and the lowest valley a minimum. Starting at a point on the surface one can walk in a straight direction (one coordinate) until a hill (or valley) is reached. Turn at right angles (second coordinate) and walk until a higher spot is reached. Turn at right angles again (in the direction of first coordinate) until a higher spot yet is reached. Continue doing this until the level no longer changes and you have arrived at the very top (or bottom). The preceding may have to be repeated elsewhere on the surface to ascertain that the very highest (or very lowest) point has been found.

Mathematically it is necessary first that all functional constraints have been involved in the criterion function (not always possible). Assuming the criterion function two-dimensional in x and y, start at initial values x_1 and y_1. Keep x_1 constant and vary y until an optimum value is computed at x_1,y_2. Now keep y_2 constant, and vary x until an improved optimum value is found at x_2,y_2. Keep x_2 constant until a new improved optimum is found at x_2,y_3. Continue repeating the process until the magnitude of the criterion function no longer varies in the number of significant figures needed. At this point the desirable optimum has been determined. When regional constraints exist, the search must remain within the specified region.

The procedure appears tedious and time consuming, and it is. But it can be carried out rapidly using a digital computer once it is programmed. The method can be extended to criterion functions in more than two parameters. Again, with a computer the complexity is readily surmountable.

12-6. JOHNSON METHOD OF OPTIMUM DESIGN

R. C. Johnson proposed in his book [4] and many other writings an optimizing process which does not vary in theory from that already presented. It is, however, systematized, clearly phrased, and possibly simplified. It is well worth much consideration.

The basic functional constraint equation containing the parameter to be optimized and therefore controlling the final design has been called the *primary design equation*, PDE. It thus contains the desirable effect that must be maximized or the undesirable effect to be minimized. Additional, applicable functional constraints, that do not contain the optimizing parameter, are the *subsidiary design equations*, SDE. The third group of equations are the regional constraint or the *limit design equations*, LDE.

The steps generally are as follows. The primary design equation is written in terms of the functional, material, and geometrical parameters, including the quantity to be optimized. The subsidiary equations are written next and introduced to the maximum extent possible into the primary design equation. This is accomplished by the algebraic elimination of common parameters. The combination is the *developed* or combined *primary design equation*, DPDE. The designer then considers the effect of each of the limit equations singly or in some combination upon the features to be optimized. Substituting the desired limit into the developed primary equation derives the *final primary design equation*, FPDE, which is then solved for the optimized quantity.

To determine the magnitudes of the design parameters eliminated from the primary equation, the optimized parameter is carried into the original subsidiary equations. These are solved for the remaining quantities, completing the design.

When a single primary equation does not contain all of the subsidiary and limit functions, the solution is not explicit and unique. At times, it might even be that not all subsidiary and limit relations can be satisfied with a single value of the significant design parameter; and the solution becomes more complex, requiring considerations of the interaction among the variables. Trial, iteration, judgment, and experience play an important part in the final solution.

For a complete presentation and study of the method, Reference [2] should be consulted. Where not all subsidiary and limit equations can be combined into the one primary design equation, we have an example of *redundant specifications*. Furthermore, where a single design cannot possibly satisfy every subsidiary and limit equation, we have *incompatible specifications*. Both of these are well illustrated in Johnson's book.

Example 12–4. A flat rectangular tray is to be mass produced. The container is to be of volume V, and of height h, and be made of sheets of thickness t. Determine the dimensions, and select the material and fabrication method for minimum cost.

Solution: The cost per tray can be expressed symbolically as

$$C = c_{\text{material}} + c_{\text{tooling}} + c_{\text{labor}} + c_{\text{overhead}} \qquad (PDE)$$

The volume $= V = bhl$ where b is width and l is length. The volume of material used per tray is $\qquad\qquad (SDE)$

$$V_m = blt + 2hlt + 2hbt \qquad (SDE)$$

The regional constraints are

$$b \le l \le 1.5b \qquad (LDE)$$
$$h \text{ as given} \qquad (LDE)$$

Materials and fabrication methods under consideration, and their density and unit cost, are indicated in the table. It can be safely assumed at this

| | | Cost | | Fabrication | |
Material	Density, lb/in.^{3}	\$/lb	\$/in.^{3}	Method	Cost
Aluminum	0.102	1.14	0.116	press-forming	high
Stainless steel	0.283	0.87	0.246	press-forming	high
Lucite	0.040	2.00	0.080	vacuum-forming	fair
Polystyrene	0.038	0.65	0.025	vacuum forming	fair
Vinylite	0.045	1.42	0.064	vacuum-forming	fair

point that tooling, labor, and overhead costs will vary negligibly, so long as the selection is made from the above table. Thus

$$C = c_m \rho V_m = \rho c_m (btl + 2htl + 2bht) \qquad (DPDE)$$

where C_m = cost of material per lb. Since $l = V/bh$

$$C = \rho t c_m (V/h + 2V/b + 2bh) \qquad (FPDE)$$

It is clear that ρc_m will determine the cost. Polystyrene and vacuum-forming are therefore the material and fabrication technique to be used.

To determine the optimum proportions,

$$\frac{\partial C}{\partial b} = \rho t c_m \left(\frac{-2V}{b^2} + 2h \right) = 0$$

Thus,

$$b_{\text{opt}} = \sqrt{\frac{V}{h}}$$

and

$$l_{\text{opt}} = \frac{V}{h} \left(\sqrt{\frac{V}{h}} \right) = \sqrt{\frac{V}{h}} < 1.5b$$

The square is the best rectangular shape.

The minimum material cost is

$$c_{\text{min}} = \rho t c_m \left(\frac{V}{h} + 4 \sqrt{Vh} \right)$$

It is quite possible that a particular maximum tray width may apply, because of the space the tray must fit in. For instance, b cannot exceed a certain value b_M which is less than b_{opt} just determined. The length would thus have to be

$$l = \frac{V}{hb_M}$$

and the cost could be computed, of course, by using the FPDE equation above and the width value b_M.

12–7. OPTIMUM DESIGN, REDUNDANT SPECIFICATIONS

The optimum design of mechanical elements often involves situations not as normal as that of the previous article. That is, the FPDE is not a combination of all significant subsidiary and limit relations. Optimization in such cases may best proceed [4] in general as follows.

The redundancy results in, say, two equations; one is the ideal PDE, which combines all but one SDE effect, which depends upon some of the same parameters. Inclusion of this particular SDE into the PDE would eliminate from both an independent parameter that affects the optimization. Thus, in a way, separate evaluations of the *ideal* and the *relating*, PDE and SDE, equations must be made and later superimposed.

Suppose that the formulation has reduced to the following.

$$Q = f(x, y, z)$$

is the ideal PDE upon which the optimum design is based, and

$$u = g(x, y)$$

is the relating equation. Parameter z is independent of x and y, which are related or interdependent parameters. The *eliminated* (from PDE) parameter u depends upon the same related x and y parameters. All parameters are subject to limit conditions as indicated.

$$x_m \leq x \leq x_M$$
$$y_m \leq y \leq y_M$$
$$z_m \leq z \leq z_M$$
$$0 \leq u \leq u_M$$

If the independent parameter z is taken at the optimum value z_o that maximizes Q (z_m or z_M, or possibly some intermediate value if circumstances demand), the ideal PDE defines a Q-surface in x and y. On the other hand, the relating equation defines a second u-surface in x and y. Taking u at its maximum value, u_M, reduces the surface to a plane. The u-plane intersects the Q-surface along curve mn sketched in the control diagram of Fig. 12–2. Points on the intersection, which is only sketched [5] to help visualize features of interest, can be determined by assuming x_n, finding y_n from $u_M = g(x, y)$; taking z_o, x_n, and y_n and calculating Q_n from $Q = f(x_n, y_n, z_o)$ and plotting the curves.

By inspection it can be established that Q increases in the direction shown by the arrow. It is similarly found that the Q-surface, say typically, toward the x and y coordinates contains possible solutions because $u \leq u_M$ in this area. The addition of x and y limits completes the sketch. It can now be concluded that points of possible optimum

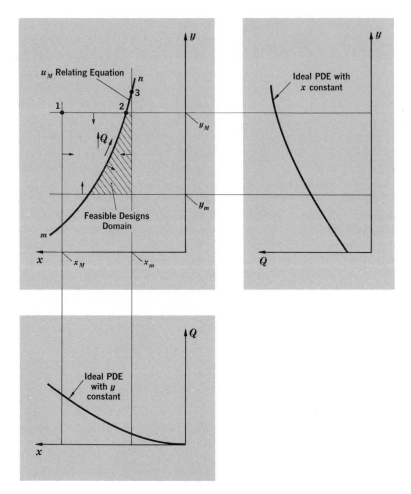

Fig. 12–2. **Control diagram for calculations of optimum parameters, schematic only.**

design are 1, 2, and 3. To determine which one is actually the optimum solution check as follows.

1. Calculate u_1 from $u = g(x_M, y_M)$. If $u_1 \leq u_M$, point 1 is optimum. If $u_1 > u_M$, proceed to—
2. Calculate x_2 from $u_M = g(x, y_M)$. If $x_2 \geq x_m$, point 2 is optimum. If $x_2 < x_m$, proceed to—
3. Calculate y_3 from $u_M = g(x_m, y)$. If $y_3 \geq y_m$, point 3 is optimum. If $y_3 < y_m$, an optimum solution does not exist within the established constraints. This means the specifications are

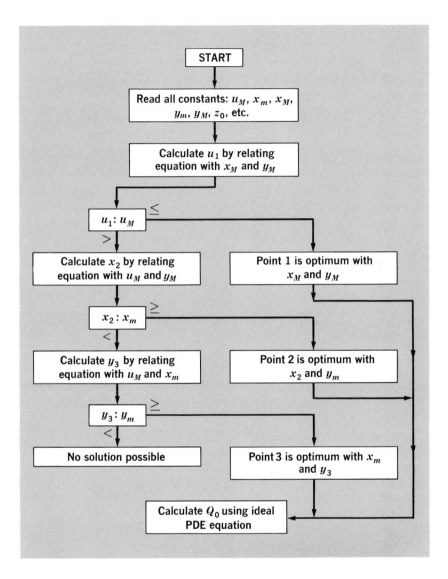

Fig. 12–3.   Block diagram for optimum design calculations.

incompatible and a compromise within the domain of feasible design is in order.

The optimum design steps are summarized in Fig. 12–3. The scheme can be used to program the optimization.

The process can be extended to more than one relating equation as well as more than three design parameters.

Example 12–5. A torsion shaft (Fig. 12–4) acting as an energy-absorbing spring is subjected to a sinusoidally pulsating $(O - T_M)$ torque T. The shaft absorbs 150 in.-lb of energy E each cycle. Space restrictions limit the length L to between 8 and 15 in. and the diameter d to a maximum of 2 in. The permissible maximum shaft twist θ_M is 25°. A factor of safety f_s of 1.5 is

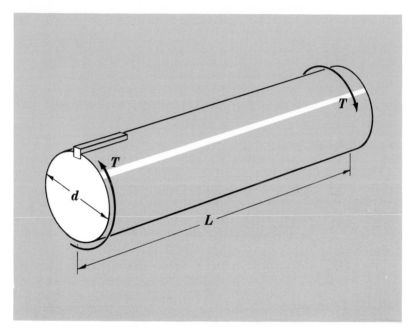

Fig. 12–4. Torsion shaft for Example 12–5.

decided proper, and the keyway stress concentration factor k is established at 1.8. The torque T_M, which transfers to the machine to which the shaft is attached, is an undesirable effect, and so must be minimized. Determine optimum shaft length and diameter dimensions.

Solution: Formulation using standard shaft stress theory is.

$$T_M = \frac{2E}{\theta} \qquad\qquad (PDE)$$

$$\tau_M = \frac{16kT_M}{\pi d^3} \qquad\qquad (SDE)$$

$$\theta_M = \frac{32T_M L}{\pi d^4 G} \qquad\qquad (SDE)$$

$$\tau_d \leq \frac{S_e}{f_s(1 + S_e/S_y)} \qquad\qquad (LDE)$$

$$d_M = 2 \text{ in.} \qquad (LDE)$$
$$8 \text{ in.} \leq L \leq 15 \text{ in.} \qquad (LDE)$$
$$\theta \leq 25° \qquad (LDE)$$

The design shearing stress τ_d is based on the maximum shear stress theory. The endurance strength S_e of the AISI-1020 shaft material is 30,000 psi, its yield strength S_y is 35,000 psi, and its shear modulus of elasticity G is 12,000,000 psi.

If the design shearing stress and the angle of twist are taken as the eliminated parameters, the final formulation becomes

$$T_M = \frac{2E}{\theta} = \frac{2EG\pi d^4}{32LT_M}$$

or

$$T_M{}^2 = \frac{\pi EGd^4}{16L} \qquad \text{(ideal } PDE\text{)}$$

$$\tau_M = \left(\frac{16k}{\pi d^3}\right)\left(\sqrt{\frac{\pi EGd^4}{16L}}\right)$$

or

$$\tau_M{}^2 = \frac{16k^2EG}{\pi Ld^2} \qquad \text{(relating equation)}$$

$$\theta = \left(\frac{32L}{\pi Gd^4}\right)\left(\sqrt{\frac{\pi EGd^4}{16L}}\right)$$

or

$$\theta^2 = \frac{64EL}{\pi Gd^4} \qquad \text{(relating equation)}$$

The control diagram (typical) is now sketched (Fig. 12–5) from an inspection of the above equations. If L is kept constant, $T_M{}^2$ will increase with d, somewhat as indicated on the side $T_M{}^2$ vs d view. If d is kept constant, $T_M{}^2$ will decrease with L, somewhat as depicted on the bottom $T_M{}^2$ vs L view. Analyzing the relating equations reveals their intersections with the T-surface are approximated by the curves shown on the top view.

$$\left[\frac{S_e}{F_g(1 + S_e/S_y)}\right]^2 = \frac{16k^2EG}{\pi}\frac{1}{Ld^2}$$

or

$$K_1 = \frac{K_2}{Ld^2}$$

and

$$L = \frac{K_2}{K_1d^2} = \frac{K_3}{d^2}$$

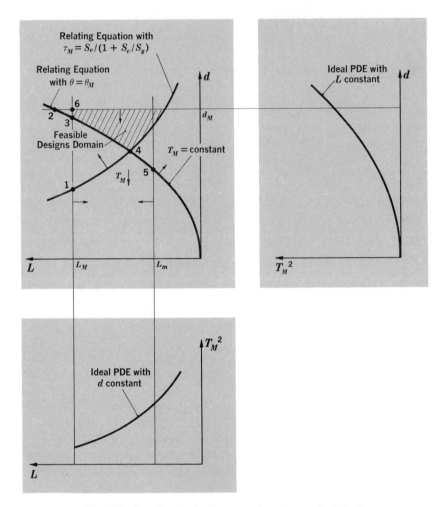

Fig. 12–5. Control diagram for Example 12–5.

Thus L decreases with d somewhat as sketched, and $T_M{}^2$ decreases in the direction shown by the arrow alongside the curve. Since τ_M could be less than the design value, K_1 can be smaller. K_3 would thus be larger and for the same length L the diameter d will have to increase in proportion. The feasible design domain is, therefore, above the T_M intersection as indicated by the small arrows. Also

$$\theta_M{}^2 = \frac{64E}{\pi G}\frac{L}{d^4}$$

or

$$K_4 = K_5 \left(\frac{L}{d^4} \right)$$

and

$$L = \frac{K_4 d^4}{K_5} = K_6 d^4$$

Thus L increases as d increases somewhat as sketched. If L is eliminated from the ideal PDE by substitution from the θ relating equation, the result is

$$T_M{}^2 = \left(\frac{\pi E G d^4}{16} \right) \left(\frac{64 E}{\pi G \theta_M{}^2 d^4} \right) = \frac{4E^2}{\theta_M{}^2}$$

T must therefore be constant at T_M along the θ_M intersection. Also since θ_M can be smaller than 25°, K_4 and in turn K_5 can be smaller. Thus for the same L, d would have to be larger. The feasible domain for the θ_M intersection is therefore above the curve as depicted by the small arrows. Points 1, 2, 3, 4 and 5 mark the possible optimum design parameters. A check will uncover which is optimum.

$$d_1 = \frac{4k}{\tau_d} \left(\sqrt{\frac{EG}{\pi L_M}} \right) = \left[\frac{4kf_s(1 + S_e/S_Y)}{S_e} \right] \left(\sqrt{\frac{EG}{\pi L_M}} \right)$$

$$= \frac{4 \times 1.8 \times 1.5(1 + 30/35)}{30,000} \sqrt{\frac{150 \times 12 \times 10^6}{3.14 \times 15}}$$

$$= 6.68 \times 10^{-4} \times 6.18 \times 10^3 = 4.41''$$

Since $d_1 > 2$ in., the τ_M relation is out of range:

$$d_5 = \sqrt[4]{\frac{64 E L_m}{\pi G \theta_M{}^2}} = \sqrt[4]{\frac{64 \times 150 \times 8}{3.14 \times 12 \times 10^6 (0.436)^2}}$$

$$= \sqrt[4]{107 \times 10^{-4}} = 0.321''$$

and

$$\tau_M = \frac{4k}{d} \sqrt{\frac{EG}{\pi L_m}}$$

$$= \frac{4 \times 1.8}{0.321} \sqrt{\frac{150 \times 12 \times 10^6}{3.14 \times 8}}$$

$$= 22.4 \times 84,600 = 1,895,000 \text{ psi}$$

$$d_3 = \sqrt[4]{\frac{64 E L_M}{\pi G \theta_M{}^2}} = \sqrt[4]{\frac{64 \times 150 \times 15}{3.14 \times 12 \times 10^6 (0.436)^2}}$$

$$= \sqrt[4]{201 \times 10^{-4}} = 0.377''$$

and

$$\tau_M = \frac{4k}{d} \sqrt{\frac{EG}{\pi L_M}} = \frac{4 \times 1.8}{0.377} \sqrt{\frac{150 \times 12 \times 10^6}{3.14 \times 15}}$$

$$= 19.1 \times 6,180 = 118,000 \text{ psi}$$

but

$$\tau_d = \frac{S_e}{f_s(1 + S_e/S_y)} = \frac{30,000}{1.5(1 + \frac{30}{35})}$$

$$= \frac{30,000}{1.5 \times 1.86} = 10,750 \text{ psi}$$

Therefore, since $\tau_M > \tau_d$ for θ_M relation, the specifications are incompatible and some compromise is necessary.

Suppose point 6 is tried:

$$\tau_M = \frac{4k}{d_M} \sqrt{\frac{EG}{\pi L_M}} = \frac{4 \times 1.8}{2} \sqrt{\frac{150 \times 12 \times 10^6}{3.14 \times 15}}$$

$$= 3.6 \times 6,180 = 22,250 \text{ psi}$$

and

$$\theta_M = \frac{8}{d_M{}^2} \sqrt{\frac{EL_M}{\pi G}} = \frac{8}{2^2} \sqrt{\frac{150 \times 15}{3.14 \times 12 \times 10^6}}$$

$$= 2 \times 0.00773 = 0.0155 \text{ radians}$$

Thus one might select a higher strength steel such that

$$\tau_d = \frac{S_e}{f_s(1 + S_e/S_y)} \geq 22,250 \text{ psi}$$

A smaller f_s may have to be satisfactory as well. And there are other possible compromises.

REFERENCES

1. R. Bellman, *Dynamic Programming*, Princeton Univ. Press, Princeton, N.J., 1957.

2. J. E. Mulligan, "Basic Optimization Techniques—A Brief Survey," *Journal of Industrial Engineering*, v. XVI, n.3 (May–June, 1965) pp. 192–197.

3. Westinghouse Electric Corp., "A Technique for Optimizing Engineering Designs," R&D Letter, April–May, 1964.

4. R. C. Johnson, *Optimum Design of Mechanical Members*, John Wiley & Sons, Inc., New York, 1961.

5. R. C., Johnson, *Three-Dimensional Variation Diagrams for Control of Calculations in Optimum Design*, ASME Paper No. 66–WA/MD–9, Nov. 27, 1966, 7 pp.

PROBLEMS

12–1. Identify several effects that may be undesirable in engineering design situations.

12–2. Identify several effects that may be desirable in engineering design situations.

12–3. Define and illustrate a criterion function and distinguish it from a functional constraint.

12–4. Compute the maximum power in watts that can be delivered to a load through a 25-ohm resistor at 220 volts.

12–5. The girth plus the length of a parcel-post package cannot exceed 84 in. according to postal regulations. Determine the dimensions of acceptable package having the greatest volume.

12–6. Show that an I-beam is an optimum section for a flexure member. Which effects are optimized in this consideration?

12–7. For another application the spring of Problem 12–D4 is to be designed for a maximum natural frequency. All values given still apply. Derive the PDE equation, and discuss its application.

12–8. Derive the expression

$$\tau_d = \frac{S_e}{f_s(1 + S_e/S_y)}$$

used as the design shearing stress in Example 12–5.

12–9. A triangular piece of sheet material has a base b units long and an altitude of h units. The owner wants to salvage the largest rectangular piece possible. What are the dimensions of the rectangle he can cut out of the triangle?

12–10. Discuss why even an optimum design may not be absolute.

12–11. Discuss the difficulties that may be encountered with material parameters.

DESIGN PROBLEMS

12–D1. A car manufacturer has estimated an annual demand for his car of 500,000. He also estimates the cost of storage awaiting sale of $3/car as well as a cost of $20,000 to stop and restart production. Since the demand is only an estimate, the continuous production of the 500,000 units presents too much of a risk. Thus he must determine the most economical lot size. Establish the lot size for him.

12–D2. The smaller an electrical conductor, the lower its cost; but the power loss grows greater with decreasing size. Using the dual-variables method, optimize generally the cross section so that it will continuously conduct direct current at minimum cost.

12–D3. Space limitations are such that a column member of a machine cannot be permitted to buckle, because of possible interference with other parts. The available space is defined by $h_M \times b_M$ with $h_M > b_M$ and the column is l units long. The column is pin-connected with the pins parallel to the b side. Determine the cross section size, and select the material (cast iron, Inconel, or SAE-4130), if cost and axial load transmission capability are to be optimized. The member can be assumed a long column.

12–D4. A helical compression spring is needed for an application in which the spring constant must be maximized. The spring unloaded is to be l units long. Its coil diameter cannot exceed D_M. The top load it must transmit is F_1. Design for optimum wire diameter and select the best material.

12–D5. Assume the torque T is applied statically instead of cyclically, all other data remaining as given in Example 12–5. Determine optimum shaft diameter and length, the torque still being the optimizing criterion.

12–D6. Find a steel that would satisfy the compromise suggested in Example 12–5.

12–D7. A part d inches in diameter and l inches long is to be finished by turning on a lathe. The production cost per piece is established at

$$c_p = \frac{\pi dl}{f}\left(\frac{1.5}{v} + 13 \times 10^{-17}v^5\right) + 68\cancel{c}$$

Production time per piece is, on the other hand,

$$t = \frac{\pi dl}{f}\left(\frac{0.083}{v} + 70 \times 10^{-17}v^5\right) + 4 \text{ min}$$

In the above equations, f is feed in in./rev, and v is surface speed in ft/min. All costs from overhead to tool life are included in the above relations, and so are all production times from machine down-time to cutting time. It is decided to optimize the operation by determining the best speed. Analyze the situation, determine the speed, and discuss your recommendation.

12–D8. Identify two other possible compromises in the incompatible specification case of Example 12–5. Carefully consider the product significance of the four compromise proposals (your two plus the two suggested in the test) and using your utmost engineering judgment select the optimum compromise. Justify your selection clearly.

12–D9. Eliminating the maximum shaft twist limit in Example 12–5, determine the optimum design.

13

Computers

The computer has fantastically increased man's capacity to perform intelligently. It has enabled him not only to solve problems at unimaginable speeds, but it also permits him to analyze engineering situations that are so complex and time-consuming that without a computer they would be left undone. Watt's steam engine extended man's muscle power, the computer is extending his brainpower.

It must be clearly noted, however, that the computer cannot think. It can only provide an output when supplied with an input, and that output can be only as correct as the input. The computer simply performs physical operations that have been described by mathematical relations and proper instructions.

An engineer who understands the structure and detail operation of the computer fully can probably use it more effectively. But, a lack of such knowledge does not preclude his using it with success. Cognizance of computer languages plus an appreciation of the functions and limitations of computers will save him much of the drudgery of complex calculation. He must be, as he always has been, fully capable of analyzing the problem and defining it in mathematical terms. He must still synthesize or create the alternate solutions.

13-1. COMPUTER FUNCTIONS

Computers perform several functions. They compute, simulate systems, control processes, and monitor operations. Business data can be processed, information stored and retrieved, and even languages translated. Future functions are unforeseeable. A thorough expounding of these matters is not necessary here, but a brief review of the major functions is appropriate. Many textbooks are available that treat the subject effectively.

The most common computer function is the solution of formal mathematical problems. It permits the engineer to quickly solve intricate problems, eliminating the drudgery of routine computations. Specifically, computers perform only the basic arithmetical operations of addition, subtraction, multiplication and division. But, these operations are performed with great rapidity. This of itself would be of little value were it not for the "memory" of the computer. The memory enables the computer to store great quantities of data and to produce the data for use as quickly as the rapid calculations require.

As an illustration, consider a simple case such as the size-index (of a four-bar linkage) equation:

$$UN = \frac{Q + R + S + T + (M + N)/2}{5}$$

If only one or two index numbers were needed, the parameters could be easily substituted, and the UN's determined. The computer would be of little value. If, however, hundreds of these values had to be determined, the computer might prove helpful. But, if each set of parameters had to be a separate input, little time would be saved; the process would be equivalent to that of using a desk calculator. On the other hand, if hundreds of sets of the parameters could be easily and quickly stored within the computer and then could be recalled quickly, one set at a time, the computer would be much more helpful. The computer can do even better, because you need only 'inform' it that parameter Q, for instance, is to range from 1 to 50 in increments of 0.1, and the computer can, of course, do this with extreme speed. It can also hold its output, compare it with information in its memory and in this way make decisions.

Numerical methods enable the computer to solve differential equations that may be so complex that analytic solutions are not available. Thus all engineering situations whether expressible in simple algebraic relations or cumbersome differential equations can be solved by a computer at astronomic speeds.

The second function of computers, of direct importance to designers, is simulation. The computer makes possible the thorough investigation of the mathematical model of a system. How variations in any or all the parameters affect the characteristics, functioning, and the output of the system can be readily examined. Even noise can be simulated and its effects upon the system studied.

The real importance lies in that it is even possible to test one or more components without a completed system. That is, the portion of the computer that simulates a given part can be appropriately replaced by the actual component. An important component frequently so tested is the human being. He is thus spared the possible hazard of being part of an untried system. It is often more economical as well, because field testing can be quite expensive. Many more parameters can, furthermore, be more completely investigated in computer simulation.

Computers are also being used to efficiently control many processes on-line. By interposing the computer between the measuring instruments and the controls, irregularities can be quickly corrected. The computer receives the instrument reading, compares it with the required, stored in its memory, and sends out signals changing the controls to keep the system running properly. Because this is accomplished rapidly, accurately, and automatically, very precise system outputs are assured.

A very popular application of the control function is the numerical control (NC) of machine tools [1]. Working drawings are converted into tape instructions, which in turn take the machine through its cycle of operations, fabricating the workpiece to very close tolerances. NC possesses great advantages over ordinary automatic machining. Unless a great many duplicates are to be made, tooling costs for automatic production become prohibitive. In NC, on the other hand, it is only necessary to convert the blueprint into tape instructions which then direct the machine to produce the part once or over and over again as needed.

Two basic types of NC systems exist: positioning and contouring. Positioning, illustrated schematically in Fig. 13–1, locates individual points in sequence with reference to previously established x–y coordi-

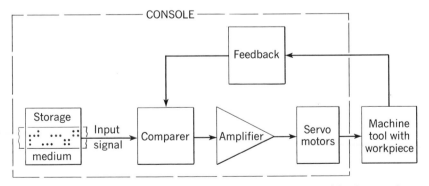

Fig. 13–1. Numerical control machining system, positioning cycle.
From J. P. Vidosic, *Metal Machining and Forming Technology.* Copyright © 1964, The Ronald Press Co., New York.

nates. Exact location of hole centers in drilling, boring, and reaming, for instance, is typical of numerical positioning. The same tape instructs the press to next drill to the required depth or perform whatever operations follow.

In contour systems, NC controls closely the two- or three-dimensional motion of the tool, making it cut the desired shape. Series of minute, overlapping straight lines or parabolas, none of which is longer than the tolerance, generate the continuous, mathematically defined path. Because of the thousands of points needed, a computer becomes

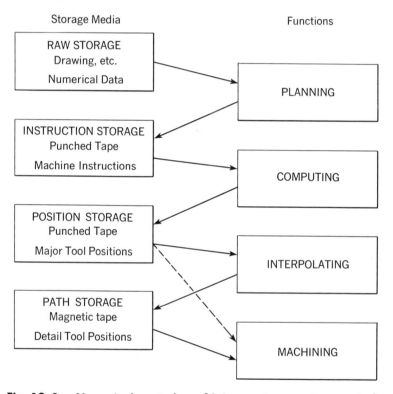

Fig. 13–2. Numerical control machining system, contour control.
From J. P. Vidosic, *Metal Machining and Forming Technology.* Copyright © 1964, The Ronald Press Co., New York.

essential. A contour-control NC system is depicted in Fig. 13–2. Milling machines are well suited for such NC machining.

It is probably obvious that the computer input of instrument readings is a monitoring operation. Thus the computer can be used to monitor events and decide when a function must be corrected, a process modified, or a system closed down. This is all performed automatically and possible failures due to unexpected conditions prevented.

The store of knowledge is growing at a terrific rate. Finding the information an engineer needs in a particular situation can be a burdensome and time-consuming task. Computers are, however, being put to good use in solving this problem too. Summaries of information are compiled, sorted, and stored in computer systems. When needed, the facts and figures can be quickly and automatically retrieved for instant use. Even vast dictionaries are stored in computers that can read and translate foreign languages. And, by the way, the computer can do this much faster than the best translator.

13–2. DIGITAL AND ANALOG COMPUTERS

The fundamental difference between digital and analog computers is that the former counts while the latter measures. The digital computer, operating discretely, takes number inputs and calculates single answers for each set of inputs. The analog computer, on the other hand, accepts varying inputs and provides continuous solutions.

The typical digital computer functions on the binary number system, base 2, instead of the customary decimal. The convenience of the binary system lies wholly within the computer, enabling it to work simply on the basis of the presence or absence of an easily observed quantity, such as of voltage. The electronic digital computer has a magnetic memory unit that can hold thousands of bits of information and instructions. These data travel when instructed in the form of electronic pulses from the memory to the arithmetic unit. The computations performed are then either sent back to storage for later use or sent out to the printer. Digital computers are classified as general-purpose, possessing great flexibility; or as special-purpose, designed to provide one particular function such as controlling the feed of a lathe.

An analog computer simulates mechanically, electromechanically, or electronically a physical event that is described mathematically. The analog operates continuously on an easily controlled and measured variable as electrical pressure or mechanical displacement. In mechanical analog computers mechanisms of many types perform the arithmetical operations producing linear or angular displacements as the result. In electronic analogs, continuous voltages simulate the quantities involved. The electromechanical combines the two.

There seem to be only minor differences in the speed of computers as well as in their accuracies and ranges. The greatest difference is to be found in the memory capacity, which is much larger in the digital computer. There are advantages in the type of input and output each uses. Since, in general, most events are continuous, analog computers may have an edge. The digital computer is, on the other hand, more flexible. Each, the analog and the digital, has no doubt its proper application.

Recent developments have resulted in so-called hybrid computers. These are combinations of analog and digital machines, the combinations capitalizing upon the advantages of each. Where problems are such that continuous as well as discrete characteristics are desirable, the hybrid can prove most useful.

Another development is the time-sharing plan. Computing facilities are rapidly becoming necessities. This is being met partly by small computers which can be made available more economically. Another solution to this demand is the centrally located, large installation, access to which is available on a time-sharing basis through remote terminal consoles. The inconveniences of data communication may prove deterrent to the widespread adoption of time-sharing. It is quite possible that with cost decreases in computer components the small computer might become the more popular. Eventually computers of many types will certainly be handling most of the repetitive mental and physical chores.

13-3. DIGITAL AND ANALOG TECHNIQUES

The major units of a digital computer already presented are depicted in Fig. 13-3. The arithmetic unit, appropriately so named, is where all the calculations are performed. Since it can perform these calculations with great speed and accuracy, the computer becomes most useful where the solution of ordinary equations is extra long, where the solution involves numerous repetitive calculations, or where the current impossibility of a closed-form solution dictates long iterative numerical methods.

A system of n independent equations in n unknowns has a unique solution which is arrived at analytically by simple algebraic steps. When say, more than three equations are involved, the task though simple, is practically cumbersome and time-consuming. As the number of equations and unknowns increases, solution without a computer becomes in a real sense impossible.

Transcendental equations of the algebraic, trigonometric, and exponential form constitute another group best solved on the computer. Such equations contain no explicit solution and must be solved by

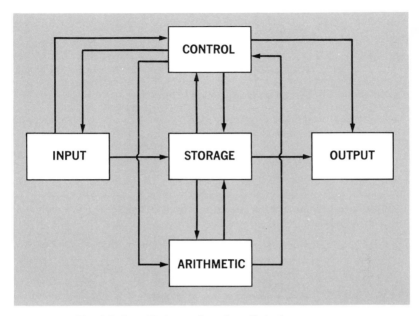

Fig. 13–3.   Major units of a digital computer.

trial-and-error or iterative methods.   For instance:

Example 13–1.   As a simple but illustrative problem, consider the solution of the equation

$$x^2 = \sin x$$

Solution: It can easily be found as a first step that, at $x = 1$,

$$x^2 - \sin x \approx 0.16$$

and at $x = 0.8$,

$$x^2 - \sin x \approx -0.20$$

Repeating at $x = 0.9$,

$$x^2 - \sin x \approx 0.027$$

and at $x = 0.85$,

$$x^2 - \sin x \approx -0.027$$

The answer is therefore somewhere between the last two x values.   To determine the x value more exactly could take much time, especially were the value needed to six or more significant figures.

Of course, $\sin x$ vs. x, and x^2 vs. x, can be plotted and the intersection value of x read.   But this cannot be accomplished readily to more than two or three figures.   The best procedure is to program the problem and have the computer do the iterating; it will take it only a very, very small fraction of the time.

Another most appropriate task for the digital computer is the evaluation of integrals not capable of exact analytical determination. For instance,

$$I = \int_m^n f(x)\,dx$$

can be solved by Simpson's rule, which reduces to

$$I = \frac{\Delta x}{3}\,(f_0 + 4f_1 + 2f_2 + 4f_3 + 2f_4 + \cdots + 4f_{n-1} + f_n)$$

Doing this manually, except for very few increments, is prohibitive. Furthermore, if large increments are taken to save time, the accuracy may likely prove too low.

Differential equations are another group of problems where the computer becomes most useful, especially when closed solutions are unavailable. For initial-value problems, Taylor series become valuable. That is, for $\dfrac{dy}{dx} = f(x, y)$, and $y = y_0$ at $x = x_0$, the numerical solution takes the form

$$y_{n+1} = y_n + \left(\frac{dy}{dx}\right)_n \frac{\Delta x}{1!} + \left(\frac{d^2y}{dx^2}\right)_n \frac{\Delta x^2}{2!} + \left(\frac{d^3y}{dx^3}\right)_n \frac{\Delta x^3}{3!} + \cdots$$
$$+ \left(\frac{d^ny}{dx^n}\right) \frac{\Delta x^n}{n!}$$

A computer can quickly calculate successive values of y.

Another powerful tool is finite-difference calculus. The original differential equation is rewritten in finite-difference form, and the recursion relation established. Starting at a point of known value, and assuming another (which should be checked whenever possible), the complete relationship is determined, point by point, by the recursion equation. For instance, note the following:

Example 13-2. The equation of motion of a vibrating mass m suspended from a spring of constant k and a viscous damper of coefficient c is

$$m\frac{d^2y}{dt^2} + c\frac{dy}{dt} + ky = 0$$

Determine the recursion equation that may be used to find successive values of the displacements.

Solution: The first derivative in finite-difference form is

$$\frac{dy}{dt} \approx \frac{\Delta y}{\Delta t} \approx \frac{y_{n+1} - y_n}{\Delta t}$$

and the second is

$$\frac{d^2y}{dt^2} \approx \frac{\Delta(dy/dt)}{\Delta t^2} \approx \frac{(\Delta y/\Delta t)_{n+1} - (\Delta y/\Delta t)_n}{\Delta t}$$

$$= \frac{y_{n+2} - 2y_{n+1} + y_n}{\Delta t^2}$$

Thus,

$$m\left(\frac{y_{n+2} - 2y_{n+1} + y_n}{\Delta t^2}\right) + c\left(\frac{y_{n+1} - y_n}{\Delta t}\right) + ky_n = 0$$

or

$$y_{n+2} = \left(\frac{2m - c\Delta t}{m}\right)y_{n+1} + \left(\frac{c\Delta t - k\Delta t^2 - m}{m}\right)y_n$$

If y_{n+1} and y_n are known or somehow established, the recursion can be continued for successive values of y_{n+2}.

Boundary-value problems involve a little more work. In the Taylor series approach, it becomes necessary to assume a solution in terms of unknown parameters, which are later found so the solution satisfies several points, including the boundaries. A similar situation arises with finite-difference techniques. To proceed with the recursion it becomes necessary to assume a value for some unknown. If the recursion does not take the solution to the second boundary, the assumption is modified and the process retraced. This is repeated until the boundary value is satisfied to the accuracy desired.

Techniques associated with the analog computer are most suitable for the solution of time-variable problems. Linear differential equations can be readily solved, and linear as well as non-linear systems simulated for analysis and study. Constants and other applicable parameters are easily set on the potentiometers of electronic or electromechanical computers; those of the bulkier mechanical type require that such constants be built in. The basic reason for the great usefulness lies in the fact that the physics of a problem in many different engineering situations is defined by the same differential equation that defines the corresponding electronic circuit. As a result, all such problems can be studied using the one analogous circuit. Though the computer was unknown as such, Kingsbury used an electrical analogy to determine the pressure distribution in the oil film around a journal bearing, back in 1931 [2]. The effect of changes in system parameters or input conditions is determined by simple manipulations of circuit components. Outputs are displayed on oscilloscopes, recorded on tape, read on meters, drawn on $X-Y$ plotters, or exhibited in some other suitable manner.

Besides the coefficient-setting potentiometers already mentioned, the analog computer consists of electronic (or mechanical) units capable of adding, multiplying, integrating (with respect to time), and generating functions. These are the negative-feedback operational amplifiers coupled to resistors and capacitors that form the circuit that determines the particular amplifier operation. Since all such elements can be interconnected as needed to simulate the particular relation being analyzed, and the parametric values readily changed, the response to manipulated variables are immediately observed. Interconversion between displacement and voltages is accomplished via servomechanisms in electromechanical computers.

Critical considerations in analog simulation are the scale factors. The magnitudes of the voltages, usually limited to ± 100 volts must be exactly related to the problem variables, which possess finite values of large range.

As an example, the equation of motion of the vibrating mass of Example 13–2 is considered.

Example 13–3. The differential equation of motion with a driving force input $F(t)$ added for a more complete illustration is

$$m\frac{d^2y}{dt^2} + c\frac{dy}{dt} + ky = F(t)$$

Develop and picture the analog computer circuit needed to study the motion.

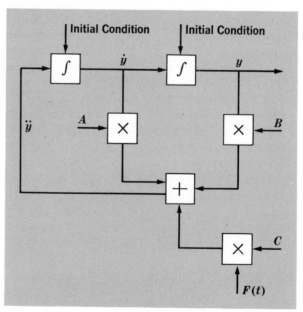

Fig. 13–4. Flow diagram for Example 13–3.

Solution: The first step is to solve for the highest derivative. Thus,

$$\frac{d^2y}{dt^2} = -\frac{c}{m}\frac{dy}{dt} - \frac{k}{m}y + \frac{F(t)}{m}$$

For simplicity the equation is rewritten in dot form, and the parameters restated in single-letter symbols.

$$\ddot{y} = -A\dot{y} - By + CF(t)$$

A flow diagram may be drawn to indicate the mathematical operations and the order in which these are performed (Fig. 13–4). The flow diagram is next transformed into the block diagram, in which standard graphic symbols are employed to represent each of the basic functions of the electronic circuit. Note that since the integrators and adders multiply by -1, sign inverters (operational amplifiers) are introduced at appropriate places. Note also that similar circuitry will be incorporated to handle $F(t)$, the circuitry depending upon the exact function. When the constants and initial conditions are assigned the circuit, and the scale factors correctly established, the computer will provide the mass displacement y. Other outputs could also be recorded, such as at y (Fig. 13–5).

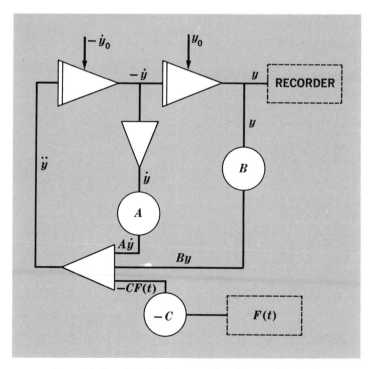

Fig. 13–5.　Block diagram for Example 13–3.

To summarize the programming of an analog computer, the following steps are enumeratured.

1. Write the equation that constitutes the mathematical model of the problem. This may be algebraic as well as differential.
2. Arrange the algebraic relations in some convenient form and solve the differential equation for the derivative of highest order.
3. Introduce appropriate scale factors in the equations of step 2.
4. Develop the electrical circuit that is analogous to the scaled mathematical model relations established in steps 2 and 3.
5. Write the equations in terms of the electric parameters for the circuit developed in step 4.
6. Determine the actual values of each scale factor, based upon the estimated maximum values for the physical quantities involved.
7. The required magnitudes of the electrical elements are now determined, and the circuit set up and readied for the investigation.

13–4. COMPUTER LANGUAGES

Originally, communication between man and computer had to be in the language of the binary system. Unfortunately, this machine language is complex and difficult to write. Special languages have been and are being developed to simplify programming. The computer still operates in the binary rather than the commonly known decimal system, but devices are available that translate the simpler-to-write decimal expressions into the machine binary language.

It may be asked why not redesign the computer. The binary code, though seemingly awkward, is simplicity itself to the computer. Basic electronic elements can only exist in one of two states: a switch is either open or closed, the current is either flowing or not, a card is either punched in a given position or not, a light is either turned on or off, and a material is magnetized in either one direction or the other.

The first step away from the binary language was to a symbolic assembly language, a more easily understandable mnemonic form. The calculations must still be outlined as before in a step by step fashion simplifying the programming only a little. Translating programs, called *assemblers*, developed by computer experts, change the symbolic language into the binary that the computer can accept as input.

The next step was to procedure-oriented languages such as FORTRAN (FORmula TRANslation). It permits the engineer to program the problem using statements that closely resemble the algebraic and logic expressions he is accustomed to. Again, of course, translation into the language of the computer must follow. The compiler accepts the engineer's procedure-oriented program (source) and produces the machine (object) language equivalent as in the case of assemblers.

There exist classes of problems within which there is much similarity. These are not exactly alike, but the treatment is sufficiently repetitive for each type. All gears, for instance, require the same design procedure, and so do heat exchangers, and building structures, and many other classes of product. For such situations, problem-oriented languages are developed. Since each applies to a particular type of problem, some synthesizing in terms of the terminology peculiar to the area is possible; this tends to further simplify the programming the engineer must do. Again though, it must be translated into the ever-required binary machine instructions, here by use of programs called *processors*. Some of the problem-oriented languages developed for various types of problems are PACER of Purdue University for mass and energy balances, STRESS of MIT for stress analysis, AGILE of the University of Michigan for subdivision layout, and DYANA of General Motors for dynamic system study.

Problem-oriented languages are actually not revolutionizing programming. Each must be designed for a particular purpose, and therefore little in the way of general quality is found in any single program. In general, nevertheless, four basic steps are normally involved in the preparation of a program:

1. Completely define the problem.
2. Prepare a flow chart of the logic the computer must follow.
3. Write the source program.
4. Debug the program; finding the more subtle errors sometime requires sample runs for comparison with manual calculations.

Frequently used operations, like computing hyperbolic functions or keeping track of the decimal point, can be stored as sub-routines in the computer's library for call by the main program whenever needed. Furthermore, packages of sub-routines for performing more complex operations, such as the solution of simultaneous linear equations or a Fourier analysis, are available for instant use as well. Each of these short cuts helps to ease the engineer's task of programming the problem.

As is well known, punched cards, magnetic tape, magnetic ink, and even optical scanners are used to transfer programs into the computer complex and activate it. At the other end, high-speed printers, electric typewriters, and cathode-ray screens record results or outputs.

A simple algebraic problem is presented, to only very briefly illustrate programming.

Example 13–4.   Program the following computation, which is the deflection relation for a short machine beam, in FORTRAN for x from 6 to 12:

$$7x^2 + 12x - y = 9$$

Program:

1. Solve the equation for the unknown y, and factor into simplest computer form (least number of multiplications).   Thus,

$$y = (7x + 12)x - 9$$

Select a suitable increment Δx, say 0.1, for the independent variable x.

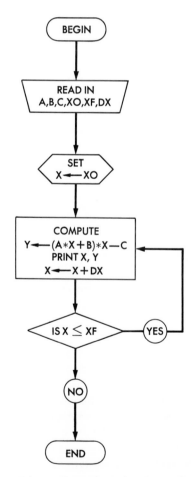

Fig. 13–6.   Flow chart for Example 13–4.

2. The flow chart, Fig. 13–6, is prepared to establish the logical flow of calculations.

3. The source program is written below:

```
COMMENT, 6 IS INITIAL VALUE OF X, 12 IS FINAL VALUE,
0.1 IS X INCREMENT DX.

READ 5, 7, 12, 9, 6, 12, 0.1, DX

      X ← 6

1     Y ← (7*X + 12)*X — 9

PRINT 10, X,Y

      X ← X + DX

IF (X. LE. 12) GO TO 1

STOP

5  FORMAT (6F10.1)

10  FORMAT (2F12.3)

END
```

4. The program is now ready for punch cards and the computer.

13–5. DESIGNING MECHANICAL COMPUTERS

The slide-rule and planimeter were early mechanical computers. Except for the electric motors that power them, most desk-top calculators are mechanical. Preference is found for mechanical computers in many industrial control operations as well, because of the inherent ruggedness, reliability, and simplicity of incorporation. Mechanical computing mechanisms are also important elements in electromechanical machines. Lack of great versatility, however, limits such mechanical devices to special-purpose applications.

Gears, racks, disks, cams, and linkages are the primary machine elements that form mechanical computers. Such units are necessarily bulkier than solid state devices; proper compromise between size and accuracy of performance must always be considered. The arithmetical operations of addition and subtraction are readily performed by gear differentials. Multiplication and division are performed by gear-lever-linkage devices. Ball-and-disk mechanisms provide excellent integrators, and the Scotch yoke is a sine–cosine generator. The cam-follower device can be designed to generate much more complex functions. Recent developments in linkage theory have made possible the synthesis of accurate function generators and precision-position coordinators.

The mechanisms used universally as addition or subtraction components are the differentials. Probably the most popular is the bevel (or spur) gear differential such as in Fig. 13–7. It can be shown that the

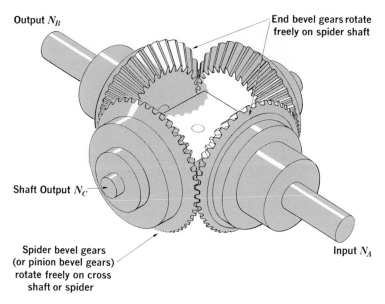

Output N_B

End bevel gears rotate
freely on spider shaft

Shaft Output N_C

Spider bevel gears
(or pinion bevel gears)
rotate freely on cross
shaft or spider

Input N_A

Fig. 13–7.   Bevel gear differential.

relation between the cross-shaft rotation N_c and the end gear revolutions N_A and N_B is

$$N_c = \frac{N_A \pm N_B}{2}$$

or

$$z = \frac{x \pm y}{2}$$

Of course either of the three legs could be the output. A link differential is shown in Fig. 13–8. The same general relation holds among the variables here as well. The exact configuration of such devices can take many appearances.

Multiplication components are much more complex, and reversals or division are limited. Most of these depend upon the relation between

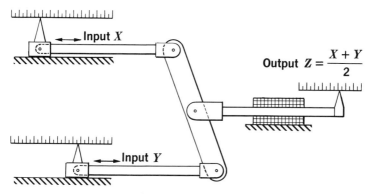

Fig. 13–8.   Link differential.

similar triangles found when links are applied inputs and are made to move according to the constraints of the mechanism.   That is, the relation takes the form $z/y = x/a$, or $z = xy/a$, where a is a constant, a fixed length on the mechanism.   For additional information see the article by Michalec [3].

Integrators are generally some adaptation of the ball-disk type shown schematically in Fig. 13–9.   Assuming full non-slipping contact between disk rotations and perfect slip in radial displacements,

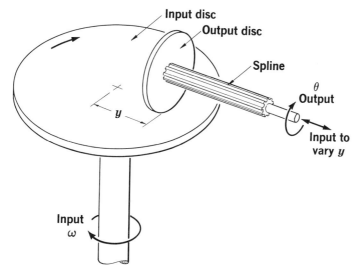

Fig. 13–9.   Ball-disk integrator.

the relation

$$ydω = rdθ$$

is realized.   Thus

$$θ = \frac{1}{r} \int yd\omega$$

The Scotch yoke has already been mentioned as a sine–cosine generator.   Another sine–cosine generator (approximate) is the eccentric-cam shown in Fig. 13–10.   Other trigonometric functions can be generated

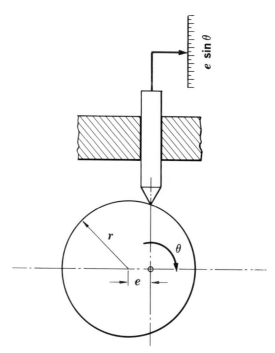

Fig. 13–10.   Sine-cosine generator (approximate).

by several types of mechanisms.   Cams are versatile function generators.   The cam surface can conceivably be shaped to provide any desired function $y = f(x)$.   Cylindrical cams having two degrees of freedom generate two-variable functions $z = f(x,y)$.   Reference [4] contains much valuable cam information.

Bar linkages are another kind of mechanism that are most versatile. These can be synthesized to generate many functions of varied type. Figure 13–11 is included as an example of the number of bar linkages

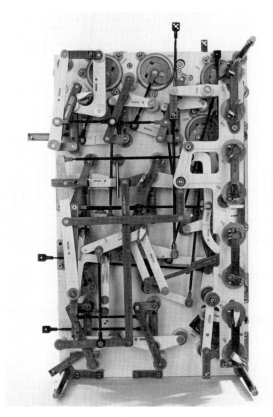

Fig. 13–11.   Typical linkage computer.

that may appear in a typical mechanical computer.   Much theory and many techniques are available for designing such mechanisms.

It must be realized that all mechanisms experience errors.   Backlash, manufacturing tolerances, and the imperfections of human design and fabrication are the unfortunate contributors.   The assumptions always required when mathematics is given physical realization contribute greatly too.   All errors must, therefore, be accurately analyzed and properly accounted and provided for.

The design of mechanical computers can best be reviewed by means of examples.   It is sufficient to develop the block diagram to illustrate what is involved.   It shows the computing components, units, or cells needed to perform the complete computation.   Each cell is a unit such as described in the preceding paragraphs.   The detail design of each unit is beyond the scope of this presentation.

Example 13–5. Construct the block diagram for a mechanical computer that will provide the deflection y across a beam subjected to the bending moment $M = Ax^2 - Bx + C$.

Solution: The elastic curve of the beam is defined by the differential equation

$$\frac{d^2y}{dx^2} EI = M = Ax^2 - Bx + C$$

or

$$y = \iint \frac{Ax^2 - Bx + C}{EI} \, dx^2$$

The cell system needed to perform the calculations required is as depicted in the block diagram below.   The capacity of the cells depends upon the limiting magnitudes of variables x and y (Fig. 13–12).

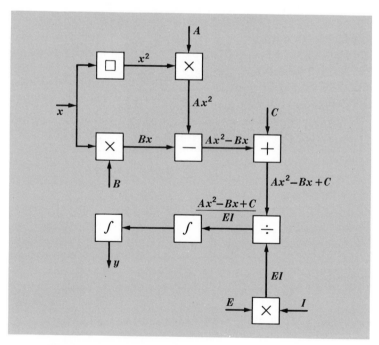

Fig. 13–12.   Block diagram for Example 13–5.

Example 13–6. A refining process requires that oil condensing under a pressure head h be removed from the condenser through an orifice. The area A of the orifice is to be varied, so that the flow Q will meet the varying demand of the succeeding process. Construct the block diagram of the mechanical analog computer that will control the flow.

Solution: If the discharge coefficient is C, the equation governing the flow is

$$Q = CA \sqrt{2gh}$$

The orifice is to be rectangular and include a slide valve changing the size of the orifice opening. Since C and g are constants, the equation obviously reduces to

$$Q = KA \sqrt{h}$$

or

$$A = \frac{Q}{K \sqrt{h}}$$

The cell system needed to govern the flow is as shown in Fig. 13–13. The

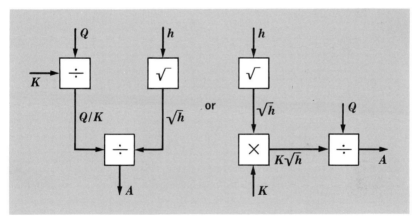

Fig. 13–13. Block diagram for Example 13–6.

system on the right is preferable because it includes one division cell only. Satisfactory division cells are more difficult to realize than multiplication cells.

13–6. LINKAGE COMPUTER ELEMENTS

The slider-crank and four-bar linkages are, as already indicated, very adaptive function generators. That is, one can design these to mechanize a function such as $y = f(x)$. One can also design them to generate particular coupler paths and to control displacement and motion.

Much attention has been given to such problems in recent years under the title of mechanism synthesis.

Linkage computers are complex combinations of the basic mechanisms (Fig. 13–11). The over-all design of mechanisms consists of three somewhat interrelated phases. The first phase is that of *type synthesis*, necessary in reaching a conclusion on the type or form of mechanism best suited to the particular need. Not only are link chains considered, but gears, cams, and other types of machine elements, also. The number of links required to mechanize the function, or provide the motion to convert the input (degrees of freedom) into the desired output, is the second or *number synthesis* phase. Finally the links must be so proportioned that the desired output will be closely approximated and the motion will be constrained to repeat itself identically, cycle after cycle. This, the most challenging part of the problem, is called *dimensional synthesis*.

Dimensional synthesis of linkage mechanisms is a complex matter, the presentation of which would require more pages than contained within the covers of this book. It will, therefore, not be attempted except in a very introductory way. It should first of all be recognized that dimensional synthesis normally provides only an approximate solution. Exact synthesis is limited, because few arbitrary functions can be so handled. The approximation is, on the other hand, not such as to nullify the very practical use of linkages for the purpose. Approximate synthesis can provide a most satisfactory and sometimes the only mechanization of almost any function within a limited range of the variables involved. For instance, the straight-line functions dealt with in the investigation of straight-line mechanisms [5] deviate from exactness only a fraction of one per cent.

Graphical as well as analytical methods are available to dimensionally synthesize linkages. Algebraic and complex-number approaches are generally more precise. Graphical procedures are, however, relatively faster, and often more understandable, because of the closer touch with physical reality. The analytics are generally based on displacement relations; that is, equations that relate the output to the input in terms of fixed parameters.

A displacement equation for a four-bar linkage can be obtained by considering a rectangular coordinate system as illustrated in Fig. 13–14. The coordinates of pairs A and B are

$$x_A = a \cos \theta \quad \text{and} \quad y_A = a \sin \theta$$
$$x_B = c \cos \beta - d \quad \text{and} \quad y_B = c \sin \beta$$

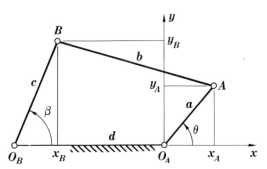

Fig. 13–14.   Geometry of four-bar linkage.

Since link AB (b) is rigid and fixed in length, the Pythagorean theorem yields

$$(a \cos \theta - c \cos \beta + d)^2 + (a \sin \theta - c \sin \beta)^2 = b^2$$

Trigonometric substitution and simplification further yields the following expression for the angle β:

$$\beta = 2 \arctan \frac{M \pm \sqrt{M^2 + N^2 - P^2}}{N + P}$$

where $M = \sin \theta$
$N = d/a + \cos \theta$
$P = d/c \, (\cos \theta) + (a^2 - b^2 + c^2 + d^2)/2ac$

An analysis of the β-relation easily reveals the complexity involved in simplifying the equation after the corresponding values for θ and β are established and substituted. To mechanize a function such as $y = \log x$, for instance, is indeed a long, slow process. It can, nevertheless, be solved when necessary, especially with the use of a computer.

If the displacement equation is written in terms of complex numbers, it becomes possible to consider not only link lengths and angles but velocities and accelerations as well. The mechanism links forming the four-bar chain close as shown in Fig. 13–15 to yield the vectorial equation

$$\overrightarrow{a} + \overrightarrow{b} + \overrightarrow{c} = \overrightarrow{d}$$

where the arrow over the scalar is used to denote a vector quantity.

Rewriting the equation, using exponentials, results in

$$ae^{i\theta_a} + be^{i\theta_b} + ce^{i\theta_c} = de^{i\theta_d} = d$$

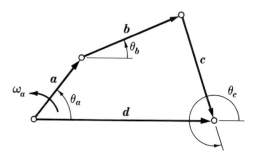

Fig. 13–15. Four-bar linkage as a vector chain.

The right-hand side of the equation reduces to d because angle $\theta_d = 0$. Differentiating twice, solving simultaneously, and collecting terms results in a system of equations that define the link lengths:

$$\overrightarrow{a} = \omega_b\omega_c(\omega_b - \omega_c) + i(\omega_b\alpha_c - \omega_c\alpha_b)$$

$$\overrightarrow{b} = \omega_a\omega_c(\omega_c - \omega_a) + i(\omega_c\alpha_a - \omega_a\alpha_c)$$

$$\overrightarrow{c} = \omega_a\omega_b(\omega_a - \omega_b) + i(\omega_a\alpha_b - \omega_b\alpha_a)$$

where the ω's are the instantaneous angular velocities and the α's the instantaneous angular accelerations of links with lengths a, b, and c.

Slider-crank mechanisms can be treated similarly; one need only note that the follower link becomes infinitely long.

Examples will illustrate two of the above approaches.

Example 13–7. Design a four-bar linkage that will transfer a link AB through the three positions A_1B_1, A_2B_2, and A_3B_3 (Fig. 13–16).

Solution: The intersection of the perpendicular bisector a_{12} and a_{23} of the distances A_1A_2 and A_2A_3 is the fixed center 0_A, and that of b_{12} and b_{23} is the fixed center 0_B. Therefore the four-bar linkage that will transfer link AB from position 1 to positions 2 and 3 cyclically is 0_AAB0_B.

Example 13-8. A four-bar linkage is to be designed to satisfy the following instantaneous velocity and acceleration requirements.

$$\omega_a = 10 \text{ rds} \quad \text{and} \quad \alpha_a = 0 \text{ rds}^2$$
$$\omega_b = 5 \text{ rds} \quad \text{and} \quad \alpha_b = 10 \text{ rds}^2$$
$$\omega_c = 2 \text{ rds} \quad \text{and} \quad \alpha_c = 20 \text{ rds}^2$$

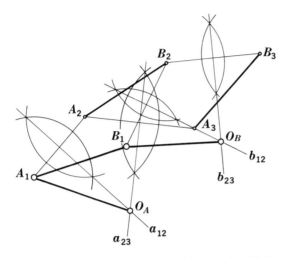

Fig. 13-16.　Linkage layout of Example 13-7.

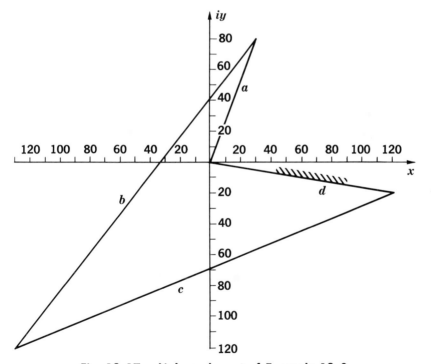

Fig. 13-17.　Linkage layout of Example 13-8.

Solution: Substituting in the link length equations and simplifying yields the following relations and values:

$$\overrightarrow{a} = 5 \times 2(5 - 2) + i(5 \times 20 - 2 \times 10) = 30 + i80$$

$$\overrightarrow{b} = 10 \times 2(2 - 10) + i(2 \times 0 - 10 \times 20) = -160 - i200$$

$$\overrightarrow{c} = 10 \times 5(10 - 5) + i(10 \times 10 - 5 \times 0) = 250 + i100$$

$$\overrightarrow{d} = (30 + i80) + (-160 - i200) + (250 + i100) = 120 - i20$$

If the above points are plotted as shown in Fig. 13–17, the four-bar linkage is physically described. The length of each link in units is computed from the real and imaginary components. Thus,

$$a = \sqrt{30^2 + 80^2} = 85.4 \text{ units}$$
$$b = \sqrt{(-160)^2 + (-200)^2} = 256.2 \text{ units}$$
$$c = \sqrt{250^2 + 100^2} = 269.6 \text{ units}$$
$$d = \sqrt{120^2 + (-20)^2} = 121.8 \text{ units}$$

The specific link lengths may be made any desired value by assigning a length to one link and apportioning the rest in accordance with above units. It must be recognized, however, that deviations between the design (precision) points may differ with the linkage size.

Suppose link a is assumed 1 in. long. Then
$$a = 1 \text{ in.}$$
$$b = \frac{256.2}{85.4} = 3 \text{ in.}$$
$$c = \frac{269.6}{85.4} = 3.15 \text{ in.}$$
$$d = \frac{121.8}{85.4} = 1.43 \text{ in.}$$

13–7. ERROR ANALYSIS

There are many reasons for man's inability to accomplish perfection, and even the mechanical computer is not error-free. The design of its components and assemblies, its fabrication, its intrinsic functional discrepancies, and even formulation of the problem to be solved using it, add to the error in the solution. Such error must be analyzed, minimized, and accounted for. Generally speaking, extreme accuracy must be practiced in the design, manufacture, and use of computer mechanisms if precision of results is to be of maximum dependability. At best, though, error analysis must be practiced since perfection is unattainable.

Errors of concern at this point are structural, and mechanical in origin. The structural error ϵ_s is the maximum deviation between the true function and the value given by the computer. That is,

$$\epsilon_s = F(x) - f(x; q_i)$$

where $F(x)$ is the desired or true function and $f(x; q_i)$ is the actual computer output necessarily influenced by all the design and operating parameters q_i.

Mechanical errors are the statistical deviations that occur because of deflection, play in joints, and manufacturing errors. These are inevitable; materials will yield under load, allowances are necessary if relative motion is to take place with appropriate ease, and tolerance must be permitted the fabricator because both he and the machines he uses are imperfect. The total mechanical error of a computing device is the sum of the individual error of each parameter involved. If the design and operating parameters are identified as q and the output variable is y, the significant expression is

$$f(q_1, q_2, \cdots q_n, y) = 0$$

If the parameters are each subject to the errors Δq_i, the mechanical output error ϵ_m is determined thus:

$$\frac{\partial f}{\partial q_1} \Delta q_1 + \frac{\partial f}{\partial q_2} \Delta q_2 + \cdots + \frac{\partial f}{\partial q_n} \Delta q_n + \frac{\partial f}{\partial y} \Delta y = 0$$

or

$$\epsilon_m = -\frac{(\partial f/\partial q_1)\Delta q_1 + (\partial f/\partial q_2)\Delta q_2 + \cdots + (\partial f/\partial q_n)\Delta q_n}{\partial f/\partial y}$$

$$= -\sum_{i=1}^{n} \frac{\partial f/\partial q_i}{\partial f/\partial y} \Delta q_i$$

REFERENCES

1. W. C. Leone, *Production Automation and Numerical Control*, The Ronald Press Co., New York, 1967.
2. A. Kingsbury, "Problems on the Theory of Fluid Film Lubrication with an Experimental Method of Solution," *Trans. ASME*, v. 53, n. 59 (1931).
3. G. W. Michalec, "Analog Computing Mechanisms," *Mach. Design*, Mar. 19, 1959, pp. 158–79.

4. H. A. Rothbart, *Cams—Designs, Dynamics, and Accuracy*, John Wiley & Sons, Inc., New York, 1956.

5. J. P. Vidosic, *Theoretical Analysis of Four-Bar Mechanisms*, Final Report, NSF Grant GP-2748, Ga. Inst. of Tech., Atlanta, Ga., 1966.

PROBLEMS

13–1. Identify and describe five primary functions that computers perform.

13–2. How does a computer differ from a desk calculator?

13–3. Explain the simulation function of the computer.

13–4. Describe numerical control of machine tools.

13–5. What is a hybrid computer?

13–6. By what means are voltages converted into displacements in electro-mechanical analog computers?

13–7. Distinguish between procedure-oriented and problem-oriented languages.

13–8. Solve the equation

$$y^2 = \tan y$$

to at least three significant figures.

13–9. Solve the equation

$$x \times \log_{10} x = 1.2$$

to at least two significant figures.

13–10. Determine the recursion equation that can be used to compute successive values of the variable in the differential equation

$$(D^2 + 3D + 5)x = 4t^2 \qquad (D = d/dt)$$

13–11. Establish the recursion equation for

$$(D^2 + 0.01gD + 2g)x = 0 \qquad (D = d/dt)$$

13–12. Construct flow and block diagrams for analog simulation of the situation described by the differential equation of Problem 13–10.

13–13. Construct flow and block diagrams for analog simulation of the differential equation of motion

$$\frac{d^2x}{dt^2} + 2a\frac{dx}{dt} + b^2x = 0$$

13–14. Derive the three complex-number link length equations.

13–15. Derive the displacement equation

$$ae^{i\theta_a} + be^{i\theta_b} + ce^{i\theta_c} = de^{i\theta_d} = d$$

13–16. Discuss the problem of computer storage and retrieval of knowledge.

13–17. Discuss the fundamental difference between the analog and digital computers.

13–18. Discuss the possible future popularity of small computers and the time-sharing plan of large computers.

13–19. Discuss the critical consideration in the circuitry of analog simulation.

13–20. Discuss the reasons for retaining the binary system as the machine language of the computer itself.

13–21. Discuss what may be found in a computer library.

DESIGN PROBLEMS

13–D1. Construct a flow chart for finding the roots of the equation

$$1 + 5x - \sec \sqrt{x} = 0.$$

13–D2. Construct the digital computer flow chart for computing the roots of the transcendental equation of Example 13–1.

13–D3. Construct the digital-computer chart for the solution of the deflection equation derived in Example 11–4. The beam is l units long.

13–D4. The pressure in a closed vessel increases with distance x from the axis of rotation as the vessel is rotated about its axis at an angular velocity ω according to the relation

$$p = \frac{\rho \omega^2 x^2}{2g}$$

where ρ is the specific weight, and g the gravitational acceleration. Prepare a flow chart of the logic the computer must follow to calculate the pressure increase for a cylindrical vessel 20 in. in diam for a range of speeds from 5 to 12 radians/sec.

13–D5. Prepare a flow chart of the logic the computer must follow in solving the equation

$$y = (x_i - x_0)x_i$$

where x_i varies between x_m and x_n.

13–D6. Construct the block diagram for a mechanical computer that will yield the rate of heat transfer q across a homogeneous tube of inside radius r_i and temperature T_i, and outside radius r_0 and temperature T_0. The equation is

$$q = \frac{2\pi L k (T_i - T_0)}{\ln (r_0/r_i)}$$

where L is the length of the tube, and k is the thermal conductivity.

13–D7. A centrifugal device is to provide a constant force of 1 lb. The force is to be developed by a mass of 0.05 slug revolving at the appropriate radius. The angular velocity of the motor powering the device may vary from 60 to 90 rpm. A computer is to automatically displace the mass radially to the correct radius. Design the computer showing on a block diagram all the cells required.

13–D8. An object moving in the x–y plane is to be kept located in terms of its x and y coordinates. The coordinate positions are to be indicated continuously on counters, the instantaneous direction on a 360° dial, and the instantaneous speed on another computer, to the nearest mile. The total distance traveled is also to be displayed on a counter. The input information is to be the instantaneous speed and its direction. The speed ranges from 0 to 100 mi/hr. Construct the block diagram, labeling clearly all components involved.

13–D9. Synthesize the four-bar linkage, satisfying the following instantaneous angular velocities and accelerations. Layout the mechanism.

$$\omega_a = 5 \text{ rds} \qquad \omega_b = 2 \text{ rds} \qquad \omega_c = 1 \text{ rds}$$
$$\alpha_a = 0 \qquad \alpha_b = 20 \text{ rds}^2 \qquad \alpha_c = 10 \text{ rds}^2$$

13–D10. Synthesize a four-bar linkage to satisfy the following instantaneous values. Layout the mechanism.

$$\omega_a = 6 \text{ rds} \qquad \omega_b = 4 \text{ rds} \qquad \omega_c = 2 \text{ rds}$$
$$\alpha_a = 0 \qquad \alpha_b = 7 \text{ rds}^2 \qquad \alpha_c = 5 \text{ rds}^2$$

13–D11. Design a four-bar mechanism satisfying the following instantaneous values. Lay the mechanism out.

$$\omega_a = -10 \text{ rds} \qquad \omega_b = 5 \text{ rds} \qquad \omega_c = -2 \text{ rds}$$
$$\alpha_a = 0 \qquad \alpha_b = 10 \text{ rds}^2 \qquad \alpha_c = 20 \text{ rds}^2$$

14

Intellectual Property Protection

Man must have had ideas since his very beginning. Ideas, the products of his brain, are what distinguish him materially from other animals. Ideas have made his struggle for survival easier, his search for food and shelter less urgent, his labor more productive, and his life generally more abundant.

Ideas must be revealed, if they are to be of much benefit. Yet ideas can be stolen when revealed. To prevent such loss, and yet induce the inventor to reveal his idea so it can benefit mankind, patent, trademark, and copyright protection has been made available. Like all man-written laws, the protection of these intellectual properties is not a direct and absolute matter. Nevertheless, every engineer whose research, development, and design may lead to invention should possess at least some knowledge of patent, trademark, and copyright procedures. The purpose of this chapter is to present a brief introduction to the subject.

14-1. BRIEF HISTORY

In ancient times there were only the conquerors and the conquered. The first group, consisting of the few, were the owners; the second, the slaves, had little if any rights. The question of "whose idea" was no problem. Later, a discovery or invention was simply kept secret, passed only from father to son. Such is still possible, but not profitable. It then became customary for governments to grant monopolies of manufacture or commerce—the making of soap, the sale of salt—to individuals.

Such monopolistic practice, greatly abused, forced the British Parliament to pass the Statute of Monopolies in 1623 which eliminated monopolistic grants. Privileges were now granted to only the "true and first inventor . . . of any manner of new manufacture." This marks the beginning of patent statutes, which were eventually extended to the entire western world.

The first patent issued on the American continent was granted in 1641 to a Samuel Winslow by colonial Massachusetts for a better way of producing salt. The Colonial patents and even some early state issues were granted by special acts of individual legislatures. Probably because some leaders of the Constitutional Convention like George Washington, Thomas Jefferson, and Benjamin Franklin were inventors, and possessed of strong conviction of the importance of encouraging creativeness in others for the welfare of the nation, a patent provision (Article I, Section 8) was included in the United States Constitution. It gave Congress the power "to promote the progress of science and useful arts, by securing for limited times for authors and inventors the exclusive right to their respective writings and discoveries."

The first United States patent was granted on July 31, 1790, to Samuel Hopkins for a new potash making process. This, however, was not Patent number 1, because the practice of serially numbering issued patents started on July 13, 1836. Hence Patent 1 was issued to a John Ruggles for his locomotive steam engine. Close to three million patents, granted since, have contributed to the advancement of technology and the welfare of mankind. Were it not for the patent law, many potential inventors would be unwilling to develop their inventions and so would abandon their ideas, while others would keep them secret as long as possible, stimulating no one to further improvement and invention.

14-2. INVENTIONS AND PATENTS

Invention is a difficult word to define from the patent viewpoint. The statutes proclaim a patent can be obtained for "a new and useful process, machine, manufacture, or composition of matter, or any new and useful improvement thereof." The statement is obviously broad and so freely interpretable. Not even the courts have defined what really constitutes an invention; actually it is determined subjectively in the last analysis in any particular case.

An invention is thus understood generally to be something that did not exist previously. It does not include the discovery of something, such as a law of nature, that has always existed even though unknown to man. An invention must be *new*, *useful*, *fully disclosed*, and must not have been *abandoned*.

Very often an invention is established by negative rules that attempt to state what does not constitute invention. For example, a combination of two or more known features into one structure in which the separate features do not cooperate to produce the desired result is merely an aggregation and so does not constitute invention. The Supreme Court, for instance, held that no invention was involved in the addition of an eraser to one end of a pencil because each component, the eraser and the pencil, continued to perform its job independently. The combination is merely a convenience. A potential patentee must always remember, however, that because of the subjectivity involved there may be exceptions to this and every other patent rule.

It should be realized that because there exists no exact definition of invention there can be no advance assurance a patent will be granted in any particular case. And it must also be realized that a patent does not guarantee the patentee a profit. It does not mean the Government of the United States will take steps to prevent others from using the patent. It simply gives the patentee the right to pursue the manufacture and sale of the invention for some number of years (Congress is considering changing the present grant period of seventeen years, as well as other patent legislation). The patentee can, however, file suit in a Federal Court against anyone using his invention unlawfully.

What gave our forefathers the foresight to provide intellectual property protection? For around 1,000 years prior to the formation of a patent system, no industrial improvement of any appreciable value occurred anywhere in the world. The American Indian had not even "invented" the wheel (used by the Sumerians in Mesopotamia ca. 3500 B.C. [1]). The answer is probably found in the word incentive. The patent law provides benefit generally by:

1. Inducing the inventor to make the invention,
2. Giving the public the opportunity to use the invention, and
3. Making the invention known to everyone, which in turn may lead someone else to further invention.

Thus, as indicated in the Constitution, the patent system promotes the progress of science and art and therefore of mankind; both the patentee and the public profit, and so progress is better sustained. It encourages the risk of capital investment in new products and processes. It stimulates competitors to invent improved techniques that assure them of better competitive positions in industry.

14–3. PATENT GRANTING

The Patent Office is organized to examine both patent and trademark applications, to maintain and develop public patent information sys-

The head **28** comprises a disc-like member having an upper frusto-conical fluid contact surface **29** facing the direction of fluid flow from the bore **14**. The head **28** is of minimum radius capable of providing sealing contact with the sharp circular seat **17**. The under or outer side of the head **28** is here shown as a flat circular surface **30** disposed in a plane normal to the axis of the head and joining the outer periphery of the surface **29** at an acute angle to provide a short, thin, sharp and acutely angled lip **31** of minimum overhang. As more clearly illustrated in FIG. 3, the sharp lip **31** when seated, will contact the sharp seat **17** to provide a thin circular line contact. While, as indicated with respect to angularity forming the seat **17**, the angle between the surfaces **29** and **30** may not be critical; it is, however, preferable that this angle be acute to provide a sharp edge for the lip to insure a quick and complete discharge of fluid, eliminating the danger of fluid drag or adherence and insuring rapid decrease of fluid pressure.

It will be noted that the substantially equal diameter of the head **28** with respect to the diameter of the seat **17** at the end of the fluid outlet passage **14** provides a minimum marginal lip **31** extending outwardly and downwardly from the seat **17**. The frusto-conical surface including the lip will insure a radial spread of fluid discharged and the desired degree of atomization and diffusion. It will further be noted that since the diffusion element is retained in position merely by the relatively light spring **24** which is fully flexible, both laterally as well as longitudinally, the element is free floating and may move rapidly and fully from its seat **17** to be unguided and floatingly suspended by the spring. It will also be noted that the conical configuration of the surface will insure proper seating of the element against the seat, such conical formation providing a guiding action for the seating of the element under spring tension when fluid pressure is terminated.

From the foregoing, it will be seen that the present nozzle structure may be characterized as including a discharge orifice bounded by a sharp smooth circular seat from which the fluid may be rapidly discharged with minimum drag friction and without the retention of moisture or liquid droplets. This sharp terminus, externally bounded by the reversely inclined walls **16**, gives a substantially instantaneous pressure drop insuring rapid diffusion. The conical diffusion head with its minimum overhang of peripheral edge, also formed at an acute angle, similarly precludes adhesion and insures rapid atomization. Such minimum overhang also diminishes the length of restrictive passage of fluid between head and seat, effectively maintaining friction at a minimum.

Fig. 14–1. Sample portion of a patent specification.

tems, and to provide the administrative services for conducting the patent granting operation.

To obtain a patent one must file a formal written application with the patent office. The application consists of four major parts: *formal papers, specification, claims,* and *drawing(s).*

The formal part is the petition for the patent, an oath stating the applicant is the actual inventor, the filing fee (at present this is $30 plus $1 for each claim over twenty), and the power of attorney, if someone is to represent the inventor.

The specification provides a description of the invention. It should be sufficiently full and clear to convey to a person skilled in the art how to make and use the invention. Part of the specification for a fuel injection nozzle (R. L. Allen, inventor; Georgia Tech Research Institute, assignor) is presented in Fig. 14-1. It may be noted that not only does the specification start with a general description, but it even refers to figures and part numbers identified on drawings. Observe the extensive, and carefully worded, detail.

The claims constitute a most important part of the application. They should cover the invention fully enough to give the patent the best possible chance for commercial success. The claims should be broad enough to establish sufficient boundary rights, yet not so inclusive as to be obviously excessive or encompass earlier inventions. Thus, briefly, a claim should be written for each feature that distinguishes the invention from related earlier ones plus any additional claims needed to provide sufficient and proper protection. The claim portion of Patent 3,105,640 (R. L. Allen, inventor; Georgia Tech Research Institute, assignor) is shown in Fig. 14-2. Although most patents contain many claims, three precisely worded claims were sufficient in this case.

If the invention can be described graphically, a representative drawing or two should also accompany the application. Sketches and views that best illustrate the novel features of the invention should be included in the drawing. Every essential element recited in the specification and claims should be illustrated and identified on the drawings. Drawings must be made in India ink on special paper of given size known as "Patent Office Bristol Board." Margins must be as specified, and only approved drafting symbols are acceptable. The Patent Office may even require a model of the invention for a better understanding of the claims, but it seldom exercises the requirement. Figure 14-3 is an illustration of a drawing as it appears in the patent certificate.

In the process of obtaining a patent it often becomes necessary to prove when the idea was first conceived. The date it was first described, a drawing made, possibly built and tested, these and other steps in the procedure may have to be proven. It is thus wise, very wise, to obtain and preserve unquestionable substantiation for each fact and date. This can be accomplished by having one or more persons witness the idea and progress of invention. An example of a record of a step in the development or progress of an article believed to be patentable is shown on Fig. 14–4. Witnesses must be sufficiently informed to generally know what the invention constitutes. They should sign and date drawings and other records of whatever steps are taken in working out the invention. Copies of all correspondence should be kept, any drawings and models made saved, and sale slips for purchase of material used retained.

Another critical function involved in the process of obtaining a patent is the search to avoid conflict with other patents. The validity of a patent must be assured by ascertaining that the idea was not anticipated by an earlier patent, or publication, or commercial use. Who should conduct the search? The Patent Office makes a preliminary search after the application is submitted. The inventor can make the search himself in the search rooms of the patent office, or he can hire a professional to conduct the search.

Every inventor can prepare, file, and prosecute his application for a patent. The legal matters involved are, however, often too complex for the lay person. It is, therefore, normally safer to obtain the services of an attorney. His legal knowledge and experience should result in a stronger patent. He should have been, however, qualified by the Patent Office and listed in their roster if he is to protect his client fully.

In considering the present invention, it will of course be understood that numerous changes, modifications and the full use of equivalents may be resorted to without departing from the spirit or scope of the invention as defined in the appended claims.

I claim:

1. A spray nozzle including a generally cylindrical body defining a threaded bore, a fluid cavity in axial alignment with said bore and an axial cylindrical outer bore communicating therewith and forming a discharge orifice, the outer wall of said body being tapered to said orifice at an acute angle to provide a sharply swept back circular seat at said discharge orifice, a diffusion head, resilient means suspending said head from within said

Fig. 14–2. Patent claims.

body for free universal movement with respect thereto, said diffusion head having a frusto-conical inner surface from the edge to adjacent the center, the diameter of said surface being slightly greater than the diameter of said orifice, the opposite outer surface of said element presenting a flat face having a radially outermost peripheral sharp edge portion lying in a flat plane normal to the axis of said inner surface, said suspending means providing yieldable contact of said inner surface with said seat, and being threadedly adjustable in the threads of said threaded bore.

2. A spray nozzle including a generally cylindrical body defining a threaded bore, a fluid cavity in axial alignment with said bore and an axial cylindrical outer bore communicating therewith, the outer wall of said body being tapered to said outer bore at an acute angle to provide a sharply swept back circular seat at the discharge orifice of said bore, a diffusion head, resilient means suspending said head from within said body for free universal movement with respect thereto, said diffusion head having a frusto-conical inner surface from the edge to adjacent the center, the diameter of said surface being slightly greater than the diameter of said orifice, said element having an outer surface with a radially outermost peripheral sharp edge portion joining the outer periphery of said inner surface and presenting a flat face lying in a flat plane normal to the axis of said inner surface, said suspending means providing yieldable contact of said inner surface with said seat, and being threadedly adjustable in the threads of said threaded bore, said suspending means including a wire annulus adjustably engageable in the threads of said threaded bore.

3. A fluid spray nozzle including a generally cylindrical body defining a through axial fluid passage, said passage including an upper threaded bore, a central cavity communicating with said bore and a lower cylindrical outlet bore communicating with said cavity and forming a fluid outlet orifice, fluid inlet means secured in said threaded bore, a wire annulus threadedly adjustable in said threaded bore, a spring suspended from said annulus, a diffusion element suspended from said spring, the lower outer wall of said body being tapered inwardly to said outlet bore at an acute angle to define a sharply swept back circular seat at said orifice, said diffusion element including a head having a conical inner surface of slightly greater diameter than the diameter of said orifice to rest upon said seat, said element also having a flat outer surface with a radially outermost peripheral sharp edge portion joining the outer periphery of said inner surface and lying in a flat plane substantially normal to the axis of said conical inner surface and forming at its junction with the edge of said inner surface a sharp peripheral edge on said diffusion element.

Fig. 14-2—Continued.

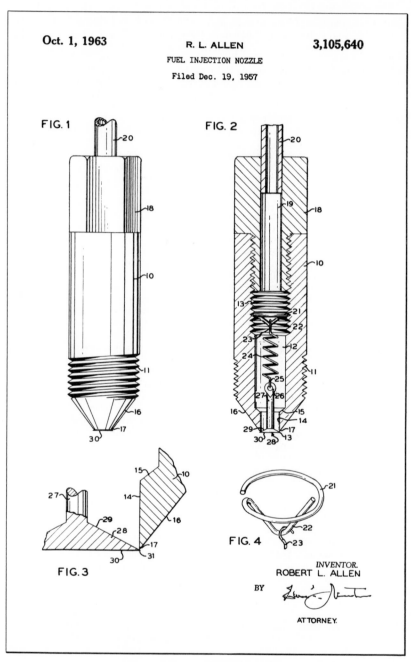

Fig. 14–3.　Patent drawing.

The work of patent examination is carried out by a corps of assistant examiners organized into groups as indicated in Fig. 14–5. Each group examines applications falling into a specific classification, such as petroleum chemistry, electronic devices, mechanisms and elements, or furniture and receptacles. Each set of groups is organized into an examining operation as depicted, headed by a director. Even though well organized, the Patent Office has a long backlog of pending applications.

13 July 1951 Record of Invention - Article of Invention:
It is claimed that I have this date had made a small disc of titanium which rotated at high speed and held in contact with a glass surface cuts the glass surface by a process of chemical decomposition. Hence I claim this titanium wheel to be used in the manner described as an article of invention with all rights for its manufacture and sale in accordance with the patent laws of the United States of America. 13 July 1951 Richard B. Belser
Witness: W.M. Spicer – 8/6/51
Witness: R J Raudebaugh 8-6-51

Fig. 14–4. Record of invention progress.
Copied with permission from a Projects Book of Mr. R. B. Belser, Research Engineer, Georgia Institute of Technology.

A potential patentee should also note the following facts. A patent cannot be obtained (currently) for something that has been on the market for more than one year or has appeared in public print over a year prior to application. Correspondence concerning a patent in the process of execution from the Patent Office must be answered within six months, otherwise the application becomes legally abandoned. When a patent is granted, a final fee similar to the initial one must be paid.

14–4. DESIGN PATENTS

In addition to the industrial patent just considered, the Patent Office issues design patents and plant patents. Plant patents are granted

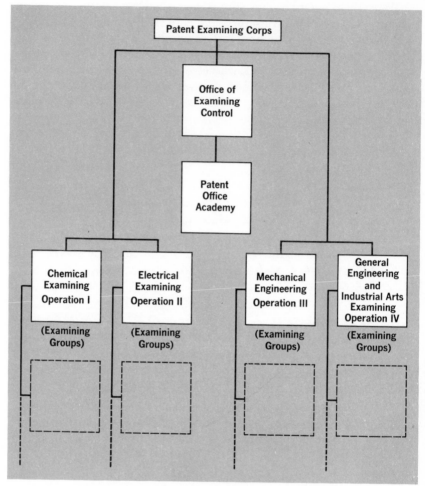

Fig. 14-5. The flow of patent examination.

for the asexual reproduction of a distinctly new variety of plant, such as a rose bush. Not many such patents are, as may be expected, granted.

The distinctiveness and aesthetic appeal of the appearance of one design over another often determines the preference of a customer. Therefore, although the utility of two products is very nearly alike, one manufacture will be selected over another. To protect such a configuration or ornamentation, design patents are granted under the statute reading: "Whoever invents any new, original and ornamental design for an article of manufacture may obtain a patent there-for . . . ."

The design must be new and novel and must have nothing to do with utility or functional qualities of the product to which it applies. It is applied for in a manner similar to that of the industrial patent. The application consists primarily of the drawing depicting the special configuration or ornamentation. Normally, only one claim is required, which simply states: "The ornamental design for a ＿＿＿＿＿＿＿＿ as shown." A design patent can be obtained for $3\frac{1}{2}$, 7, or 14 years, as desired by the applicant.

14–5. TRADEMARKS

The Patent Office also grants trademark rights. A trademark is a word, letter or symbol that identifies certain products or the origin of

---

United States Patent Office　　628,667
Registered June 12, 1956

PRINCIPAL REGISTER
Trademark

Ser. No. 697,633, filed Nov. 3, 1955

THERMOPOSITOR

Roy A. Martin, doing business as Roy A. Martin Company
809 Wellesley Drive, N. W.
Atlanta, Ga.

For: AEROSOL SAMPLERS, in CLASS 26.
First use on or about July, 1954; in commerce on or about July, 1954.

Fig. 14–6.　Sample trademark; in this case, a word.

the products. An example of one is Fig. 14–6. Four types of such marks are defined by statutes:

1. *Trademarks*, which identify goods of a particular manufacturer or merchant.

2. *Service Marks*, which identify and distinguish the services of one person from another. An advertising slogan, for instance, is such.

3. *Certification Marks*, which certify the origin or some other quality of a product or service. An example of such certification is the Underwriter Laboratories' approval mark found on many consumer products.

4. *Collective Marks*, which indicate a cooperative, association or other organization. The ASME clover leaf is an example.

A trademark must not be confused with a "trade name," which is not registrable. A trade name merely identifies commercially an item or individual or organization. "Skylark," for example, is the trade name of a particular model of Buick car, whereas Buick's trademark consists of three elongated shields inside a ring.

A trademark can be registered for a period of twenty years (and renewed as many times as desired) either in the Principal or Supplemental register by application to the Patent Office. The mark must have been used in interstate commerce prior to application; for Supplemental registration it must have been in use for a full year. Before granting the certificate of registration, the Patent Office tries to assure itself that the mark is distinctive enough not to cause confusion with others already in use. A mark can be used without registration, but its use can be better restricted if officially registered.

Trademarks are also granted by states for intrastate commerce. A trademark should be registered in all the states as well as the U. S. Patent Office to be fully protected. Like the patent right, a trademark right can be lost for mis-use or non-use for too long a period.

14–6. COPYRIGHTS

A copyright provides statutory protection for certain types of intellectual property. Among these are such properties as books, periodicals, maps, musical compositions, drawings, lectures, sermons, addresses, photographs, artistic jewelry, tapestries, and even motion pictures. Both published and unpublished works can be copyrighted. As is the case with patents, copyrighting does not provide the owner with any direct governmental protection. It simply gives the owner statutory basis for the prosecution of an infringer.

The Copyright Office is organized to provide copyright examination, cataloging, reference, and service. To obtain a certificate of copyright registration good for some number of years (the present 28 years

will likely be changed), the applicant must submit copies of the work
with the proprietor's claim to copyright noted thereon and the registration fee of four dollars.   Figure 14–7 is part of a copyright claim; it is

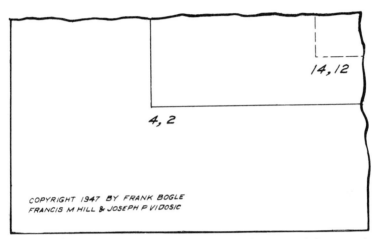

Fig. 14–7.   Portion of a copyrighted sheet showing claim notation.

the corner of a sheet of copyrighted material that contains the required
notation.   It must be realized that the copyright applies to the words,
form of expression or arrangement and not the idea or thought
expressed.   It must also be realized that everyone has an inherent com-
mon-law copyright to his private writings and drawings, but without
action to reserve it the right is lost as soon as the material is published.

14-7. INTERNATIONAL RIGHTS

An international patent is not available as such.   Therefore a patent
obtained in one country does not grant the patentee protection in any
other country.   Protection in another country can only be realized by
filing a separate application in that country.   And the applicant must,
of course, conform with all the particular requirements of each country
in which he wishes a patent.   This is in general quite expensive,
because of the cost of prosecuting an application and because some
countries also require the payment of taxes to maintain a patent when
granted.

Each country has its own granting procedure, and statutory criteria
of patentability vary from bare novelty to industrial utility.   In many

countries an opposition rather than an interference procedure is used to determine who shall be granted the patent. That is, an application is published so third parties can oppose the granting of patents for various reasons including prior coverage of the concepts. The life of a patent varies, as well, from 15 to 20 years, and in some countries an application is void if the invention has been used or publicly described prior to filing.

To simplify and possibly minimize the problems involved, foreign patent treaties have been signed by some countries. International patent relation groups have been formed for the purpose as well. Probably the major of these is the International Union for the Protection of Industrial Property established in 1883 by the Paris Convention. Over sixty countries have agreed to abide by its rules. It is much easier to file a patent in a member country once a patent is granted in the home country. Trademarks, trade names, and designs are also covered by this Convention. An international agreement concerning copyrights is also in existence. Copyright in member countries is established by marking the work with the owners name and the date "in such a manner and location as to give a reasonable notice of claim . . . ." Probably the most difficult problem involves the life of a copyright. In some cases copyright is granted for the life of the author plus some number of years, while others grant protection for some fixed number of years starting either from the date of registration or from the date of first publication.

14-8. RECOGNITION FOR INVENTION

The patent system was established to provide incentive for invention and to promote competition. Unfair competitive practice is, however, obviously to be discouraged and actually unlawful when intentional. Breach of confidential relations where one party gains while the other is defrauded, and the intentional misrepresentation to gain advantage are unlawful acts that impede beneficial competition. Such problems concern employees and employers as well. Well-known motivating devices are the suggestion award and the bonus system. Yet special awards for invention have found little acceptance.

Engineers are usually employed on the condition that they assign to their employer all right to any inventions made while in the company's employ. Engineers usually accept this as a matter of course but some do object, claiming vigorously that it is unfair and restrictive to full exercise of creativity. The claim is not resolved. Eugene Raudsepp reports [2] arguments that are made both for and against extra compensation.

Mr. Edward Hartshorne of Olin Mathieson said, for instance, "Patentable invention, made in the course of solving problems chosen because of their commercial interest to the company, is valuable property which should be protected by patent application. The prestige coming to the inventors by reason of these patents is all the extra incentive needed for best effectiveness."

Looking at the question from the combined effort of modern engineering teamwork, Mr. William R. Gentry, Electro Metallurgical Company wrote, "It is hard to determine who in a team is responsible for an invention or idea, and recognition or reward to the wrong man will lead to jealousy which results in poor teamwork."

On the other side of the argument, one industry manager said: "A well advertised bonus plan could be a powerful means of motivating research workers, while a liberal patent plan would certainly be no bar to inventive solutions of research and development problems. The company should patent all original ideas in which it is interested, grant immediate cash awards to the inventor, and develop a plan of subsequent royalties."

And Mr. Robert M. Page thinking of the individual's reputation among his colleagues has said: "If important new ideas are not publicly identified with their real originators, the real originators may become less productive, or leave the organization. People sometimes wonder why scientists are sensitive about the matter of credit for their achievements, but is it difficult to imagine how a normal father would feel if the paternity of his own children were a subject of public conjecture?"

And so arguments continue. Some companies have instituted awards of fifty and one hundred dollars per patent while a very few have increased the award per patent to a figure as high as one thousand dollars.

REFERENCES

1. A. F. Burstall, *A History of Mechanical Engineering*, M.I.T. Press, Cambridge, Mass., 1965, p. 42.
2. Eugene Raudsepp, "Special Pay for Patentable Inventions," *Machine Design*, v. 34, n. 27 (Nov. 22, 1962), pp. 126–28.

PROBLEMS

14–1. Why did several of the Constitutional Convention leaders insist on a patent provision in the Constitution?

14–2. Identify four features that make an invention valid.

14-3. Identify clearly the four major parts of a patent application.

14-4. Explain how priority may be established in a patent application litigation.

14-5. What is a design patent granted for?

14-6. Identify four types of marks for which rights are available from the Patent Office.

14-7. Distinguish between a trademark and a trade name.

14-8. Discuss the difficulty of defining distinctly what is invention.

14-9. Discuss the benefits of having a patent law.

14-10. The general rule that an inventor may claim his invention as broadly as permissible in view of prior art, provided the claim is not indefinite or functional, has its limitations in chemical or metallurgical cases. Why may this be so? Discuss.

14-11. Discuss the possibility of obtaining a patent for a new use of an old device.

14-12. Discuss the importance of a thorough and authoritive patent search.

14-13. Discuss the value of a copyright.

14-14. Discuss the value of the International Union for the Protection of Industrial Property.

14-15. It has been said that rewards or bonuses for invention interfere with teamwork and affect morale unfavorably. Discuss.

15

Engineering Ethics

President William Howard Taft proclaimed at a Georgia Tech dedication on May 11, 1911:

I consider the honest engineer the most valuable asset of the Government. These are the reasons: Dishonesty in any other branch of the service can be overcome in some way. In some way we can recover from it. In some way we can rally from it. But dishonesty on the part of the engineer is always so far reaching, in the loss of property, of money, of time, of human lives, that dishonesty on the part of the engineer is irreparable.

15–1. PROFESSIONAL INTEGRITY

A profession is a group of men or women trained by education and experience to perform certain needed functions better than their fellow beings. Members of the group possess knowledge of particular disciplines and the mental capacity to use this knowledge effectively. Such calling involves also the individual possession of unwavering principles, a high conception of personal honor, lofty ideals, logical thought, a deep sense of responsibility, moral courage, distinguished ability, and great energy.

Engineering is such a calling. The engineer is involved in the development, design, and fabrication of products that are generally used by many, most of whom lack any knowledge about the technology of the product. The public depends upon the profession to supply it with safe, dependable, and functional products and services. Society expects that the works of the professional engineer will evolve it favorably. Society depends upon and believes in the professional integrity of the engineer.

Professional integrity implies the intellectual conception of what is right and what is wrong. It recognizes what is good for its general rather than personal application. It understands and appreciates human values. The engineer of integrity is a man of principles, of uncompromising character, and of real honesty.

Laws are enacted to protect the individual and thereby society. Laws are enacted to afford the greatest possible degree of justice and equity under normal conditions of life and human relations. The beneficial effect of the written law is complimented by the obligations of the common, unwritten, law. A profession that would observe only specific legal rights would quickly lose its effectiveness and status, and would deteriorate into a group of practitioners whose work and conduct would have to be strictly regulated and controlled.

Moral and ethical principles began to develop, no doubt, long before the establishment of even the first written law. Such principles resulted in the common law. Moral and ethical standards established by custom, and public opinion, and common agreement recognize the imperfections of the written law and of language. The exact application of the law to specific situations often needs authoritative court interpretation. And legal action consumes both time and money which could well be unwarranted by the results attained. The exercise of well-founded ethical standards which conscience recognizes as morally just and equitable has been and still is the final answer to human relations, to social organization, and to professional practice.

15-2. MORAL VALUES

Values are attributes of things and the level of quality of the intangibles of human behavior. As has been indicated in earlier chapters the value of things, of commodities, depends upon the law of supply and demand. Intangibles, like health, happiness, love, friendship and security, on the other hand, do not depend upon supply and demand. These intangibles defy quantitative evaluation.

There exists another group of values that cannot be measured or calculated, referred to as moral values or virtues. These are qualities such as honesty, justice, goodness, kindness, truthfulness, universal love, loyalty, and altruism. Such values are inherent in human action or reaction to a greater or lesser extent. Like creativity they must be practiced to stay effective. Laws are written to govern and control the action of any single individual so the welfare of society is not endangered. The relations among men are, however, only poorly governed when men depend only upon laws. It is quite possible for a man to abide by all of the laws to which he is subject and yet be undesirable as a citizen. The man could be unfair, untruthful, and selfish without avoiding a single legal obligation.

Laws that define individual rights in many matters are not necessarily always fair and just. The conduct of the individual in matters not strictly governed by statute has much to do with character, and principles, and morals, and conscience. A professional man will not exercise legal rights that are not also morally sound as applied to his particular situation. "Over and above the requirements of the law are the obligations of the good neighbor, the helpful colleague, and the practicing professional" [1]. Honesty is always the best policy.

15-3. RESPONSIBILITY

Every man since the beginning of time has known the inner struggle between individualism and loyalty to the society of which he is a part. It is the battle between self-interest and social interest. Self-sacrifice for a worthy cause brings much satisfaction, whereas self-seeking is seldom without unpleasant consequences. Selfishness can be controlled only by a sense of responsibility. Without its possession by both man and society, the friendly interaction breaks down. Even though one lives in accord with his society, he need not and should not lose his individuality, his hopes and dreams for improvement of that society. This indeed is the real sign of the responsible citizen.

Responsibility then is what a man possesses when he discharges his obligations to himself and to society. To do this effectively is not an easy matter; it takes character, and courage, and adherence to principles and sound morals. It is assuming responsibility.

The greater the benefits a man receives from his society, the greater his obligations to society. The more educated man is capable of deeper understanding, of more effective reasoning, of less biased judgment, of more appropriate decision, and of more constructive action. Responsible living is the duty of the professional man. His effect upon human destiny and that of his profession must be exemplary, and progressive, and beneficial. The responsible professional cherishes, extends, preserves and passes on knowledge and experience. And he uses this knowledge and experience with full responsibility for the benefit and the betterment of mankind.

15-4. ETHICS FOR ENGINEERS

As already stated the engineer designs and builds machines, structures, and systems and provides services the safety and functional capacity of which the average user cannot evaluate. He must instead depend upon the integrity and responsibility of the engineer as he does upon his doctor to cure him, his attorney to protect him, and his spiritual advisor to guide him. This inability to pass on the validity, or even understand technical statements, scientific factors and engineering works, is growing as rapidly as the expansion of scientific knowledge.

A high standard of responsibility, an accurate use of awareness of social forces and their relationship to engineering, are essential. If the engineer is to work for his employer faithfully, serve the public well, and advance his profession, high ethics must guide his conduct and way of life. The major requisite for being ethical is probably a strong will to be ethical. Ethics involves happiness, the fulfillment of purpose, and the seeking of the optimum good. The engineer who knows and applies the engineering method to the solution of his professional problems should be capable of ethical decision. He can use the same engineering approach of define, search, evaluate and select to decide what he should do ethically to gain real satisfaction and inner happiness. To assist the individual engineer, a human being subject to temptation, codes of ethical practice have been evolved. These codes differ from law because compliance is voluntary and limited to members of the profession.

15–5. CANONS OF ENGINEERING ETHICS

Although both the American Society of Civil Engineers and the American Society of Mechanical Engineers adopted codes of ethics as early as 1914 and the American Institute of Electrical Engineers even before, in 1912, a concerted effort to unify and systematize did not come until later. The Engineers' Council for Professional Development, a select body of distinguished engineers, prepared the "Canons of Ethics for Engineers" in 1947 (Fig. 15–1). Some eighty professional, technical, and industrial organizations have adopted these Canons. A careful study is essential because honest success in engineering entails one's absolute duty to practice accordingly.

Besides the expression of the three fundamental principles, there exist three groups of proposed relations: relations with the public, with employers and clients, and with engineers. A brief discussion of each should strengthen their significance.

The section dealing with relations with the public cautions the engineer to act modestly, prudently, and with dignity. He will endeavor to keep the public truthfully informed of engineering and its achievements, without exaggeration and with honest conviction. Regard for the safety, health and welfare of the public shall be paramount in his professional work.

In relations with employers and clients the engineer is petitioned to be faithful, impartial, and just. He will not permit financial interest or friendship to bias his opinions and contributions. He will not disclose proprietary information without consent of the owner, accept compensation for the same service from more than one party without proper consent, nor engage in work for which not qualified. Where his judgment is over-ruled, he should carefully point out any adverse outcomes he honestly believes may result as a consequence.

Where relations with other engineers are involved, he will compete fairly, endeavor to provide opportunity for the development of subordinates, and cooperate with everyone in advancing the profession of engineering and interchanging knowledge. He will not slander the professional reputation of his colleagues and will see that credit is granted to those to whom it is due.

Thus the Canons constitute a guide for the members of the engineering profession as to what is expected of each and what one can expect from another. The Canons declare before all the world what the Profession holds high in the way of standards and what the public may expect in their dealings with members of the profession and in their use of the services and products of the profession's effort. The adhesion to such ethical ideals is mutually beneficial to both the giver and receiver; it builds respect for oneself as well as for a profession upon which mankind depends so greatly.

15–6. CASES OF ETHICAL REVIEW

Ethical questions do arise. It is hoped that these are infrequent and only of minor consequence. Serious infringements can quickly arouse public indignation and condemn the profession, and a strong indignation could force undesirable legislation that could prove quite burdensome to practitioners. Many of the professional societies appoint committees or boards whose duty it is to render judgments. Probably the major one of these Boards of Review is that of the National Society of Professional Engineers. Issues of its periodical, *Professional Engineer*, contain cases that have been reviewed. Several of these cases are extracted with NSPE permission to illustrate the application of the Canons of Ethics for Engineers.

Case 1   (July 1967, p. 53)

FACTS: A state association of municipal officials conducts an annual meeting at which papers and discussions are [presented] pertinent to engineering problems and developments. A number of consulting engineers in the state attend the meeting. The program for the meeting shows that there will be a reception

FUNDAMENTAL PRINCIPLES OF PROFESSIONAL ENGINEERING ETHICS

The Engineer, to uphold and advance the honor and dignity of the engineering profession and in keeping with high standards of ethical conduct:

   I. Will be honest and impartial, and will serve with devotion his employer, his clients, and the public;

   II. Will strive to increase the competence and prestige of the engineering profession;

   III. Will use his knowledge and skill for the advancement of human welfare.

RELATIONS WITH THE PUBLIC

1.1 The Engineer will have proper regard for the safety, health and welfare of the public in the performance of his professional duties.

1.2 He will endeavor to extend public knowledge and appreciation of engineering and its achievements, and will oppose any untrue, unsupported, or exaggerated statements regarding engineering.

1.3 He will be dignified and modest in explaining his work and merit, will ever uphold the honor and dignity of his profession, and will refrain from self-laudatory advertising.

1.4 He will express an opinion on an engineering subject only when it is founded on adequate knowledge and honest conviction.

2.6 He will not disclose information concerning the business affairs or technical processes of any present or former employer or client without his consent.

2.7 He will not accept compensation—financial or otherwise—from more than one party for the same service, or for other services pertaining to the same work, without the consent of all interested parties.

2.8 The employed engineer will engage in supplementary employment or consulting practice only with the consent of his employer.

RELATIONS WITH ENGINEERS

3.1 The Engineer will take care that credit for engineering work is given to those to whom credit is properly due.

1.5 He will preface any ex parte statements, criticisms, or arguments that he may issue by clearly indicating on whose behalf they are made.

RELATIONS WITH EMPLOYERS AND CLIENTS

2.1 The Engineer will act in professional matters as a faithful agent or trustee for each employer or client.

2.2 He will act fairly and justly toward vendors and contractors, and will not accept from vendors or contractors, any commissions or allowances, directly or indirectly.

2.3 He will inform his employer or client if he is financially interested in any vendor or contractor, or in any invention, machine, or apparatus, which is involved in a project or work of his employer or client. He will not allow such interest to affect his decisions regarding engineering services which he may be called upon to perform.

2.4 He will indicate to his employer or client the adverse consequences to be expected if his engineering judgment is over-ruled.

2.5 He will undertake only those engineering assignments for which he is qualified. He will engage or advise his employer or client to engage specialists and will cooperate with them whenever his employer's or client's interests are served best by such an arrangement.

3.2 He will provide a prospective engineering employee with complete information on working conditions and his proposed status of employment, and after employment will keep him informed of any changes in them.

3.3 He will uphold the principle of appropriate and adequate compensation for those engaged in engineering work, including those in subordinate capacities.

3.4 He will endeavor to provide opportunity for the professional development and advancement of engineers in his employ or under his supervision.

3.5 He will not injure maliciously the professional reputation, prospects, or practice of another engineer. However, if he has proof that another engineer has been unethical, illegal, or unfair in his practice, he should so advise the proper authority.

3.6 He will not compete unfairly with another engineer.

3.7 He will not invite or submit price proposals for professional services, which require creative intellectual effort, on a basis that constitutes competition on price alone. Due regard should be given to all professional aspects of the engagement.

3.8 He will cooperate in advancing the engineering profession by interchanging information and experience with other engineers and students, and by contributing to public communication media, to the efforts of engineering and scientific societies and schools.

Fig. 15-1. Canons of ethics for engineers.

and social hour during the meeting, "sponsored by the Blank Engineering Company," a well-known consulting firm in the state.

QUESTION: Is it ethical for an engineering firm to sponsor a social hour at the meeting and be so identified in the program? *Consider Canon 1.3.*

PORTIONS OF BOARD'S DISCUSSION: "Motivation for the sponsorship of the social hour by the engineering firm could be an expression of appreciation to the members of the association for past professional assignments, or it could be a means of advertising the firm and hoping that such a gesture of support might lead to future assignments. Or it might be both.

"In any event, we believe that the motivation is not the controlling element of the case. The fact is that the firm has put itself into the position of such questions being raised in the minds of those who attend the social hour or those who see the program. Promotion of engineering engagements should be handled on a personal basis rather than by a broad-scale offering to one and all.

"In addition, . . . we believe that the sponsorship of a social hour under these circumstances may unfavorably reflect upon the profession. . . ."

BOARD'S CONCLUSION: "It is unethical for an engineer to sponsor a social hour at a meeting of a state association of municipal officials if he is identified as the sponsor."

Case 2   (Aug. 1965, p. 41)
FACTS: A consulting engineer is contacted jointly by several manufacturers of competing products and requested to perform comparative evaluation of the products of these several manufacturers. It is understood that the manufacturers may, by mutual consent, disseminate the engineer's report to third persons.

QUESTION: May a consulting engineer ethically serve joint clients (manufacturers of competing products) and have his comparative evaluations of the products circulated to third persons with the mutual consent of the clients? *Consider Canon 2.7.*

PORTION OF BOARD'S DISCUSSION: "Applying these principles to the facts of the case, there obviously can be no objection to the engineer rendering the services requested by joint clients, even though it is indicated that the engineer's comparative evaluations of competitive products may be used to the detriment of one or more of the joint clients. For reasons best known to the joint clients, they regard such a service as being of value for their purposes.

"As to circulation of the comparative evaluation reports, the joint clients have the determining voice in deciding their interests in providing for this possible use of the reports. Full disclosure would be accomplished under the arrangement between the engineer and the joint clients.

BOARD'S CONCLUSION: A consulting engineer may ethically provide manufacturers of competing products with comparative evaluation reports and
permit their circulation to third persons if desired by all the joint clients.

Case 3   (April 1967, p. 47)

FACTS: An engineer has served as expert witness for which he was paid on a
per diem basis. He is asked to provide similar services for a plaintiff on
the basis of being paid a percentage of the amount recovered by the plaintiff.
If the judgment is in favor of the defendant he will not be paid for his services.
The attorney for the plaintiff is handling the case on a similar arrangement
for his fee.

QUESTION: Is it ethical for an engineer to provide technical advisory services
or serve as an expert witness in a lawsuit on a contingent fee basis? *Consider
Canon 3.3.*

PORTION OF BOARD'S DISCUSSION: ". . . The duty of the engineer as a
technical advisor is to provide his client with all of the pertinent technical
facts related to the case, favorable and unfavorable alike, and to perform one
or more duties. He may prepare a written technical report to his client; he
may sit with the client's attorney during the trial or other hearings to suggest
questions to witnesses involving technical points; and he may serve the attorney with regard to explanation of technical facts which are developed in
testimony. Whichever of these duties are performed, we think it reasonable
to assume that the engineer will offer certain conclusions of a technical nature.
On that basis he could not ethically serve on a contingent fee basis because
his conclusions might be influenced by the fact that he stood to gain financially
by having his conclusions coincide with his personal interest in his remuneration, which is dependent upon his client being successful in the litigation. . . .'"

BOARD'S CONCLUSION: "It is not ethical for an engineer to provide technical
advisory services or serve as an expert witness in a lawsuit on a contingent
fee basis."

Case 4   (Jan. 1967, p. 26)

FACTS: A local public body signed a contract with an engineering firm for
complete engineering services for a new airport, including the establishment
of fees for preliminary planning, general consulting services, preparation of
construction plans and specifications, field engineering during construction,
and other technical services, including coordination of a unique mechanical
passenger conveyor system with the basic design.

Certain public officials charged publicly that the fee structure was excessive
and the question was referred to a grand jury. The controversy received
considerable publicity in the local press and on radio and television stations.
During the period of public discussion of the fee structure, a group of local
consulting engineers, none of whom had had airport design experience issued

a report, concluding that the fee was substantially in excess of the fee schedule published by the state professional engineering society. The report of the local group was made public and received general press and radio and television coverage.

QUESTION: Is it ethical for a group of consulting engineers to issue a public report criticizing the fee arrangements contained in a contract with an engineering firm? *Consider Canons 1.4 and 3.5.*

PORTION OF BOARD'S DISCUSSION: ". . . It is evident in this case that the criticism of the fee for an airport design was not based on "adequate knowledge" in that the critics had never done airport work and hence could not be in a position to properly evaluate the fee structure for that type of work.

"It was likewise improper for the committee of engineers to publicly conclude that the fee was in excess of that established by the state professional engineering society. Such an interpretation of the society fee schedule should obviously be determined by an appropriate body of the society which is in a position to know the background, intent and application of various portions of the fee schedule. State society fee schedules are necessarily general in nature and are intended to be guides. They serve a valuable purpose in providing a basis for the negotiation of the fee between the engineer and the owner, but the fee must reflect the unusual or special requirements of the project.

BOARD'S CONCLUSION: "It is not ethical for a group of consulting engineers to issue a public report criticizing the fee arrangements contained in a contract with an engineering firm under the circumstances described.

Case 5   (Sept. 1965, p. 68)

FACTS: A government agency programs the construction of a bridge. It retains a consulting engineer to design the total structure. An engineer who is a sales representative of Firm A, which produces and sells prestressed concrete bridge members, contacts the consulting engineer and requests him to consider using Firm A's material. The engineer of Firm A indicates that his firm will provide the design of the superstructure incorporating its product at no charge to the consulting engineer, and that this design will be performed by licensed professional engineers.

QUESTIONS: 1. Is it ethical for the engineer employed by Firm A to make such an offer?

2. Is it ethical for the consulting engineer to accept such an offer? *Consider Canon 2.2 and 2.3.*

PORTION OF BOARD'S DISCUSSION: "Under the circumstances in the facts, the consulting engineer is in violation of (Canon 2.2) and would also appear to violate his responsibility to be honest and impartial.

"If, on the other hand, the consulting engineer believes the construction material (product) proposed by Firm A is best in the client's interest, and proposes to contract for an appropriate fee with Firm A for the necessary engineering design, he must under (Canon 2.3) disclose such activity to his client.

BOARD'S CONCLUSION: 1. "It is unethical for the engineer employed by Firm A to make such an offer which involves "free" engineering service.

2. "It is unethical for the consulting engineer to accept such an offer under the circumstances stated in the facts."

15–7. PROFESSIONAL ENGINEERING REGISTRATION

Over 200,000 registered professional engineers attest to the fact that registration is the law in everyone of the fifty states.   It began over half a centruy ago when Wyoming decided the need for the protection of the public in engineering services existed.   Public protection is the sole criterion under which registration can be enforced.   The consulting engineer, therefore, working either alone or in partnership, must register if he is to sell his services publicly.   And consulting engineers in industrial organizations consider the registration certificate an important legal measure of professional competence.   Furthermore, any engineer appearing as a witness in a court of law finds his testimony more acceptable if licensed.   Enforcement under state law is now generally accepted.   Pleading unconstitutionality is no longer a certain defense argument.   The Supreme Court of the State of Delaware declared, in upholding the registration law, that "It has been recognized since time immemorial that there are some professions and occupations which require special skill, learning, and experience with respect to which the public ordinarily does not have sufficient knowledge to determine the qualifications of the practitioner.   The layman should be able to request such services with some degree of assurance that those holding themselves out to perform them are qualified to do so. For the purpose of protecting the health, safety, and welfare of its citizens, it is within the police power of the State to establish reasonable standards to be complied with as a prerequisite for such pursuits." And the Court added: "Professional engineering is recognized as one such occupation."

The application of registration laws to engineers in the employ of corporations, and with regard to intercorporation business, is not too clear.   What about the engineering involved in the design and manufacture of products marketed in and out of the state of plant location? Who bears responsibility when one organization provides engineering services to another in its development of a public product?   Such questions are yet unresolved. It appears certain, however, that professional engineering practice will be governed more and more strictly. Registration requirements will include more and more professional engineering categories. Codes of ethics may even be incorporated to protect the public from misuse of registration.

It seems appropriate to encourage registration, particularly of the young engineer. It is probably true that standards of registration should be significantly upgraded. Nevertheless, registration should be considered a must and entered upon early. Time dulls the memory; basics, clear in the mind at the time of graduation, become obscure when not used regularly. The Engineers-In-Training examination, which must be passed to establish eligibility, does not take unretentiveness into account.

The feeling of representative corporations employing many professional engineers is well expressed in the following statements.

"The duPont Engineering Department has made it clear that it considers registration as a Professional Engineer to be a significant personal accomplishment which merits recognition as achievement of professional status. Registration, like all other aspects of professional development, is supported through education, encouragement, and persuasion. The Department believes that true professional development is necessarily a function of the individual, that management efforts to 'legislate' professional development would be self-defeating."

The General Electric Company has stated: "Engineers are informed that registration is one of the several important measures of their professional standing. Departments encourage engineers to display their registration certificates which are framed at Department expense."

The laws enacted by the States to govern the practice of professional engineering and the issuing of certificates customarily establish a Board of Registration whose duty it is to administer the Act. Provisions usually permit the Board to register anyone who is determined by the Board to possess the minimum requirements specified by the Act. In general, however, the process consists of three steps.

1. Qualifying as an Engineer-In-Training by graduation from an approved engineering curriculum and the successful passing of an examination covering the fundamentals of engineering.
2. Four or five years of successful practice and experience in engineering of a type satisfactory to the Board.
3. Passing of a final examination designed to establish the applicant's competence to practice professional engineering in his particular area.

In addition the applicant is expected to subscribe to the state's code of ethics, which generally reads about as the following, which is the code of the State of Georgia.

It shall be considered unprofessional and inconsistent with honorable and dignified bearing for any Professional Engineer:

1. To act for his client, or employer, in professional matters otherwise than as a faithful agent or trustee, or to accept any remuneration other than his stated recompense for services rendered.
2. To attempt to injure falsely or maliciously, directly or indirectly, the professional reputation, prospects, or business of any one.
3. To attempt to supplant another Engineer after definite steps have been taken toward his employment.
4. To compete with another Engineer for employment by the use of unethical practices.
5. To review the work of another Engineer for the same client, except with the knowledge of such Engineer, or unless the connection of such Engineer with the work has terminated.
6. To attempt to obtain technical services or assistance without fair and just compensation commensurate with the services rendered.
7. To advertise in self-laudatory language, or in any other manner derogatory to the dignity of the Profession.
8. To submit proposals for services where fees alone are used as the basis of employment.
9. To practice in a field of engineering in which the registrant is not proficient.

Registration in one State does not generally enable an engineer to practice under the law of another state. He must register in every state in which he wishes to practice engineering. Many states, however, have reciprocal arrangements that make it easier to obtain registration in a second state. The National Bureau of Engineering Registration maintained by the National Council of State Boards of Engineering Examiners can, for instance, issue Certificates of Qualification. These are then offered as evidence of qualification for registration with other member State Boards. Of course, a particular Board does not have to accept the certificate as complete evidence. It may require additional proof of competence, although in some states recognition of the Certificate of Qualification is mandatory. In any case, registration in a second State is likely to be simpler for one already registered in the first state.

ENGINEERS' CREED

As a Professional Engineer, I dedicate my professional knowledge and skill to the advancement and betterment of human welfare.

I pledge:

To give the utmost of performance;

To participate in none but honest enterprise;

To live and work according to the laws of man and the highest standards of professional conduct;

To place service before profit, the honor and standing of the profession before personal advantage, and the public welfare above all other considerations.

In humility and with need for Divine Guidance, I make this pledge.

(Adopted by The National Society of Professional Engineers, June 1954.)

REFERENCES

1. N. W. Daugherty, "Your Approach to Professionalism," Engineers Council for Professional Development, New York.

PROBLEMS

15–1. You are in the library looking for a book. In the next stack you observe a fellow student take a book from the shelf, place it under his coat and walk out. You have seen library books in his room before.

What action would you take?

15–2. The Goodbuild Construction Company, a nationally known concern, has obtained the primary contract for a large suspension bridge. General Contractors, a local engineering firm, has sub-contracted to build the underground foundations. A few days before the starting date, General Contractors learns a prominent financial manipulator with a questionable reputation has bought much Goodbuild stock very recently.

Should General take any action and, if so, what?

15–3. Van County has voted a bond issue to install a water system. The county engineer accepts a supplier's bid for the pipe. You, a professional engineer and a member of the county's Planning Commission, learn of this bid. Furthermore, you know the contract price for the pipe is much too high and the supplier's reputation somewhat questionable.

What action, if any, should you take, though it is really not your responsibility?

15-4. Mr. X, director of R & D of a large glass manufacturer, supervises the development of a new resin. The resin proves quite useful as a transparent plastic for curved aircraft enclosures (bubbles) and other such applications. Mr. X conducts additional investigations and convinces himself further improvements in the resin would make it suitable for plastic laminates for which there is a fair demand. He fails to convince management, however, to appropriate sufficient money to carry on the necessary development program. Instead, they decide to drop all experimentation and simply manufacture the resin for its present use.

Mr. X is displeased, resigns from the glass company and organizes a new firm and proceeds to develop the resin.

Is Mr. X justified in doing so or has he acted unethically?

15-5. You have been hired by the Vidosic Specialty Company at a good salary. You are working on the design of several devices intended for public use. After being with the company several months, you notice that your company's advertising tends to be misleading and that some design operations are carried on without full regard of customer welfare. A ski-lift was designed, and sold to a construction company for installation, which you are certain is not fully safe. As a matter of fact, several people are killed shortly after installation in an accident involving this equipment. Your company is unconcerned because the construction company is legally responsible.

As an ethical member of your profession what course of action might you take, if any. You have a large family to support and installment payments to meet.

15-6. You are one of four design engineers working for the Atnalta Machine Tool Company. One of the designers with whom you are rather unfriendly because of previous unpleasant incidents has conceived a new chipless cutting device. He obtains a quarter million dollars from management for its development along with a substantial raise. You have seen the basic description of the device and are honestly convinced it cannot work.

Considering your responsibility to your company as well as your associate, what action, if any, should you take? Which factors might influence your decision?

15-7. John, Joe, and Bill are engineers. John is out of work and in real need of a job. Joe is a good friend of John. Bill is chief engineer for the firm Tech, where an opening exists. John goes to see Bill who is impressed with John's personality. John gave Joe as a reference. Bill, therefore, writes to Joe, explaining the position he has in mind for John, and asks for his serious opinion. Joe who is in position to well understand the work Bill has for John, believes that John does not have the necessary experience and is poorly fitted for the work.

Should Joe advise Bill concerning John's lack of experience and inability? Or should he write the letter without endangering his long friendship with John and let Bill find out for himself?

15–8. The chief design engineer of company A calls the chief engineer of a larger company B to ask if he knows where he might be able to find a qualified engineer for a particular vacancy in his department.   The position pays $10,000 a year.   Chief engineer B knows only of a young man in his organization who is doing good work and would be well qualified for the job.   He is being paid $7,500 a year for his work at B.   Therefore B, not wanting to lose the young man, tells A he knows of no one out of work and, of course, tells the young man nothing about the opportunity.

Has B acted ethically, remembering that the young man is doing an excellent job on some work that may otherwise suffer?

15–9. A sales engineer finds a company shopping for a certain piece of equipment that would net him a nice, much-needed commission.   His company does not manufacture the exact machine needed; he knows the nearest thing he has will probably prove somewhat unsatisfactory.   There is no time available to redesign the equipment.   The sales engineer also knows that another manufacturer does make a machine that would do well in this case.

What should the sales engineer do, consider the client or his company first?

15–10. You are the purchasing agent for the concern Large.   You purchase annually a number of small trucks for your concern from the company Auto. This truck has proved very satisfactory.   Company Auto also manufactures a passenger car you are thinking of buying for yourself.   The same dealer handles both the truck and passenger car.   He offers you the car at a noticeably reduced price.

Should you buy the passenger car from this dealer?

APPENDIXES

Case Studies

The design process and its many ramifications are illustrated in the case studies that follow. A thoughtful study of each will reveal much of the methodology and theory that is covered in the chapters of this book; the review can be most beneficial. Cases are, however, presented only briefly to conserve space; in its entirety, each case would be a series of lengthy engineering reports. The reader should inject his own detail in accordance with the subject matter studied. Enough is presented to illustrate major steps involved, the reasoning applied, decisions made, creativity exercised, and alternate solutions considered. Not every case will necessarily illustrate each of the steps. Nevertheless, something important can be learned from each, especially if one reads into the case.

Case A-1. A Latent Need for Nuclear Crash Equipment

Nuclear-powered cargo airplanes are being considered for extra-long cross-country commercial runs. The Nuclear Power Authority has decided that the possibility of crashes and failure of other experimental as well as operational, peaceful nuclear equipment must be accepted and prepared for. The Authority, therefore, issues a call for proposals for some type of unmanned, crash equipment. The general specification the Authority furnishes reads as follows.

Desired a system of highly mobile, remotely-controlled vehicles, designed to operate in radiation environments. Vehicles must be capable of crossing any terrain, climb, and swim across streams. Each vehicle must be air-transportable and be capable of seeing ahead and around itself. There must be the capability of clearing land, fighting fires, collecting nuclear debris, lifting and carrying nuclear packages, and even freeing and cutting structures.

As the chief engineer of an engineering organization that does much development work for the Authority, you are given the specification and asked to organize and proceed with a tentative development of a system for the purpose.

It is decided to first conduct a feasibility study to consider whether and how the specification can be met. If the situation appears feasible, a preliminary design would be undertaken. Serious consideration would then be given on a top-level basis, including Authority personnel, as to whether to continue or drop the development.

FEASIBILITY STUDY.   The following items are analyzed and evaluated:

1. Number of vehicles necessary, and function of each.
2. Cross any terrain, climb, and swim.
3. Air-transportability—shape, size, weight, transport plane availability.
4. Power source—mechanical, electrical, nuclear, fuel, range.
5. Seeing—TV system, radar, lighting.
6. Functional equipment—clear land, fight fires; articulated claw arms, cutting tools, tool heads, lifting forks, carrying platforms; instrumentation.

PRELIMINARY DESIGNS.   Several vehicles are proposed, considered and contract designed.

All vehicles will be track type, equipped with TV cameras and penetrating lights, and will be diesel-powered, with auxiliary battery power for special manipulators where needed.

1. Vehicle *A* will be the lead vehicle, equipped with bulldozer blade and scoop bucket, a torch cutting arm, and fire fighting apparatus.
2. Vehicle *B* will provide utility support at the crash site, including fire fighting, handling of small debris components, and providing remote refueling capacity.
3. Vehicle *C* will provide extricating and lifting capability at the crash site. It will be equipped to carry debris to a burial area; possessing a turret-mounted, articulated boom.
4. A command vehicle *D* is also proposed.   This is a van-type, shielded vehicle that will house the remote-control operating personnel.   It will provide for operation of the other vehicles from a closer yet safe distance.
5. Sufficient detail and mock-up data are worked out in preliminary design to establish utility, maneuverability, effectiveness and approximate cost of the vehicle system.

Upon reconsideration and review of the proposed system by management and the Authority it is decided to proceed with detail design.

DETAIL DESIGN

1. Recognition—frame, engine, track, body, working equipment, instrumentation, for each vehicle.
2. Definition—capacity and strength design of components and assemblies.
3. Preparation—data and information covering materials, engines, fuels, controls, instrumentation, TV system, transport plane.
4. Conceptualization—extend and modify preliminary concepts.
5. Synthesis—computation of detail requirements in capacity, size, shape, equipment, dimensions of all components and assemblies.
6. Evaluation—Estimate of operational characteristics, weight, cost of each vehicle.

7. Optimization—maximize as many desirable effects, such as strength, maneuverability, range, speed and safety as possible; minimize as many undesirable effects, such as cost and operational difficulty, as possible.
8. Presentation—test and obtain operational information, explain special features, provide manufacturing drawings, specifications, etc.

Designs are now ready for final consideration. The Authority will call for bids and sign contracts; and one or two of each will be fabricated for testing, proving, further evaluation and necessary modification, and final production of the required number of each vehicle.

Case A–2. Specific Water Flow Requirement

Clear water is needed for a process at a specific flow rate. The supply coming into the plant can and does vary. A simple, economical method of maintaining the process supply, needing little attention, is desired (Fig. A2–1).

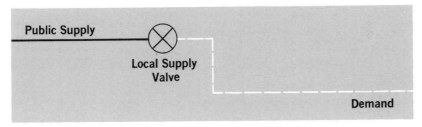

Fig. A2–1.   Supply–demand sketch.

MIND SYNTHESIS AND ANALYSIS

1. Flow responds to the supply head.
   So a constant head is needed.
2. How can a constant head be maintained?
3. Arrange control back at the water source.
   Can not, because it is a public water supply.
4. Arrange to control the local supply valve.
   Yes, but how?
5. Should it be controlled manually?
   No, labor is too expensive. Anyway, human response is insufficiently sensitive.
6. How about a storage tank with constant head interposed between demand and supply?
   Sounds feasible.
7. If used, must maintain constant head in tank automatically.
8. Use an overflow scheme?
   Too wasteful.

9. Well, recirculate overflowing water.
   Too troublesome, and need pump.

10. Use some simple device responsive to water-level changes in tank and automatically operating local supply valve.
    Sounds possible.

11. How about a float with its displacement somehow actuating the supply valve by means of a rack and gear?
    Yes, but the best valve available will probably need more turning energy than can be generated by a practical tank and float size; space is limited as well.

12. How about the float displacement sensitizing a motion pick-up?— transfer the signal to an amplifier and then to a servomotor, which can then open and close the valve as demanded by float; a dashpot could be used to stabilize disturbed float.
    Good, E. E. Joe will help us with the electric circuitry. The mechanical portion of the system will, however, be analyzed and designed (Fig. A2–2).

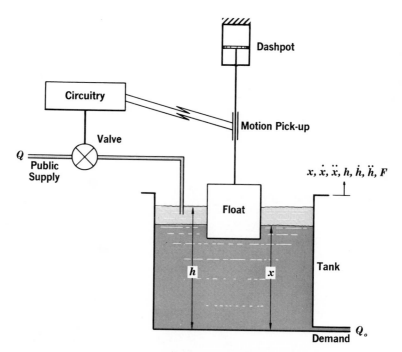

Fig. A2–2.   Paper synthesis and analysis of the system.

With laminar flow in the dashpot, the response is linear, or

$$F_d = -c\dot{x} \quad (\dot{x} \text{ down, } F_d \text{ up})$$

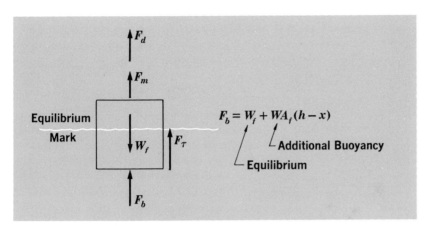

Fig. A2–3.   Free-body diagram of float.

The float free-body diagram is shown in Fig. A2–3.   The flow or skin friction is

$$F_\tau \approx f(\mu, \dot{x}, A_w)$$

and the pick-up resistance is

$$F_m \approx g(f_r, \dot{x}, A_m, p)$$

The equation of motion, based on Newton's laws is

$$\Sigma F = ma$$
$$W_f - F_d - F_b - F_\tau - F_m = ma$$
$$W_f + c\dot{x} - W_f - wA_f(h - x) - F_\tau - F_m = 1 - m_{f+p}\ddot{x} \tag{a}$$

If motion under operating conditions is likely to be turbulent, then Equation (a) would not apply, because both buoyancy and damping forces would be non-linear.   The differential equation would thus become very complex and only approximately solvable.   Cumbersome numerical methods may have to be used (with a computer this would not be bad).   Furthermore, flow friction and pick-up motion forces are difficult of exact mathematical definition.

In the usual engineering application and thus here, however, float response is slow and motion laminar.   And, viscous friction as well as pick-up motion forces are low enough, relative to the others, to be negligible for the current purpose.   Therefore,

$$-wA_f h + wA_f x + c\dot{x} + m_f\ddot{x} = 0$$

or

$$m_f\ddot{x} + c\dot{x} + wA_f x = wA_f h \tag{b}$$

The block and mathematical models are shown in Fig. A2–4 and A2–5.

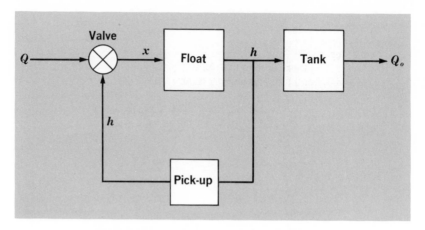

Fig. A2–4. Block diagram of system.

Under static conditions the inertia and damping forces are zero. Thus, $x = h$. This might also hold sufficiently for very slow float displacements.

A perfectly controlled system would have x equal to h at every instant, no matter how or why h varied. Since this ideal situation is not achievable, it is necessary to know the amount and kind of h deviation if the magnitude of control error is to be evaluated and the usefulness of the system established. Float and pick-up variables or parameters could be investigated and adjusted in order to optimize the control.

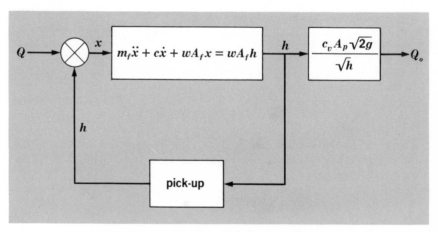

Fig. A2–5. Mathematical model of system.

1. Unit-step Input:
At $t < 0$, system is in equilibrium
At $t = 0$, head jumps suddenly to new value h.

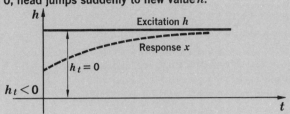

2. Unit-step velocity input:
At $t < 0$, system is in equilibrium
At $t = 0$, h suddenly starts increasing at $f(t) = h$.

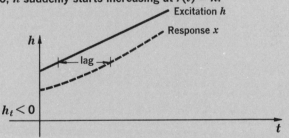

3. Harmonic or sinusoidal input:
Head h varies sinusoidally about equilibrium value.

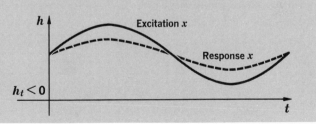

Fig. A2–6. Standard excitations.

The h variation is likely unsystematic and thus mathematically inexpressable. If this were the case, $h = f(t)$ could be substituted in Equation (b), the equation solved, and the error or difference between h and x determined. Since the h variation cannot be predicted, however, some approximation must be resorted to.

The best way would probably be to apply statistical methods to the random h variation, if the statistics were available for the actual system.

Another approach is to replace the random variation with a standard excitation. Although results will not be exact solutions of the actual situation, the response revealed will contain much indicative and useful information about the possibilities of this head-control system.

Operational methods are used in such solutions. Possible standard excitation functions are shown in Fig. A2–6.

DESIGN. If the above analysis reveals deviations of x from h that are qualitatively sufficient, the design of system proceeds.

System parameters m_f, A_f, and c can be chosen or computed to minimize $h-x$ deviation. Float, dashpot, and tank synthesized or selected (if commercially available) to provide size and strength capacity and satisfy above optimum parameters.

SYMBOLS USED

A_f float cross-section area
A_m rubbing area of motion pick-up
A_p cross-section area of tank outlet pipe
A_w wetted float surface
c damping coefficient
C_v velocity factor of tank outlet pipe
f_r coefficient of friction of pick-up material
F_b buoyancy force
F_d damper force
F_m resistance force of pick-up
F_r skin friction of float
h desired water level in tank
m_f float mass
m_p pick-up mass
p pressure against wetted pick-up surface
Q variable public supply flow
Q_o constant output flow or demand
t time
w water density
W_f weight of float
x instantaneous water level in tank
μ water viscosity

Case A-3. Deep Water Subsea Completion System*

The development of offshore oil and gas fields has largely been conducted from permanent pile-supported platforms using directional drilling techniques. But as the search for oil and gas reserves extends to deeper water, conventional offshore exploitation methods become less attractive, because of the high cost

* Abstracted with permission from the Humble Oil & Refining Company's paper: A. M. Rigg, T. W. Childers, and C. B. Corley, "A Subsea Completion System for Deep Water," *Journal of Petroleum Technology*, Sept. 1966, pp. 1049–55.

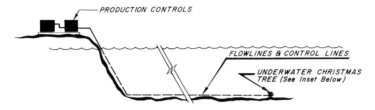

UNDERWATER CHRISTMAS TREE FEATURES.....

Installed And Retrieved By Complete Surface Operation (No Diver Assistance).

●

Flowlines Installed from The Surface After Tree is Connected On Ocean Floor.

●

Valves Operated From Remote Station Located On Land Or On A Production Platform.

●

Elimination Of External Control Line Connections Through Internal Porting Of Main Casting.

●

Contains Remotely Actuated Riser Connection So That The Well May Be Safely Re-entered From The Surface.

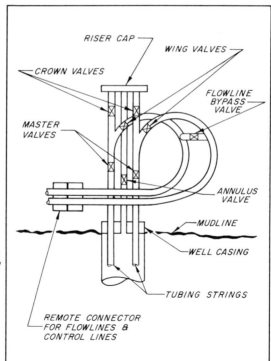

Fig. A3–1.   Deep water subsea completion system.

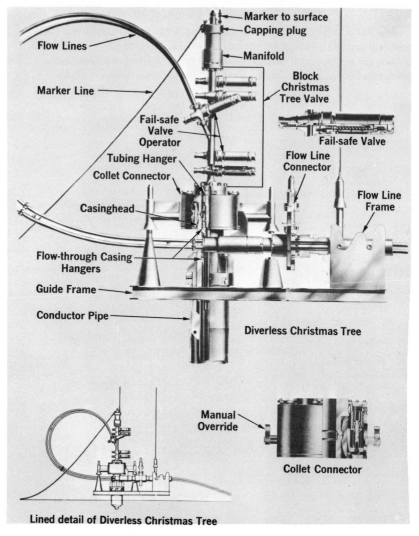

Fig. A3–2.   Christmas tree.

of fixed platforms.   The Humble Oil & Refining Company has therefore conducted extensive development and testing of subsea completion methods.   A brief record of the system thus developed and proven is presented below as an example of the solution of another engineering problem.

The first step in getting away from the fixed platform, brought about by high construction cost in water over 300 feet deep, was the use of floating vessels for exploratory drilling.   This involved the adaptation of conventional land equipment to floating vessels and the use of divers.   As the exploration proceeds to the edge of the continental shelf and beyond, the use of divers becomes inefficient, and attention turns to diverless equipment techniques needed to complete and operate a well drilled by the floating vessel.

It was decided that the completion and production maintenance of underwater wells in deep water require the development of

1. An underwater well-completion system,
2. An underwater Christmas tree system,
3. The tools and techniques needed for well-servicing and simple workover operations from remote locations.

After a well is drilled, a wellhead and production equipment must be installed and operated.

The Christmas tree contains all valves necessary for the proper operation and servicing of the well, as shown in Fig. A3–1.   An important feature is the remote flowline connector, which enables independent installation or removal of either the underwater Christmas tree or the flowlines.   Seals in the flowline connector can be installed or replaced without disturbing the tree or the flowlines.   Furthermore the tree can be completely operated, serviced, maintained, and controlled from the remote station connected to it by the flowlines.   All of this, including the remote station facility and the special tools such as the pump-down storm choke, landing nipples, operating tools, and paraffin-removal tools, had to be developed and designed.   Besides the basic equipment, the techniques for such satellite underwater well production had to be completely devised and proven.   The tree with all connections made, sitting atop the well, is shown in Fig. A3–2.   The initial operation of a subsea well so constructed proved the method and equipment fully satisfactory.   Humble Oil is therefore proceeding with such completion systems.   An important problem in the search for and production of a much needed fossil fuel has been satisfactorily solved.

Case A–4. System for Using Continuous Steel Tubing in Oil Well Operations*

During the productive life of oil or gas wells, workovers are required to maintain economic production and even to prevent complete stoppage.   Sand that accumulates in production tubing must be washed out; paraffin deposits on the tubing must be cleared; leaks must be repaired; tools sent into the well have to be retrieved; injection of heavy fluids into the tubing is often required for well safety control; and the well bore must be cemented when production is abandoned.

All such operations require a flow conduit to the producing zone with a return flow path so that fluids or material can be placed into the well, injected into the formation and washed or circulated out of the well as desired.   In the past, this was done by removing production tubing and replacing it with work

* Abstracted with permission from the Humble Oil & Refining Company's paper: J. L. Rike, "A Small Coiled-Tubing Workover Rig," American Petroleum Institute preprint, March 1967, 27 pp.

tubing, using rigs similar to those that originally drilled the well. The first step away from this expensive process was the development of wireline tools and concentric pipe strings that can be run through the production tubing. The 1-in. or $1\frac{1}{4}$-in. concentric pipe used is made of 30-ft lengths that must be screwed together one joint at a time at the well; the pipe is heavy and costly, the process is time-consuming, and the well must be controlled with a fluid

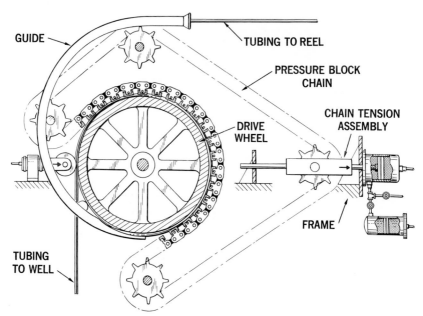

Fig. A4–1. Coiling and feeding mechanism.

heavy enough to contain the subsurface pressure. Again, Humble decided such operation was both too expensive and too cumbersome.

Continuous flexible pipe that could be fed into the well under nominal well pressure to provide the circulating path would be a great improvement. But how do you feed in and out mile lengths of pipe, and what kind of pipe?

Problems, difficult problems, were sensed immediately. The flexible conductor would collapse because of the pressure differential between the inside and outside of the tubing. The tubing would buckle whenever it would have to be pushed into place against wall friction and other possible drag. Continuous strings, however, appeared to promise advantages associated with speed, economy of personnel, improved safety, versatility, and reduction in potential well damage.

A feasibility study was thus undertaken to investigate the possibility of using thin-walled continuous-weld steel pipe that will withstand the pressure

differentials and can be coiled and uncoiled.   New equipment was needed to
straighten the pipe as it is uncoiled and run into the well and then re-bent into
a practical-size coil when removed from the well.   To accomplish this the
yield point must be reached at least twice each trip, a fatigue situation that
poses a severe life question.

Various thin-walled steel pipes were investigated and fatigue properties
determined.   Numbers of ingenious systems for straightening the pipe were
tried.   A key to such devices is in the tube running and pulling apparatus.

Fig. A4–2.   Pressure blocks on endless chain.

A $\frac{3}{4}$-in.-OD pipe, with a 0.049-in. wall of low-carbon steel having a yield
strength of 50,000 psi, was found suitable.   It could be coiled on a 3-ft-diam
mandrel 86 times before failure.   The pipe can be bought at a reasonable cost
of 15¢/ft.   It parts at a 6,500-lb tensile load, the weight of 16,200 ft of the
pipe at 0.4 lb/ft.   It collapses under a radial pressure of 7,000 psi.

A number of possible systems of coiling and feeding the pipe with a minimum
operating crew were tried.   The key element was the mechanism for running
and pulling the tubing.   The final device is shown in Fig. A4–1.   The tubing
comes out of the well, making a complete loop around the driving wheel before
going back to the storage reel.   The main wheel is grooved to fit one-half of
the pipe string.   The pulling force is provided by a friction grip on the pipe
obtained with a series of 3-in.-long pressure blocks mounted on an endless
chain, as shown in Fig. A4–2.   The pipe is gripped firmly between the pressure block and grooved wheel around approximately three-quarters of the
wheel circumference.

The pipe is straightened out before it enters the well, by two grooved sheaves
placed on opposite sides of the pipe.   One of the sheaves is mounted higher

than the other and its lateral position is controlled by an air piston that adjusts the straightening force to the character of the pipe, the weight of suspended pipe, and the work-hardening accumulating with time.   An odometer, connected by a speedometer cable to an idler sprocket, records the length of tubing in the well.   A load cell measures the pull exerted on the pipe.   The tubing is wound and unwound from a reel, Fig. A4–3.   All operations are placed under the immediate control of an operator at a console panel, Fig. A4–4.

Fig. A4–3.   Storage reel unit.

The system is shown in Fig. A4–5 feeding the pipe into a well.   The power unit has twin diesel engines driving twin hydraulic pumps.   Hydraulic motors in turn power the primary components for maximum flexibility and control.

Experience demonstrates that a novel workable solution to this problem of workover and servicing operations has been arrived at.   Several areas of refinement, however, are still being pursued.

This evolution of the coiled-tubing unit from a concept to an economic-feasibility study, to a mechanical-feasibility study, to a prototype model, to initial testing and revision, and finally to actual field testing and then further refinement, presents an interesting picture of how engineers explore and solve difficult problems of industry.

Fig. A4–4.   Operating console.

Fig. A4–5.   Coiled tubing system.

Case A–5. System for Heating Peaches*

The formation of dark spots in peach processing is a most undesirable tendency.   Such spots are due to spores that are exterminated at a temperature of 130° F, according to Agriculture Experiment Station investigations.   Immersion in water for 3 min is found more effective than dry heat.

* Courtesy Professor W. A. Hinton, Georgia Institute of Tehcnology.

Thus a machine to mechanically immerse the peaches in 130° water for 3 min is decided upon.

A capacity of 500 bushels/hr appears appropriate, since other phases of the processing plant are of this size.

Batch-processing is ruled out in favor of continuous, because a conveyor system could well eliminate damaging handling. A belt conveyor would, however, tend to bruise the fruit with the peaches piled on each other.

Damage is less likely to occur if floating peaches are moved more gently, by a stream of water.

The problem of how to move the fruit and maintain its 3-min contact must be solved.

A possible solution is the combination of a rapidly moving stream and some sort of soft-touch peach retarding device. It was thus decided that a continuous chain, carrying screen frames as shown in Fig. A5–1, would provide

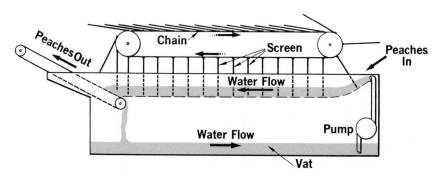

Fig. A5–1. Peach heating system.

the desirable kinematic arrangement. In order to minimize corrosion, and simplify bearing design, the chain was to be suspended above the vat as indicated.

Several extemporaneous trials indicated a screen speed of around 5 ft/min to be quite suitable. Thus a reasonable vat length of 5 fpm × 3 min, or 15 ft, would be required. A length of 20 ft was actually selected.

One bushel occupies approximately 1.25 ft³. A float cross section of

$$\frac{500 \text{ bu/hr} \times 1.25 \text{ ft}^3/\text{bu}}{5 \text{ fpm} \times 60 \text{ min/hr}} = 2.1 \text{ ft}^2$$

is therefore needed. An area 60 in. by 12 in. was selected.

If the peaches are assumed to fill 2.1 ft² of the flow area, 2 ft² remain as water space. At a water speed of 2 ft/sec, a flow of

$$2 \text{ fps} \times 2 \text{ ft}^2 \times 60 \text{ sec/min} \times 7.48 \text{ gal/ft}^3 = 1,795 \text{ gpm}$$

is required.

A commercial pump that will lift water 3 ft at 1,800 gpm is available. Thus, at an efficiency of 60%, the power needed calculates as

$$\frac{240 \text{ ft}^3/\text{min} \times 62.4 \text{ lb/ft}^3 \times 3 \text{ ft}}{33,000 \times 0.6} = 2.18 \text{ hp}$$

Since an electric motor can handle an overload of at least 10%, a 2-hp motor is decided appropriate.

Another problem involves the consideration of the heat required to maintain water and peach temperature.

The ambient temperature is assumed at 60° F while the peaches, out of cold storage, are at 50° F.

A vat 20 ft long, 5 ft wide and 44 in. deep contains 260 ft² of exposed surface. The conductance from metal to air is small compared to that of water to metal. The metal conductivity can, therefore, be neglected. Available data reveal 2.0 Btu/hr-ft²-° F to be a reasonable coefficient of heat transfer including radiation.

Thus, if a temperature of 130° F is assumed on the outside metal surface, the heat lost from the surface is

$$260 \text{ ft}^2 \times 2 \text{ Btu/hr-ft}^2\text{-}° \text{ F} \times (130 - 60)° \text{ F} = 36,400 \text{ Btu/hr}$$

The heat lost from the water surface, plus that consumed in evaporation at 130° F, is established at 1,800 Btu/hr-ft². The total heat lost from the water surface is

$$75 \text{ ft}^2 \times 1,800 \text{ Btu/hr-ft}^2 = 135,000 \text{ Btu/hr}$$

Water evaporation consumes about 1,000 Btu/lb; therefore about 133 lb/hr of make-up water will be required. If the make-up water is available at 50° F, the heat needed is

$$133 \text{ lb/hr} \times 1 \text{ Btu/lb-}° \text{ F} \times (130 - 50)° \text{ F} = 10,640 \text{ Btu/hr}$$

Determination of the heat absorbed by the peaches was not as simple. Estimation based on a little information found, and on the results of some experimentation performed, help establish a requirement of 1,470 Btu/bu of peaches. Thus,

$$500 \text{ bu/hr} \times 1,470 \text{ Btu/bu} = 735,000 \text{ Btu/hr}$$

are needed to heat the peaches.

The total heat requirement is the sum of the individual figures or

$$917,040 \text{ Btu/hr}$$

The question now becomes how to best provide the heat requirement. One possibility is a boiler supplying steam or hot water to the vat. Another is a gas burner with a heat exchanger.

Since the vat is subject to no external pressure, it was estimated that the burner method, with a shop-fabricated heat exchanger, would be more economical.

Assuming a burner–exchanger efficiency of 75%, the burner capacity becomes

$$\frac{917,040}{0.75} = 1,223,000 \text{ Btu/hr}$$

A pipe of 14-in. ID was selected because it could readily be coupled to the commercial gas burner selected.   A heat-balance investigation revealed, however, that an additional heat-transfer surface of 170 ft² was needed.   One hundred and sixty-two (162) linear feet of 4-in. tubing would provide the additional

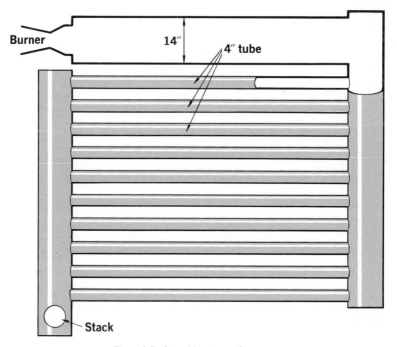

Fig. A5–2.   Heat exchanger.

surface.   Ten tubes 16 ft long, arranged as shown in Fig. A5–2, were therefore decided upon, and the heat exchanger fabricated.

Stress calculations indicated ¼-in. steel plate of sufficient strength, and so the vat was thus fabricated.

The equipment was assembled and installed.   Its operation proved fully satisfactory.

Design Projects

Exercise in creative design should form an important part of design-engineering instruction. A somewhat sophisticated system-design project should probably constitute the capstone of the basic engineering curriculum. It should tend to integrate the experiences of the entire curriculum.

Projects should require the application of scientific knowledge and the use of engineering judgment. Synthesis as well as analysis should be involved in the solution of the situation. The student must be expected to draw primarily upon his own ability, knowledge, and experience, if he is to derive maximum benefit. The complete process of design involves, among other things, problem definition; the project description is therefore kept at a minimum.

The instructor will likely be able to motivate the student to a more effective effort when the project derives from the student's own experience or making. Nevertheless, several example projects of differing degrees of difficulty are offered below, which may be used as they are, or as guides in stating others.

Project B–1. Hunt Trap System

A photographic reconnaissance orbit around the planet (Mars or Venus) has revealed indigenous life forms. Careful analysis of the photographic data reveals strong evidence of some kind of animal life, not human. A fast-shifting, rodent-type animal, which appears to glide along the surface in rapidly-changing random directions and able to rise a few feet vertically and hover for short periods, is believed spotted. Its size and shape are estimated to approximate those of a Pekingese dog. It also appears to be violently cannibalistic.

It is deemed wise to study this life before attempting more extensive exploration of the planet. A return trip in a space vehicle capable of travel at over 100,000 mph is possible. Therefore, it is decided to send two men to capture (trap?) two pairs of these animals and bring them back alive for study on earth. A maximum going load of 800–1,200 pounds and return load of 1,000–1,500 pounds (earth) are available.

Evolve the equipment needed to trap and transport the animals back to earth alive. Strength design is not the immediate task, but because of weight limitations its consideration can not to be fully neglected.   All mechanisms, environmental necessities, transportation facility, food requirements, etc., must be completely considered, accounted for, specified, and designed.   Clear sketches of the system and its components, specifications, description of function, and operating instructions are to be incorporated in the written report at completion of project.

A reference that might contain helpful information and lead to additional reading is:

> *Space Handbook: Astronautics and Its Applications* Staff Report of the Select Committee on Astronautics and Space Exploration, House Document No. 86, 86th Congress, 1st Session, Washington, D.C., 1959.

Project B–2. Project Dive

Scuba divers can go to depths of 200 to 300 feet but can work only for a few minutes at such depths.   Even hard-hat divers can labor only 20 min or so a day.   Certain industries are developing more suitable equipment.   It is claimed that work-periods of up to 8 hours at depths of several hundred feet are possible.

We have been asked by a client interested in biological underwater exploration to propose a system that will enable them to gather sea life for study.   In order to keep the cost at a safe minimum, use of available or only slightly modified equipment is suggested.   Because expected submerged periods are to be relatively long, scuba diving gear is not likely feasible.   Instead, what is probably needed is some combination of diving chamber, decompression chamber, support equipment, and gathering apparatus.

The task to be performed is explained as follows.   "We are to gather and surface species of benthos fauna living on the ocean floor.   Collection is to be at depths of 300 to 500 feet and we desire to be able to work on the bottom 3 to 5 hours a day."

A safe and suitable system capable of supporting the performance of the task must be developed for our client.   All diving, searching, gathering, and surfacing equipment must be completely specified.   Also, it must be realized that the benthos are to be surfaced alive, and kept alive, for at least several days.   In developing the system, we must select available equipment where possible, modify or redesign where necessary, and prepare operating specifications.   Sketches, charts, drawings, etc., needed to describe the system clearly must accompany our report.

Project B–3. Yard Raking Machine

The Tech Products Improvement Company is a firm of engineers organized to provide new, and improve old, designs of products desired by their clients. You were hired by the firm some three months ago to help in the design of more competitive items with improved function, reduced costs, better appearance, and simplified components.

You have just been requested to suggest three alternative designs of a yard machine.   The machine is to be capable of raking, pulverizing, and disposing of fallen leaves and pine needles.   The designs are to include manually operated as well as powered models.   Since the machine is to be used in residential neighborhoods, the dispersal of pulverized material should not be too violent. It is thought that a model with a removable collector unit may be of value, that is, a unit into which the pulverized material would collect, which when filled could be easily disconnected and detached, via a quick disconnect of some sort, and wheeled away for dumping.   You are also encouraged to remember that the equipment should be so designed that it can easily be operated by ordinary people.

The designs report must include sketches and calculations that will enable your firm to explore the feasibility and desirability of the equipment.   This preliminary design should also contain sufficient detail to estimate size, weight, and cost.   You must supply the firm with these estimates.

Project B–4. Agricultural Products Dryer

Many agricultural products need to be dried, from apricots to prunes; with beans, corn, hay, milk, and peanuts in between.   Hay probably represents the greatest bulk and probably also the greatest tonnage.   Alfalfa hay dryers have been in use for many years.

A problem in the batch-drying of a product such as corn is that when warm air is blown up through a bin (such as a wagon box) of cold kernels, the warm air picks up moisture at the bottom but soon reaches its wet-bulb temperature in the colder material on top.   It then redeposits the moisture from the bottom at the upper levels making this material dripping wet, until at long last it finally dries by air that has not been cooled and humidified while passing through the bottom material which has since been dried.   (This phenomenon has been experienced even in some combustion work where the bottom portion was incandescent.)   Drying temperatures must not be allowed to go high enough to sterilize the product.   Unless you learn of a different safe limit, assume a maximum safe temperature of 125° F.

What can you propose in the way of three alternatives for drying products such as corn, peanuts, and soy beans?

Develop the most promising of your three ideas into sketches and calculations that will enable you to explore feasibility and desirability with farmers and financiers.

Project B–5. Water Vehicle Speedometer

A speedometer capable of indicating a speed of 2–5 knots to 10–20 knots of a small motor-driven pleasure boat is desirable.   It should enable readings correct to ± 0.5 knot.   It should be simple in principle and appearance, economical to manufacture, easy to install or mount, maintenance free, and fool proof.

It will be mass produced.

The Satisfaction Specialty Company by whom you are employed decides to add such a product to its line. You are directed to develop the speedometer. In your report to management, include sufficient sketches to depict the appearance of the device as well as its principle of operation, to estimate its cost, and to predict its weight.

Project B—6. Catenary Cables

The design of electric transmission lines is based on the theory of catenary cables.   In locations where ice is likely at times to coat the cable or where winds cause flutter, trouble is sometime encountered.   Cables may sag excessively under these conditions, resulting in sparking to ground and fractures.

The strength properties of such cables are determined, using long lengths (500 inches) of cable pulled on the ends while the cable is supported in a horizontal position along its full length.   These data are used in the cable design— support tension, span length, sag, etc.

Investigate, analyze, and evaluate the significance of using cable properties so obtained in the design.   Is this practice scientifically sound?   Are improvements possible?   How?

Project B—7. Short Transportation Vehicle

A convenient but reasonably inexpensive mode of transportation from plane station to terminal lobby is becoming a great need in many of the larger airports.

Investigate the situation, analyze the facts, and synthesize possible solutions.   Consider the problem thoroughly, evaluate the alternatives, and then prepare your report for presentation to management.

Project B—8. Naval Stores Dryer

The oleoresins industry constitutes a market for a type of economical dryer. Old stumps from which additional product can be extracted contain a troublesome amount of moisture—up to 40 per cent by weight.   A reduction in the moisture content down to 20 per cent or less would simplify extraction and improve quality.

The stumps are usually cut up in a chipping hog and additionally broken down to splinter size in hammermills.   The chips are then leached out with solvents.

Drying by heating is not particularly satisfactory, because loss of valuable volatile products accompanies the operation.   Even the heating that develops during chipping can prove troublesome under high ambient-temperature conditions.

Investigate and analyze the situation; propose a workable way of drying the splinters or chips, and of reducing heating during chipping.   Design a drying facility that will handle 300 tons of material every 24-hour day.   A preliminary design extensive enough to sell management your idea is sufficient.

Index